Chemical Reactions
in Urban Atmospheres

Published Symposia
Held at the
General Motors Research Laboratories
Warren, Michigan

Friction and Wear, 1959
Robert Davies, *Editor*

Internal Stresses and Fatigue in Metals, 1959
Gerald M. Rassweiler and William L. Grube, *Editors*

Theory of Traffic Flow, 1961
Robert Herman, *Editor*

Rolling Contact Phenomena, 1962
Joseph B. Bidwell, *Editor*

Adhesion and Cohesion, 1962
Philip Weiss, *Editor*

Cavitation in Real Liquids, 1964
Robert Davies, *Editor*

Liquids: Structure, Properties, Solid Interactions, 1965
Thomas J. Hughel, *Editor*

Approximation of Functions, 1965
Henry L. Garabedian, *Editor*

Fluid Mechanics of Internal Flow, 1967
Gino Sovran, *Editor*

Ferroelectricity, 1967
Edward F. Weller, *Editor*

Interface Conversion for Polymer Coatings, 1968
Philip Weiss and G. Dale Cheever, *Editors*

Associative Information Techniques, 1971
Edwin L. Jacks, *Editor*

Chemical Reactions in the Urban Atmosphere, 1971
Charles S. Tuesday, *Editor*

Chemical Reactions in Urban Atmospheres

Proceedings of the Symposium

HELD AT

General Motors Research Laboratories
Warren, Michigan, 1969

EDITED BY

Charles S. Tuesday

Fuels and Lubricants Department
General Motors Research Laboratories
Warren, Michigan

WITHDRAWN

American Elsevier
Publishing Company, Inc.
NEW YORK · 1971

AMERICAN ELSEVIER PUBLISHING COMPANY, INC.
52 Vanderbilt Avenue, New York, N.Y. 10017

ELSEVIER PUBLISHING COMPANY, LTD.
Barking, Essex, England

ELSEVIER PUBLISHING COMPANY
335 Jan Van Galenstraat, P.O. Box 211
Amsterdam, The Netherlands

International Standard Book Number 0-444-00103-4

Library of Congress Card Number 79-154707

Copyright © 1971 by American Elsevier Publishing Company, Inc.

Manufactured in the United States of America

CONTENTS

Session I – Chairman: P. A. Leighton

J. N. Pitts, Jr.

G. R. McMillan, Jalaj Kumari, and D. L. Snyder

Edgar R. Stephens

Session II—Chairman: A. P. Altshuller

R. D. Cadle and E. R. Allen

B. Dimitriades and M. L. Whisman

Sigmund Jaffe

Session III—Chairman: S. W. Benson

Jack G. Calvert, David H. Slater, and James W. Gall

Richard B. Timmons, Henry F. LeFevre, and Gerald A. Hollinden

Julian Heicklen, William P. Wood, Kenneth J. Olszyna, and Edwin Cehelnik

Session IV—Chairman: R. J. Cvetanovic

J. J. Bufalini and K. L. Brubaker

P. J. Groblicki and G. J. Nebel

Preface

This book contains the papers and discussions presented at the Symposium on Chemical Reactions in Urban Atmospheres which was held at the General Motors Research Laboratories, on October 6 and 7, 1969.

Many of the pollutants in urban atmospheres react, even at extremely low concentrations, both with each other and with the normal constituents of the atmosphere. Although some of these reactions are thermal, photochemical reactions very often predominate. Some of these chemical reactions remove or scavenge pollutants, and thus act to "cleanse" the atmosphere. Other atmospheric chemical reactions, however, produce products that are much more detrimental to the environment than the original pollutants and thus act to "dirty" the atmosphere. Photochemical smog reactions are the outstanding example of reactions of this type.

An understanding of the chemical reactions that occur in urban atmospheres is necessary in order to achieve meaningful air pollution control and a high degree of air quality. Although much has already been learned about these atmospheric chemical reactions, many important questions are yet unanswered. This Symposium was organized in an effort to stimulate progress in answering these questions by bringing together the foremost workers and best minds in this and closely related fields. The eleven invited papers presented at this Symposium were all concerned with current research problems and are important original contributions by the authors to the literature of this field.

Although this book records these original contributions and much of the formalized discussion they elicited, the most important contribution of this Symposium may not have been recorded, that is, the many individual discussions and interactions that occurred at the many social functions included in the total Symposium format.

This Symposium could not have been held or these proceedings published without the valuable aid of many of my colleagues.

I am particularly indebted to Mr. Joseph M. Colucci and Mr. Ronald L. Scott for their devotion to the many details involved in the organization and conduct of a symposium of this type. I am also indebted to Dr. Paul F. Chenea for his timely and thoughtful address at the Symposium Banquet on "Science, Technology, and the Public Good."

Although I am listed as the editor of this volume, much of the editing was actually done by my colleagues, especially Mr. Jon M. Heuss, Dr. William

A. Glasson, and Mr. George J. Nebel, and I am certainly indebted to them for their valuable assistance.

Finally, I should like to acknowledge the valuable contribution to both the Symposium and the publication of these proceedings of the Fuels and Lubricants Department Secretarial Staff, Mrs. Barbara R. Plumley, Miss Jeanne C. Christensen, Mrs. Sharon L. Curtiss, and Mrs. Christine Dzedzie.

CHARLES S. TUESDAY

SESSION I

The Role of Singlet Molecular Oxygen in the Chemistry of Urban Atmospheres

J. N. Pitts, Jr.
Department of Chemistry
University of California, Riverside
Riverside, California

Abstract

Singlet molecular oxygen ($^1\Delta_g$) may be a previously unrecognized oxidizing species present in polluted urban atmospheres. Various methods for generating and detecting singlet oxygen, the physical and chemical quenching of singlet oxygen, and its known chemical reactions are reviewed. A number of mechanisms for the formation of singlet oxygen are critically examined. These are (1) by direct absorption of solar radiation by ground-state molecular oxygen or an olefin-oxygen complex, (2) by photodecomposition of ozone, (3) by absorption of solar radiation by organic molecules followed by transfer of energy to ground-state molecular oxygen, and (4) as a product of certain exothermic chemical reactions. Several implications of the possible presence of singlet molecular oxygen in urban atmospheres are discussed.

Introduction

The characteristic symptoms of photochemical air pollution were first encountered in the mid-1940's in Los Angeles, California. In the early 1950's researchers established that it was indeed a new kind of air pollution primarily caused by the action of sunlight on the exhaust emitted by the millions of motor vehicles in the Los Angeles Basin. Over the next two decades, qualitative and subsequently quantitative laboratory and field studies, together with Leighton's definitive monograph "Photochemistry of Air Pollution" *(1)* published in 1961, provided the basis for much of our present understanding of the chemical and mechanistic aspects of photochemical smog, whether produced in the laboratory or in the atmosphere *(2-8)*.

Despite this excellent past work, current researchers well recognize that today we are still woefully ignorant of many detailed aspects of the physical, chemical, biological, and medical effects of photochemical smog on man and his environment. Thus, while the current implementation of the United States Air Quality Act of 1967 by the National Air Pollution Control Administration is leading to more widespread and stringent control measures than hitherto existed, it would be tragic if a sizable fraction of the scientific community and the public at large were to believe that we now fully "understand" smog. Even though the application of new controls and the development of new control technology are of the

References, pp. 29-31.

highest priority today, there is continuing need for fundamental research on all aspects of air pollution.

In short, we still do not have a satisfactory set of reaction mechanisms that can explain many key physical, chemical, and biological aspects of photochemical air pollution *(9)*. For example, in the NO_x-hydrocarbon-air systems* irradiated by ultraviolet light in the laboratory, current mechanisms cannot explain such phenomena as (1) the observed substantial excess in rate of consumption of hydrocarbons over the calculated rate, and (2) the fact that overall material balances may account for only approximately 50% or less of the hydrocarbons consumed in the reaction *(8)*. Furthermore, they do not account satisfactorily for the rapid rate of oxidation of the primary pollutant nitric oxide to nitrogen dioxide and the speed with which other secondary pollutants such as ozone and peroxyacetyl nitrate (PAN) appear in actual atmospheres.† These phenomena are illustrated in Fig. 1, which shows the diurnal variations of NO, NO_2, and O_3 in the Los Angeles atmosphere on a smoggy day.

Another example of the uncertainties in the situation relates to the fact that data from several laboratories suggest that the effects of photochemical air pollution as observed in the atmosphere (for example, eye irritation and oxidant) may be reduced most effectively by further control of hydrocarbons. Other researchers propose that at this stage of time, with hydrocarbon emissions being regulated by federal law, reduction in the effects of photochemical air pollution would be better achieved by reduction in emission of oxides of nitrogen from auto exhaust.‡

The chemical and physical complexity of *real smog* is further illustrated by the fact that the composition of the polluted air mass constantly changes as it is being irradiated by the sun. This point, coupled with the obvious fact that concentrations of oxidant on the upwind side of an urban area are usually much lower than concentrations downwind, is of immense esthetic, medical, and legal implications. For example, those residents of the Los Angeles Basin who live in communities east of the Los Angeles-Pasadena area are generally downwind from this huge source of oxidant. Thus, while such cities as Azusa and Riverside generate some of their "own oxidant" on many days of the year, they are subjected to the additional impact of a "photochemically well-aged" cloud of oxidant moving in on them sometime during the afternoon from the Los Angeles area. In Riverside, some 60 miles east of downtown Los Angeles, instead of the oxidant level reaching a maximum around noon, the level peaks briefly

---

*Recall that NO_x actually stands for a mixture of NO and NO_2 plus other oxides of nitrogen present in smaller amounts in an unspecified ratio. As "it" emerges from the auto exhaust, the NO_x is predominately nitric oxide.

† Dr. Stephens will discuss this point in detail in a subsequent paper.

‡ One approach is to bypass the conflicting experimental data on relative effects of the reduction of hydrocarbons versus NO_x on photochemical smog production and simply state that emissions of oxides of nitrogen should be reduced because of their potential (or real) health hazards.

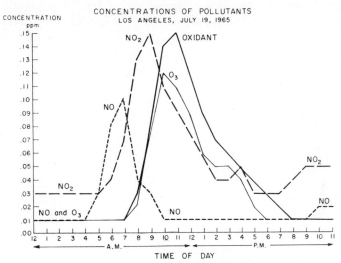

Fig. 1. Diurnal variation in concentrations of some pollutants in Los Angeles, July 19, 1965 [taken from Air Quality Criteria document on Photochemical Oxidants *(10)*].

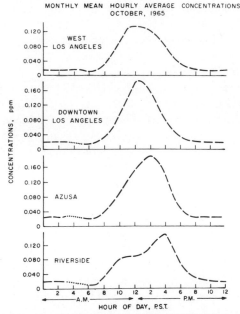

Fig. 2. Diurnal variation of concentrations of oxidants in West Los Angeles, Los Angeles, Azusa, and Riverside. These figures illustrate the eastward transport of oxidant during a smoggy period in October 1965 [taken from Air Quality Criteria document on Photochemical Oxidants *(10)*]. Original data for the first three stations are from the Los Angeles County Air Pollution Control District; data for the City of Riverside are from the Riverside County Air Pollution Control District.

in the late morning and then rises to a maximum in the late afternoon, around four to five o'clock. This is well illustrated in Fig. 2 (taken from reference *10*).

Finally, far too little attention has been paid to the important point that photochemical smog is a chemically and physically complex mixture of particulate matter and noxious gases, just as is the "London" type of smog. The latter is also a mixture of particulates (soot, sulfuric acid droplets, etc.) and gaseous pollutants (chiefly sulfur dioxide), but the overall system is chemically *reducing* in nature. From both a medical and a scientific viewpoint, in both the London and Los Angeles Types of smog, *synergistic effects* can occur which may exceed the sum of the effects due to the gases alone plus the effects due to the particulates alone. In short, the whole may be greater than the sum of the parts.

Historically this has been illustrated by the deadly effects of the London type of smog which contains both gaseous sulfur dioxide and solid particles of soot. The bulk of medical and epidemiological evidence to date strongly suggests that the 4000 excess deaths in London in 1952 were due to synergistic respiratory effects arising from the simultaneous presence of both SO_2 and soot in the atmosphere. Similar considerations apply to the excess deaths reported in an acute smog episode in New York City in 1962. Air containing only SO_2 or only soot in concentrations close to those present in actual smog does not produce nearly as severe symptoms as does a mixture of the two pollutants. This point is generally well recognized in terms of its physiological implications in the particulate-oxides of sulfur system but has *not* been generally stressed when considering the chemistry and physics, not to mention the health implications, of photochemical air pollution *(9, 11, 12)*.

While these observations on our current state of knowledge of the chemistry of urban atmospheres are in one sense depressing, they are also an exciting challenge for researchers who are interested in applying basic science to relevant problems of man. As a specific example, today we shall consider a case in which fundamental research on the spectroscopy, photochemistry, and mechanistic organic chemistry of singlet molecular oxygen recently has been applied to specific problem areas of photochemical smog. Thus, several years ago in our laboratory, in part on the basis of some earlier considerations of Leighton *(1)* and Bayes *(13)*, my colleagues (Dr. Ahsan Khan and Dr. Brian Smith of the Physical Chemistry Laboratory, Oxford University) and I came to the conclusion that the lowest electronically excited states of O_2, symbolized as $O_2(a^1 \Delta_g)$ and $O_2(b^1 \Sigma_g^+)$, may be hitherto unrecognized oxidants present in smog test chambers as well as in actual polluted urban atmospheres *(14-16)*.*
Conclusions similar to ours have been reached by Kummler *et al. (17, 18)* and by Murray and Kaplan *(19)*.

We further believe, as do an increasing number of researchers in several disciplines, that certain unexplained *chemical and biological effects observed in*

---

*We shall often abbreviate the nomenclature and refer to $^1O_2$, which may include both species.

man, animals, and plants, including some relative to certain observations on photochemical air pollution, might be attributed to these species (for example, see the review by Foote, reference *20*).*

In this paper I shall briefly review the various methods of generating singlet oxygen, and consider several aspects of the physical and chemical quenching of singlet oxygen by inorganic and organic compounds, most of which are either major or minor atmospheric constituents. Several mechanisms for the formation of $^1O_2$ will be examined critically in relation to their possible importance in the chemistry of urban atmospheres. In each, the excitation energy is derived ultimately from the sun's radiation, but the energy is utilized in different reaction paths. These are:

1. By direct absorption of radiation by ground-state $^3O_2$ (or an olefin-oxygen complex).

2. By photolysis of an atmospheric contaminant to form excited $^1O_2$ in the primary step.

3. By a spin-conserved energy transfer mechanism in which an atmospheric contaminant absorbs solar radiation and transfers its excitation to normal ground-state $^3O_2$.

4. By exothermic chemical reactions involving atmospheric contaminants which themselves originated in a photochemical process.

Published data and new results from our laboratory will be introduced into our discussion, and their implications in laboratory and atmospheric reactions considered.†

Spectroscopy

The two lowest electronically excited states of molecular oxygen, $a^1\Delta_g$ and $b^1\Sigma_g^+$, are singlets located at about 22.5 kcal (0.98 eV) and 37.5 kcal (1.63 eV), respectively, above the ground state, $O_2(^3X\Sigma_g^-)$. They are shown in the simplified potential energy diagram for the oxygen molecule (Fig. 3).

The optically "forbidden" transitions

$$O_2(^3\Sigma_g^-) + h\nu(7619\ \text{Å}) \underset{b}{\overset{a}{\rightleftharpoons}} O_2(^1\Sigma_g^+) \tag{1}$$

---

*While to date the information available on singlet oxygen comes from laboratory or upper atmosphere experiments, we feel there is good reason to believe that extrapolation to urban atmospheres is not only reasonable but should be demonstrable.

†For detailed discussions and extensive references to the original literature on singlet oxygen and its role in photooxidations, one should consult the recent reviews by Foote *(20, 21)*, Gollnick *(22, 23)*, Gollnick and Schenck *(24)*, Arnold *et al. (25)*, Pitts *et al. (15, 16)*, and Wayne *(26, 27)*.

$$O_2(^3\Sigma_g^-) + h\nu(12{,}690 \text{ Å}) \underset{b}{\overset{a}{\rightleftharpoons}} O_2(^1\Delta_g) \tag{2}$$

involve magnetic dipole interactions and are very weak relative to the "allowed" electric dipole transition:

$$O_2(^3\Sigma_g^-) + h\nu(\lambda \leqslant 2000 \text{ Å}) \underset{b}{\overset{a}{\rightleftharpoons}} O_2(^3\Sigma_u^-) \tag{3}$$

The latter is responsible for the Schumann-Runge bands which start at about 2000 Å and merge into a strong continuum beginning at 1759 Å *(28)*. The intense absorption by oxygen due to process 3 is a limiting factor in spectroscopic and photochemical studies in air *(29)*.

Despite being weak, the radiative transitions 1 and 2 have been well established in laboratory spectroscopic studies of both the absorption and emission processes. Furthermore, the emission of radiation from electronically excited singlet oxygen molecules present in the upper atmosphere has been known for some time to contribute to the day and night "airglows." The $^1\Sigma_g^+ \rightarrow {}^3\Sigma_g^-$ transition of molecular oxygen gives rise to the "atmospheric band," while the "infrared atmospheric band" results from the $^1\Delta_g \rightarrow {}^3\Sigma_g^-$ radiative transition in oxygen (see reference *27* for a review).

Since transitions to the ground state are forbidden in an unperturbed system, both the $^1\Sigma$ and $^1\Delta$ states have long natural radiative lifetimes, of the order of 7 seconds and 45 minutes *(30)*, respectively (see reference *26* for a discussion of these values). It is this very long natural lifetime of the $^1\Delta$ state coupled with its great stability toward physical quenching and demonstrated reactivity toward certain classes of organic compounds that implicates it as a possible new contributor to that catch-all classification "photochemical oxidant." On the other hand, the $^1\Sigma$ state is rapidly physically quenched by such

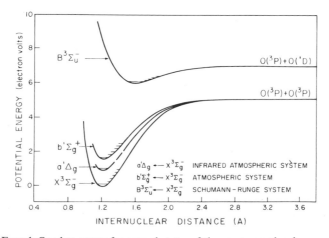

Fig. 3. Franck-Condon curves for several states of the oxygen molecule.

species as O_2 and H_2O, so it is much less likely to be a significant contributor to *chemical* processes in the lower atmosphere. We shall, therefore, confine most of our attention to the physical and chemical characteristics of the $^1\Delta$ state.

Under conditions where substantial concentrations of $O_2(^1\Delta)$ are present, collisions between two excited oxygen molecules may result and a novel energy-pooling process can occur. In this, the electronic energies of the two colliding molecules appear as a single photon (reactions 4 and 5). This "dimol" emission is responsible for the red glow readily observed visually when $O_2(^1\Delta)$ is generated chemically in an alkaline H_2O_2-Cl_2 system or by a microwave discharge.

$$O_2(^1\Delta_g)_{v=0} + O_2(^1\Delta_g)_{v=0} \left[\begin{array}{l} \longrightarrow O_2(^3\Sigma_g^-)_{v=0} + O_2(^3\Sigma_g^-)_{v=0} + h\nu \ (6340 \ \text{\AA}) \quad (4) \\ \\ \longrightarrow O_2(^3\Sigma_g^-)_{v=1} + O_2(^3\Sigma_g^-)_{v=0} + h\nu \ (7030 \ \text{\AA}) \quad (5) \end{array} \right.$$

It is not established whether the $^1\Delta$ molecules form a "stabilized dimer" or interact through a collision complex *(25)*. In any case, the process is sufficiently efficient that the dimol emission at 6340 Å is often used for monitoring the concentration of $O_2(^1\Delta)$ molecules.

Experimental Methods for the Generation and Detection of $O_2(^1\Delta)$ and $O_2(^1\Sigma)$

Physical Methods. A convenient gas phase method of generating substantial quantities of $^1O_2$ for laboratory studies is to pass normal oxygen at 1 to 10 torr through an electrodeless microwave discharge (see reference *26* for a review with original references). After the discharge, the gas stream can contain up to 10% of $O_2(^1\Delta)$, depending on the experimental conditions. Oxygen in the $^1\Sigma$ state is also formed, but it is rapidly quenched and, according to Falick and Mahan, amounts to only a few tenths of 1% *(31)*. Oxygen atoms are also formed in the discharge, but they are removed by saturation of the oxygen gas with mercury vapor prior to its entry into the discharge and by passing the effluent from the discharge over a film of mercuric oxide.

In our laboratory at UCR we have found it convenient to employ a Raytheon microwave discharge unit, Model PGM-10-X1, operating at 2450 MHz for generating $O_2(^1\Delta)$. The microwave energy is coupled from the coaxial cable to the flow system with a tunable wave guide supplied by Ophthos Instrument Company, Rockville, Maryland *(32)*.

Chemical Methods. Much of the impetus for the research on $^1O_2$ that began in the last decade came from studies of the red luminescence observed when chlorine gas was bubbled through an alkaline solution of hydrogen peroxide. Spectroscopic research, particularly that of Bowen and Lloyd *(33)*, Khan and Kasha *(34)*, and Browne and Ogryzlo *(35)*, has established that the emission is due to the formation of singlet oxygen in the reaction

$$NaOCl + H_2O_2 \rightarrow NaCl + H_2O + {}^1O_2 \tag{6}$$

"A novel and useful synthetic method for the oxidation of olefins and diene-oid compounds to give products identical with those of the well studied dye-photosensitized autoxidations" was first described in 1964 by Foote and Wexler. They went on to state: "The active species appears to be molecular oxygen in an excited state, formed *in situ* by the reaction of sodium hypochlorite and hydrogen peroxide." In a companion paper, they further proposed that singlet oxygen was "a probable intermediate in photosensitized autoxidations" *(36)*.

Since then, the solution phase reaction of alkaline hydrogen peroxide with either sodium hypochlorite or bromine has been employed by an increasing number of researchers investigating oxidations of organic compounds, including many of biochemical interest. It is now generally agreed that $O_2({}^1\Delta)$ is the principal reacting species (the ${}^1\Sigma$ state is rapidly quenched), and that the red chemiluminescence is dimol emission (reactions 4 and 5).

A particularly useful chemical method for generating $O_2({}^1\Delta)$ in the gas phase is that of Murray and Kaplan, who produced it by heating the ozone-triphenyl phosphite complex *(19, 37)*.

$$(C_6H_5O)_3P + O_3 \xrightarrow[CH_2Cl_2]{-70^\circ} (C_6H_5O)_3P{\overset{O}{\underset{O}{\diagup\!\!\!\diagdown}}}O \tag{7}$$

$$(C_6H_5O)_3P{\overset{O}{\underset{O}{\diagup\!\!\!\diagdown}}}O \xrightarrow{> -35^\circ} (C_6H_5O)_3P = O + {}^1O_2 \tag{8}$$

Energy Transfer: Photosensitization. It was three decades after the original proposition by Hans Kautsky that "The extinction of luminescence is the expression of an energy transfer between excited dyestuff molecules and oxygen, in which activated O_2 is produced," *(38)* that it became accepted that ${}^1O_2$ was produced in one class of photooxygenation reaction. In this type, the excited sensitizer molecule transfers its electronic excitation energy to molecular oxygen, producing singlet molecular oxygen which subsequently reacts with the substrate to give oxygenated products. Gollnick refers to this as a type II photosensitized oxygenation reaction. [Reviews by Bowen *(39)*, Foote *(20, 21)*, Gollnick *(22, 23)*, and Livingston *(40)* discuss in detail the mechanism of photosensitized oxidation.]

Briefly, the photosensitized oxidation by ${}^1O_2$ involves the following sequence of reactions; it is now known to be general for both liquid and gas phase systems:

$$Sens(S_0) + h\nu \xrightarrow{\text{absorption}} Sens(S_1) \tag{9}$$

$$Sens(S_1) \xrightarrow[\text{crossing}]{\text{intersystem}} Sens(T_1) \tag{10}$$

$$Sens(T_1) + {}^3O_2 \xrightarrow[\text{transfer}]{\text{energy}} Sens(S_0) + {}^1O_2 \tag{11}$$

$${}^1O_2 + Acceptor \xrightarrow[\text{reaction}]{\text{chemical}} Product \tag{12}$$

Processes 9, 10, and 11 are shown schematically on the energy-level diagram, Fig. 4.* In most cases it is the triplet state of the sensitizer that transfers the

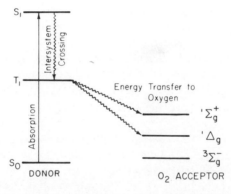

Fig. 4. Schematic representation of triplet energy transfer from donor organic molecule to molecular oxygen to produce either $^1\Delta$ or $^1\Sigma$ excited states (processes 9, 10, and 11).

electronic excitation energy to oxygen. This is presumably because of the relatively much longer lifetimes of triplet states versus singlet states of organic molecules. Thus, efficient sensitizers have high quantum yields of triplet formation; that is, the radiationless process 10, *intersystem crossing*, is efficient compared to other competing reactions of $Sens(S_1)$ species.

In terms of generation of $^1O_2$ in the laboratory, the procedure is straightforward (see references *24* and *41* for details). The sensitizer may be any one of a number of organic compounds including (1) a dye such as rose bengal, (2) an aromatic hydrocarbon such as naphthalene which is a (π, π^*) type of

---

*S_0 and S_1 refer to the ground and lowest excited singlet states, respectively; T_1 is the lowest triplet state. The wavy arrows indicate radiationless transitions.

sensitizer, or (3) a ketone such as benzophenone, an (n, π^*) sensitizer. One simply bubbles oxygen gas through a solution containing the sensitizer and substrate in a suitable solvent and irradiates the system with a lamp having a high output of radiation at wavelengths absorbed by the sensitizer. The rate of product formation depends on a variety of factors, including the efficiencies of processes 9 through 12. Gas-phase experiments on photosensitized oxygenations analogous to those conducted in solution are currently being conducted in our laboratory. Thus, Steer *et al. (42)* have recently observed the formation of an oxidation product in an irradiated gas phase sensitizer-oxygen-olefin system. In these studies, mixtures of benzene, oxygen, and tetramethylethylene (typically 20, 70, and 2 torr, respectively) were irradiated for 1 hour at room temperature. The hydroperoxide product 2,3-dimethyl-2-hydroperoxybutene-1 was isolated in large yields *(42)* (see reaction 13).

Detection of Singlet Oxygen. *Physical Techniques.* The sigma state is readily monitored by its emission in the red using highly sensitive, stable photomultiplier tubes. There are a variety of physical techniques for measuring the $^1\Delta$ state. These include (1) direct emission measurements of the red dimol emission using phototubes with red-sensitive cathodes; (2) direct emission measurements of the 1.27-μ emission from the transition $O_2(^1\Delta_g) \rightarrow O_2(^3\Sigma_g^-)$ using preferably a liquid-nitrogen-cooled germanium diode detector; (3) mass spectrometric determination of the appearance potential of the m/e 32 peak; (4) calorimetry; (5) photoionization techniques; (6) electron paramagnetic resonance (EPR) method (see Wayne, reference *26,* for an evaluation of these techniques).

A cooled germanium detector was used in the first direct observation of the photosensitized formation of $O_2(^1\Delta)$ in the gas phase by Snelling, who irradiated benzene-oxygen mixtures and detected the characteristic $^1\Delta$ emission at 1.27 μ *(43)*. Kummler and Bortner have used this technique to monitor $O_2(^1\Delta)$ emission from irradiated gas phase benzaldehyde-oxygen mixtures, a system of relevance to photochemical air pollution *(18)*, as we shall see subsequently.

In our laboratory at UCR we have found the cooled germanium diode detector to be of great utility in a number of studies including the reaction of O_3 with $O_2(^1\Delta)$ *(44)*, gas phase energy transfer from naphthalene vapor to oxygen *(42)*, and determination of quenching constants of $O_2(^1\Delta)$ for a variety of gases in urban atmospheres *(45, 46)*.*

The EPR technique developed by Mahan *et al.* is less sensitive but offers the advantage of yielding approximate values of the absolute concentrations of $O_2(^1\Delta)$. It is based on the measurement of the characteristic four-line EPR

---

*We are indebted to Dr. R. P. Wayne for fabricating our first detector from ultrapure germanium supplied through the courtesy of Mr. Adrian Mears of the Clarendon Laboratory, Oxford.

spectrum centered at $g_J \sim -2/3$ *(31, 47)*. Recently Kearns *et al. (48)* and Wasserman *et al. (49)* independently employed this EPR technique to confirm the gas phase photosensitized generation of $O_2(^1\Delta)$.

Chemical Detectors. Chemical detectors involve acceptor molecules which readily react with $O_2(^1\Delta)$ to produce a characteristic product. Particularly useful in this regard is tetramethylethylene (TME). This was first used in a gas phase system by Winer and Bayes, who followed reaction 13 by gas chromatographic monitoring of the hydroperoxide product (I) *(13)*.

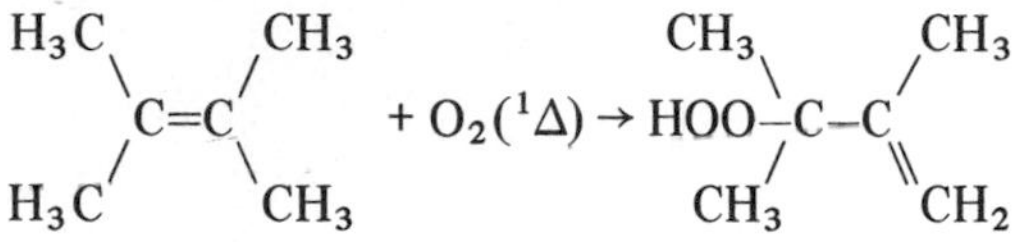

$$\begin{matrix} H_3C \\ \\ H_3C \end{matrix} \begin{matrix} CH_3 \\ C=C \\ CH_3 \end{matrix} + O_2(^1\Delta) \rightarrow \begin{matrix} CH_3 \\ HOO-C-C \\ CH_3 \end{matrix} \begin{matrix} CH_3 \\ \\ CH_2 \end{matrix} \qquad (13)$$

$$\text{(TME)} \qquad\qquad\qquad \text{(I)}$$

Recently we have employed the apparatus shown in Fig. 5 with both TME and dimethyl furan (DMF) as "traps" for $O_2(^1\Delta)$. Product formation was monitored by both gas chromatography and infrared spectroscopy in which a 10-meter-long-path infrared cell was used. Fig. 6 shows the gas phase infrared spectra of TME and the hydroperoxide product (I). My colleagues Drs. Broadbent, Gleason, and Whittle obtained virtually 100% yields of reaction products with this system with both acceptors *(32, 50)*.

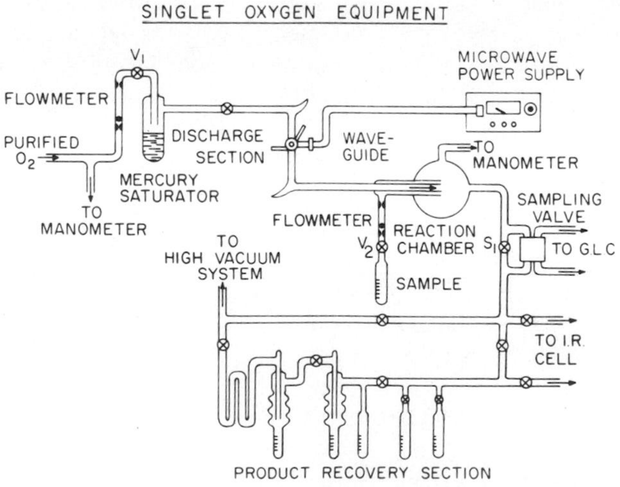

Fig. 5. Diagram of one experimental apparatus used at UCR to study the generation of $O_2(^1\Delta)$ and its gas phase reactions with organic compounds.

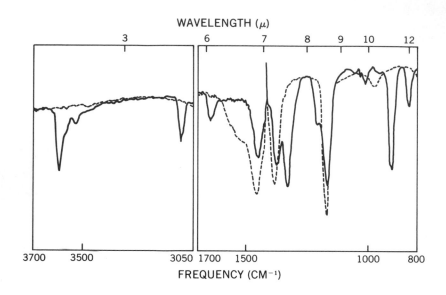

Fig. 6. Gas phase infrared spectra of TME (-- -- -- --) and its reaction product (———)
with singlet oxygen.

Photophysical Processes of $O_2(^1\Delta)$ and $O_2(^1\Sigma)$

Physical Quenching. A particularly important characteristic of the $^1\Delta$ state
is that it is remarkably stable to physical quenching. Thus Arnold *et al.* estimate
that in most laboratory flow systems it can suffer about 2×10^5 collisions with
the walls of the vessel before deactivation *(25)*.

$$O_2(^1\Delta) \xrightarrow{\text{wall}} O_2 \qquad (14)$$

Our recent value of $k_{\text{wall}} \simeq 0.1 \text{ sec}^{-1}$ confirms the stability of $O_2(^1\Delta)$
toward wall quenching *(45)*. The $^1\Delta$ state is also very stable to collisional deactivation by other molecules. This is evident from the values in Table I of the
absolute rate constants for the bimolecular physical quenching process (reaction 15) with "normal" atmospheric molecules. Nitrogen gas with a k_q of about

$$O_2(^1\Delta) + M \xrightarrow{k_q} O_2 + M \qquad (15)$$

50 is virtually ineffective as a quencher, while normal oxygen, the other major
atmospheric gas, has a k_q of only 1.3×10^3 liters mole^{-1} sec^{-1}. Thus Arnold
et al. estimate that at least 10^8 collisions with normal O_2 molecules and perhaps

Table I

Absolute Rate Constants for the Physical Quenching
of $O_2(^1\Delta_g)$ by "Normal" Atmospheric Species

$$O_2(^1\Delta_g) + M \rightarrow O_2(^3\Sigma_g^-) + M$$

M	k_q (liters mole^{-1} sec^{-1})	References
N_2	$\leqslant 80$	Steer *et al. (45)*
	$\leqslant 66$	Clark and Wayne *(26)*
	$\leqslant 1.8$	Findlay *et al.* (51)
Ar	$\leqslant 1.3 \times 10^2$	Clark and Wayne *(26)*
O_2	$1.23 \ (\pm 0.14) \times 10^3$	Steer *et al. (45)*
	$1.31 \ (\pm 0.07) \times 10^3$	Findlay *et al (51)*
	$1.3 \ (\pm 0.3) \times 10^3$	Clark and Wayne *(26)*
CO_2	$2.3 \ (\pm 0.5) \times 10^3$	Clark and Wayne *(26)*
H_2O	$9 \ (\pm 3) \times 10^3$	Clark and Wayne *(26)*

10^{10} with nitrogen molecules are necessary for relaxation of $O_2(^1\Delta)$ to the ground state *(25)*.

In condensed fluid solutions with hydrocarbons or water as quenchers, these quenching results suggest a lifetime of about 10^{-3} sec for $O_2(^1\Delta)$. In gaseous systems, however, the lifetime of $^1\Delta$ is much longer, of the order of 0.05 to 0.5 sec at 1 atmosphere pressure in air *(17;* also I.D. Clark and R.P. Wayne, unpublished data). This is highly relevant to photochemical air pollution. Thus, Bayes points out that, if $^1O_2$ were generated at the rate of 25 pphm per hour in urban air containing 25 pphm of olefin, "at least 50% of the $^1O_2$ will collide with an olefin molecule before being collisionally deactivated" *(13b)*.

Of particular relevance to the deactivation of $O_2(^1\Delta)$ by hydrocarbon pollutants are the data in Table II. These were taken in our laboratory by Mr. Ackerman and Dr. Steer, who followed the quenching of the decay of a 1.27-μ emission by a cooled germanium diode detector.* Most of the simple terminal olefins deactivate with efficiencies of the same order as normal oxygen. However, 2,3-dimethyl-2-butene (tetramethylethylene, TME) is at least two powers faster. This is partially because the value of $3 \ (\pm 2) \times 10^5$ liters mole^{-1} sec^{-1}

---

*Some of these data were obtained subsequent to the Detroit Symposium but are included for the sake of completeness.

Table II

Absolute Rate Constants for the Deactivation of $O_2(^1\Delta_g)$
by Some Simple Olefins Found in Urban Atmospheres [a]

Olefin	k_q (liters mole^{-1} sec^{-1})
Ethylene	1.1 ($\pm$ 0.19) $\times$ 10^3
Propylene	1.3 ($\pm$ 0.11) $\times$ 10^3
1-Butene	1.4 ($\pm$ 0.03) $\times$ 10^3
1-Pentene	1.9 ($\pm$ 0.34) $\times$ 10^3
2,3-Dimethyl-2-butene[b]	3.0 ($\pm$ 2) $\times$ 10^5

[a] Determined by following the rate of decay of 1.27-μ emission; Ackerman *et al.* *(46)*.
Benzene k_q = 3.2 ($\pm$ 0.2) $\times$ 10^3; Findlay *et al.* *(51)*.
[b] Average of values over the pressure range 2 to 10 torr.

includes both physical *and* chemical quenching (reaction 13). Gleason *et al. (32)* have determined k for the latter to be 1 ($\pm$ 0.5) $\times$ 10^5 liters mole^{-1} sec^{-1} by direct measurements of rates of loss of reactant and product formation on a completely different apparatus (similar to the one shown in Fig. 5 but modified for chemical kinetic studies). Despite this chemical effect, clearly TME is also a highly efficient physical quencher, possibly because it acts through some unstable, short-lived intermediate which dissociates back into TME and ground-state oxygen.

The $^1\Sigma$ state is much less stable toward deactivation; only about 100 collisions with molecules of water or a hydrocarbon are required for its deactivation, presumably to the $^1\Delta$ state *(25)* (but possibly also directly to the ground state). This corresponds to a lifetime of $^1\Sigma$ of only about 10^{-9} sec in fluid solutions *(25)*. The rate of quenching of $^1\Sigma$ depends on the nature of the quencher, M. Thus Arnold *et al.* reported quenching rate constants, k_q, ranging from 7 $\times$ 10^5 for M = helium, to 1.5 $\times$ 10^6 for N$_2$, Ar, and CO, to 6 $\times$ 10^8 for H$_2$O (all in units of liters mole^{-1} sec^{-1}) *(25)*. Izod and Wayne recently have confirmed the value for k_q of N$_2$ and have shown that normal oxygen is a very inefficient quencher with k_q = 6 $\times$ 10^4 liters mole^{-1} sec^{-1} *(52)*.

Energy-Pooling Processes – Energy Transfer from $O_2(^1\Delta)$. The excited singlet delta state of oxygen can participate in several unique electronic energy-pooling processes as well as act as an excited donor molecule in several cases of electronic energy transfer. Thus we have already considered the dimol emission at 6340 Å and 7030 Å resulting from certain collisions between two $O_2(^1\Delta)$ molecules (reactions 4 and 5).

Reaction 16 is of particular significance to upper atmosphere chemistry, for it is considered as one possible source for the substantial quantities of $O_2(^1\Sigma)$ observed there *(27, 53)*. Recent studies point to a rate constant of about 10^3

$$O_2(^1\Delta) + O_2(^1\Delta) \rightarrow O_2(^1\Sigma) + O_2 \tag{16a}$$

to 10^4 liters mole^{-1} sec^{-1} for the process *(25, 26, 52)*, far below the first reported value of approximately 10^7 liters mole^{-1} sec^{-1} of Young and Black*(53)*.
Arnold *et al.* have observed energy transfer from $O_2(^1\Delta)$ to (1) another $^1\Delta$

$$O_2(^1\Delta) + A \rightarrow O_2(^3\Sigma) + A^* \tag{16b}$$

molecule, (2) dibenzanthrone, (3) nitrogen dioxide, and (4) iodine atoms *(25)*.
The list is limited because the excitation energy of the $^1\Delta$ state, 22 kcal, is so low that few other molecules have excited triplet states at lower energies and so are capable of acting as acceptors in this system.† One other key acceptor molecule appears to be β-carotene, which Foote and Denny have found to be an extremely efficient quencher of $O_2(^1\Delta)$ *(54)*. Energy transfer from $O_2(^1\Delta)$ to nitrogen dioxide, while interesting to contemplate from the standpoint of photochemical air pollution, is apparently quite inefficient. Thus it is probably not important in the atmosphere and will not be considered here *(55)*.

Chemical Reactions of $O_2(^1\Delta)$

We should preface these remarks by noting that to date there are *no confirmed chemical reactions of* $O_2(^1\Sigma)$ *with organic molecules.*‡ Thus we shall consider only the chemical reactions of the singlet delta state with neutral atoms or molecules, and particularly those of interest in urban atmospheres [see the reviews of Wayne *(26, 27)* and Kummler and Bortner*(56)* for consideration of reactions in the upper atmosphere and with charged species].
In terms of inorganic molecules, one of the most significant reactions is that between $O_2(^1\Delta)$ and ozone, to produce oxygen atoms (reaction 17). This is quite fast, since Wayne and Pitts recently reported $k_{17} = 1.7 \times 10^6$ liters

$$O_2(^1\Delta) + O_3 \rightarrow 2O_2 + O(^3P) \tag{17}$$

---

†Conversely, electronic energy transfer from the excited triplet states of many organic molecules to normal O_2 to produce $O_2(^1\Delta)$ is a highly favored process in the laboratory and in the atmosphere.

‡This was also the consensus of the scientists participating in the International Conference on Singlet Molecular Oxygen and Its Role in Environmental Sciences, sponsored by the New York Academy of Sciences, October 23-25, 1969.

mole^{-1} sec^{-1}, as determined by direct measurement of the decay of the $O_2(^1\Delta)$ emission at 1.27μ *(44)*. This can be compared to the value of 1.2×10^7 for the reaction between nitric oxide and ozone which is very fast and most important in photochemical air pollution *(57)*.

$$NO + O_3 \rightarrow NO_2 + O_2 \qquad (18)$$

There are two general types of reaction of $O_2(^1\Delta)$ with organic molecules: (1) the oxygenation of olefins containing allylic hydrogen atoms resulting in the shift of the double bond and formation of an allylic hydroperoxide; this is analogous to the so-called "ene" reaction; (2) the oxygenation of polycyclic aromatic hydrocarbons such as cyclopentadienes and heterocycles which gives endo-peroxides (transannular peroxides); this is analogous to the Diels-Alder reaction.

Reaction 19 is a general example of case (1), the "ene" reaction; reaction 20 shows case (2), in which $^1O_2$ acts as a dienophile in a 1,4-cycloaddition reaction *(20-24)*.

$$(19)$$

$$(20)$$

$$X = CH_2, \overset{\overset{\displaystyle CH_2}{|}}{CH_2}, O, \text{etc.}$$

Reactions 13 and 21 are specific examples of the "ene" and the Diels-Alder types with TME and dimethyl furan (II) as acceptor molecules. The typical

$$(21)$$

ozonide (III) formed in reaction 21 is unstable as a pure liquid, so in solution phase reactions, methanol is present and compound IV is isolated. However, we have found that III is readily formed in the gas phase by reaction with $^1O_2$ and can be monitored by the use of the 10-meter-long-path infrared cell to monitor its characteristic absorption bands at 1334 and 1131 cm^{-1} *(32, 50)* (see Fig. 7).

Absolute rate constants for the chemical reactions of both TME and dimethyl furan have recently been obtained by Gleason *et al.* in our laboratories *(32)*. Both systems are much more complex kinetically than would appear, so there is a considerable range in their absolute values. They lie in the range $k_{TME} = 1(\pm 0.5) \times 10^5$ liters mole^{-1} sec^{-1} and $k_{DMF} = 3.7(\pm 1.4)$ liters mole^{-1} sec^{-1}.

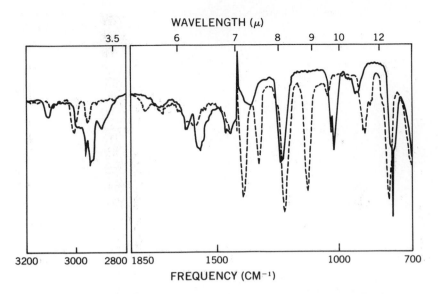

Fig. 7. Gas phase infrared spectra of DMF (———) and its reaction product (-------)
with singlet oxygen ($^1\Delta_g$).

A particularly important reaction of $^1O_2$ is the formation of the endoper-
oxides (VI) of polynuclear aromatic hydrocarbons such as 9,10-diphenyl-
anthracene (reaction 22). The $^1O_2$ can be generated internally by dye

$$\text{(V)} \xrightarrow{\;^1O_2\;} \text{(VI)} \tag{22}$$

photosensitization or the H_2O_2-NaOCl reaction, or externally by a microwave
discharge. The latter technique was used by Corey and Taylor in their definitive
paper in 1964 *(58)*.

Table III shows typical compounds that react with $^1O_2$ and the corresponding oxygenated products *(21)*. The reviews by Foote and Gollnick should be
consulted for details of the mechanisms of the reactions including their stereo-
specific aspects *(20-24)*.

Singlet Molecular Oxygen and the Chemistry of Urban Atmospheres

Having summarized the present status of laboratory knowledge about
$O_2(^1\Delta)$ and $O_2(^1\Sigma)$, we shall now apply this information plus some recent

published and unpublished research to the role of singlet oxygen in urban atmospheres.

To date, four routes have been proposed to account for the formation of singlet molecular oxygen in polluted urban atmospheres of the Los Angeles type (see references in *16* for a review). These were:

Table III

Typical "Acceptor" Molecules and Oxygenated Products for Reactions with Singlet Oxygen[a]

Compound	Product

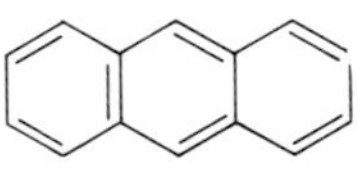

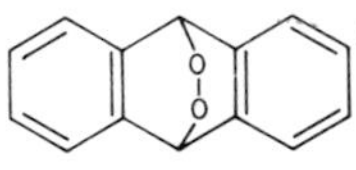

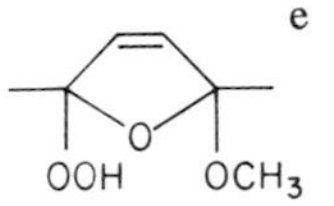

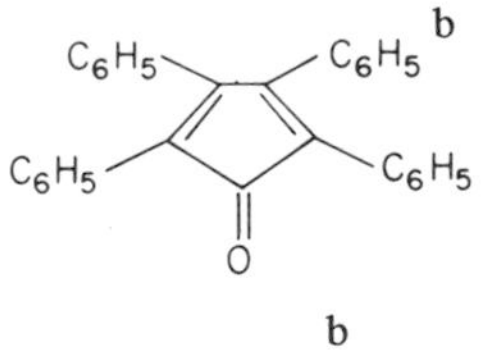

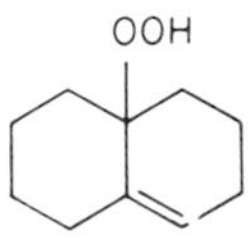

[a] Table taken from the review by Foote *(21)*.
[b] Reference *(36)*.
[c] Unstable product.
[d] Unreactive acceptor, very low yield.
[e] Methanol adduct of unstable endoperoxide.
[f] Presumably formed by loss of CO from intermediate peroxide.
[g] Reference *(41)*.

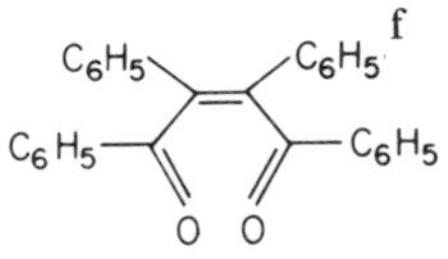

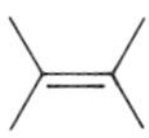

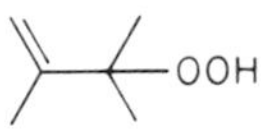

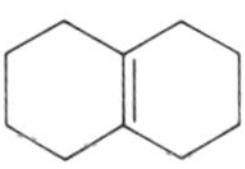

1. Direct absorption of solar radiation by ground-state molecular oxygen, $O_2(^3\Sigma_g^-)$.

2. Absorption of solar radiation by organic pollutant molecules, such as aldehydes, ketones, and polynuclear aromatic hydrocarbons, followed by transfer of energy to ground-state molecular oxygen – the Kautsky mechanism.

3. Photodecomposition of ozone.

4. A product of certain exothermic chemical reactions.

Let us briefly consider the present status of each of these mechanisms and introduce a fifth, the formation of $O_2(^1\Delta)$ by absorption of ultraviolet light by a short-lived oxygen-olefin or oxygen-aromatic hydrocarbon "collision" complex.

Direct Absorption of Sunlight. The possibility that singlet molecular oxygen plays a role in the formation of photochemical smog in the lower atmosphere was first considered in 1961 by our distinguished Chairman, Professor Leighton *(1)*. He made a critical analysis of the existing spectroscopic and photochemical data on the $^1\Sigma$ and $^1\Delta$ states of molecular oxygen (which at that time dealt almost entirely with the $^1\Sigma$ state) and concluded that excitation by direct absorption of solar radiation could not lead to significant stationary concentrations of the $^1\Sigma_g^+$ state in the lower atmosphere. He also raised the possibility that $^1O_2$ could react with hydrocarbons but noted that there was no evidence at that time for such oxidations at room temperature.

In 1964 Bayes considered the possible role of $^1O_2$ in photochemical smog (13*b*). In particular, he showed that, if the absorption coefficients for the forbidden direct absorption processes forming $^1\Delta$ and $^1\Sigma$ (reactions 1 and 2) were corrected to allow for collisional line broadening (assuming a Lorentzian line shape), the rate of direct absorption of solar radiation by oxygen in the lower atmosphere by the collisionally perturbed process 23*a* became significant and that it "may be strong enough to contribute significantly to the reactions of photochemical smog."

$$O_2(^3\Sigma_g^-) + M + h\nu \underset{b}{\overset{a}{\rightleftharpoons}} O_2(^1\Delta_g, {}^1\Sigma_g) + M \qquad (23)$$

Furthermore, he noted that the collisional deactivation of $O_2(^1\Delta)$ by O_2 or N_2 was highly inefficient and concluded that the long lifetime would "permit the average excited oxygen molecule in polluted air to encounter an olefin molecule" (and hence presumably to form a peroxide). Finally, he estimated that in the atmosphere of the Los Angeles Basin the rate of this reaction might compete with the rate of reaction of olefins with oxygen atoms produced by NO_2 photolysis.

Although Bayes' proposal was advanced in 1964, for several years it received relatively little attention. Recently Kummler *et al. (17)* have recalculated the rate of absorption of solar radiation by molecular oxygen using the data of Badger *et al.* *(30)* on the efficiency of collisionally induced absorption of oxygen, process 23*a*. They concluded that the rate of process 23*a* at atmospheric pressure is only about twice that of the unperturbed processes 1*a* and 2*a*. Similar considerations apply to the corresponding rates of emission by process 23*b* versus processes 1*b* and 2*b*. Thus the precise role in forming $^1O_2$ played by direct absorption of sunlight by oxygen in the actual lower atmosphere is still not clear and needs further detailed study.

While the situation in the atmosphere is still not clear, we have recently obtained evidence in our laboratory for the formation of $O_2(^1\Sigma)$ by direct absorption of light in the region 5700 to 7700 Å and for the production of $O_2(^1\Delta)$ following the absorption of ultraviolet light ($\lambda > 2950$ Å) by an oxygen-olefin "collision complex" *(59)*. The means by which we discovered these processes makes an amusing story, and instead of presenting it as though it were a highly organized and preplanned research project, I would rather "tell it like it was."

Dr. Coomber was actually only planning to study the production of $O_2(^1\Delta)$ by energy transfer from excited benzaldehyde (a significant pollutant) under simulated atmospheric conditions in a long-path-length infrared spectrophotometer. This was to be an extension of the work of Kummler and Bortner, who had observed the 1.27-μ emission of $O_2(^1\Delta)$ when they irradiated mixtures of benzaldehyde and oxygen in the millimeter pressure range with the unfiltered output of a 500-watt Hg-Xe arc lamp *(18)*.

Dr. Coomber's experimental technique involved utilizing a modified Perkin-Elmer Model 621 Infrared Spectrophotometer with 40-meter-path-length cells, one of which was fitted with six 7 X 6-cm Pyrex windows through which the gaseous systems could be irradiated (see Fig. 8). In a typical experiment, a mixture of 2.5 ppm of benzaldehyde and 640 ppm of TME in 700 torr of dried laboratory air was irradiated for 4500 seconds, and the transmissions at 3594 cm^{-1} and 906 cm^{-1} were monitored at 200-second intervals *(59)*. These particular infrared frequencies are characteristic of the hydroperoxide product (I) produced in reaction 13 (see Fig. 6).

Upon irradiating such a mixture, and indeed an entire series where various ratios of reactants were employed, he found increased absorptions at both of these key characteristic frequencies. These absorptions neither increased or decreased when the light was switched off, and the ratio of their extinction coefficients was 3.2, in good agreement with the value of 3.1 obtained earlier in our laboratory for authentic macro samples of the hydroperoxide *(32, 50)*.

The results of this series of experiments seemed to confirm clearly that benzaldehyde, even in the ppm range, could absorb radiation and effectively transfer excitation energy to ground-state molecular oxygen to form $O_2(^1\Delta)$.

However, as a check, Dr. Coomber removed all the benzaldehyde from the system and simply irradiated with the full arc a mixture of TME with air

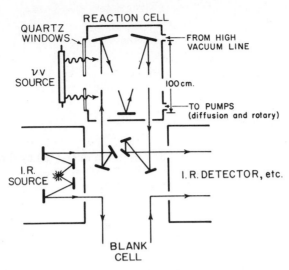

Fig. 8. Diagram of optical path for long path infrared spectrophotometer at UCR.

through the Pyrex windows. Presumably there could be no absorption of radiation under these conditions because TME is transparent at wavelengths of 2950 Å and longer. To our astonishment, the hydroperoxide (I) was still produced under these conditions, although at a substantially slower rate and only when the light was on. The big question was, How could a photochemical reaction occur in this system in the absence of a sensitizer to absorb the radiation from the light source?

To make a long story short, after a number of experiments under a variety of conditions including the use of filters isolating various spectral regions, we finally reached the conclusion that, in addition to the benzaldehyde-sensitized process, two other processes were occurring *(59, 60).* * These were:

1. The direct absorption of visible radiation in the region 5500 to 7700 Å by normal oxygen to produce $O_2(^1\Sigma)$. This probably was quickly quenched to the $^1\Delta$ state which actually reacted with the TME.

2. Absorption of ultraviolet light in the approximate region 3000 to 3400 Å by a short-lived collision complex between normal oxygen and tetramethylethylene. This produced either $O_2(^1\Delta)$ which then reacted with TME,

---

*The question has been raised as to whether we might have actually been observing a free radical attack on TME rather than its reaction with singlet oxygen. This possibility cannot be ruled out unequivocally, but it seems unlikely under our experimental procedures and in view of the reproducible results we obtained.

or TME in the triplet state which could have reacted with normal oxygen to form the hydroperoxide.*

While it is too early to discuss our experimental results in detail, our observed rates of formation of hydroperoxides suggest that both of these latter processes will be relatively insignificant in urban atmospheres compared to other possible sources of $^1O_2$, including energy transfer and possibly the direct photolysis of ozone. Thus, they will not be discussed further except to note that we are continuing our studies on the effect of oxygen in the 0.20- to 1-atm range on the absorptions of various olefins, aromatic hydrocarbons, and other organic molecules of environmental interest. This is far from the conditions of Evans, who used up to 50 atm of oxygen in his pioneering spectroscopic studies of the absorption spectra of systems of oxygen-organic molecules *(61)*.† We have observed, however, that even at the oxygen concentrations in air, significant enhancements can be observed in the liquid phase absorptivities of these compounds, and their absorption edges are shifted to significantly longer wavelengths *(60)*. This is particularly significant in atmospheric photochemistry because many olefins which have been assumed to be transparent to sunlight because of the cutoff of solar radiation at about 2950 Å might actually have weak absorptions above 2950 Å because of this oxygen-induced red shift. The absorptions, of course, would be very weak because of the relatively low concentrations of organic molecules in urban atmospheres. However, this is partially compensated for by the very long path lengths that are involved, of the order of a kilometer.

This oxygen-induced red shift in the absorption spectra of organic molecules might have applications in a variety of environmental areas including photodegradation of polymers such as polyvinylchloride, the photoconversion of provitamin D to vitamin D in animal skin, and the photooxidation of benzene at 3130 Å. These are considered briefly in a paper we have recently submitted to *Environmental Science and Technology (60)*.

Production of Singlet Molecular Oxygen by an Energy Transfer Mechanism. This mechanism, which my colleagues Drs. Khan and Smith and I first proposed in 1967, bypasses the problem of very weak direct absorption of solar radiation by suggesting that significant concentrations of singlet oxygen could be produced indirectly by triplet electronic energy transfer from electronically excited organic molecules *(15, 16)*. Thus a high yield of singlet oxygen can be obtained if solar radiation is absorbed first by an organic molecule and then, on collision, electronic energy is transferred from this donor (in its triplet state) to oxygen to produce electronically excited oxygen, $^1O_2$. This overall atmospheric mechanism

---

*Another possibility is that the hydroperoxide was formed directly in the dissociation of the excited collision complex.

†For detailed studies of this phenomenon, see the papers of Tsubomura and Mulliken *(62)* and the recent review by Hoytink *(63)*.

is identical with the Kautsky mechanism for laboratory photosensitized oxygenation reactions discussed earlier and shown in processes 9, 10, and 11 and in Fig. 4.

At the time we initially advanced our proposal, there was substantial laboratory evidence supporting the Kautsky energy transfer mechanism in liquid solutions but virtually no evidence for its validity in gas phase systems. Furthermore, there were conflicting reports as to the rate of the gas phase reactions of $O_2(^1\Delta)$ with olefins such as TME. However, during the last year this theory has been greatly strengthened by experimental confirmation of both ideas. Thus, as we have seen, there has been direct spectroscopic confirmation of $O_2(^1\Delta)$ being produced by gas phase energy transfer to oxygen from irradiated gaseous aromatic hydrocarbons with (π, π^*) triplet states such as benzene and naphthalene *(42, 43, 48, 49)* and carbonyl compounds with (n, π^*) triplets such as benzaldehyde *(18, 59)*. Furthermore, $O_2(^1\Delta)$ generated externally by a microwave generator reacts rapidly and efficiently in the gas phase with the olefin tetramethylethylene and the heterocyclic molecule 2,5-dimethyl furan *(32, 50)*.

Finally, we have confirmed chemically the generation of $^1O_2$ by a gas phase energy transfer process by using TME as a "trap" for $O_2(^1\Delta)$ and detecting the hydroperoxide product (I) when either benzene *(42)* or benzaldehyde *(59)* was the sensitizer.

It is particularly significant that a wide range of different chemical species of donor molecules is effective in producing $^1O_2$, and that energy transfer has been shown for heterogeneous gas-solid systems as well as gas-liquid and homogeneous gaseous systems *(64)*. Thus, singlet oxygen may be formed by quenching of triplet aromatics in the solid phase, as Kautsky originally proposed.

Clearly the transfer of energy at gas-solid interfaces may be of considerable significance in view of the presence of not only organic but also inorganic particulate matter in polluted urban air. At present, the possible role of inorganic particulates such as lead compounds in such a mechanism is not clear but it merits careful examination.

The rate of formation of singlet oxygen in the energy transfer mechanism depends on the rate of absorption by the donor molecules. In the lower atmosphere these donors must absorb radiation at wavelengths longer than 2950 Å because the ozonosphere cuts off solar radiation below that wavelength. With this stipulation, the donors may be aromatic hydrocarbons directly emitted to the atmosphere, carbonyl compounds such as aldehydes which may be either primary contaminants or secondary contaminants produced by photochemical reactions of olefins in smoggy atmospheres, or a variety of other absorbing species. The absorbing donor molecule may be in the solid, liquid, or gaseous state, or adsorbed on a solid.

With these considerations in mind, we calculated a very approximate value for the rate of absorption of near-ultraviolet solar radiation in a polluted atmosphere by making certain, necessarily drastic, simplifying assumptions *(14, 15)*.

We estimated that in a column of air extending from the earth's surface to the inversion level, about 1 km, the production rate of excited organic molecules on a smoggy day in the Los Angeles Basin is approximately 4×10^{-12} mole liter^{-1} sec^{-1}.

A comparable calculation of the absorption by NO_2 of solar ultraviolet radiation in the wavelength region 2900 to 3850 Å *(1)* indicates that, if the drastic assumptions cited above are valid, the absorption rates by NO_2 and by organic compounds will be approximately equal when the nitrogen dioxide concentration is around 10 pphm *(15)*. The calculations therefore suggest that the absorption by polynuclear aromatic hydrocarbon and carbonyl compounds in typical polluted atmospheres may be significant relative to absorption by NO_2 in the photochemically reactive region. Confirmation of this estimate awaits more accurate measurements of the absorption of solar ultraviolet light in urban atmospheres and possibly direct measurements of the $O_2(^1\Delta)$ concentrations in urban air.

Singlet Molecular Oxygen from Ozone Photolysis. If ozone is irradiated with ultraviolet light in the Hartley band (2000 to 3200 Å), it photodissociates into an electronically excited oxygen atom, $O(^1D)$, and molecular oxygen.

$$O_3 + h\nu \, (\lambda < 3200 \text{ Å}) \rightarrow O(^1D) + O_2 \text{ (possibly } {}^1O_2) \qquad (24)$$

Considerable evidence has accumulated that singlet molecular oxygen is produced in the photolysis *(26, 65)* and that reaction 24 is particularly important in the upper atmosphere (see reference *27* for a review).

With regard to the lower atmosphere, Kummler *et al.* have suggested that O_3 photolysis could also be a source of singlet molecular oxygen in polluted atmospheres, though probably a minor one relative to the energy transfer mechanism [see the detailed arguments of Kummler *et al. (17)*].

One important consequence of the formation of $O(^1D)$ atoms in reaction 24 is its probable participation in the energy transfer process (reaction 25).

$$O(^1D) + O_2 \rightarrow O_2(^1\Sigma) + O(^3P) \qquad (25)$$

The reaction of $O(^1D)$ with normal O_2 results in the formation of two oxidizing species — singlet molecular oxygen and ground-state atomic oxygen. The excess photochemical energy carried by $O(^1D)$ has been made available for photooxidation. Secondly, this enhancement of oxidant potential by reaction 25 makes it important to look for other atmospheric sources of $O(^1D)$. The photolysis of NO_2 itself is excluded, since the formation of $O(^1D)$ in reaction 26 requires more energy than is available in the solar radiation reaching polluted atmospheres.

$$NO_2 + h\nu \rightarrow NO + O(^1D) \tag{26}$$

However, it may be important in its photochemistry of the upper atmosphere where ultraviolet radiation of short wavelength is present.

Singlet Molecular Oxygen from Exothermic Chemical Reactions. The possibility that singlet molecular oxygen can be the product of an exothermic chemical reaction in which photochemical excitation is not the direct source of energy (although it may well be the indirect source) is intriguing. In photochemical air pollution, the most obvious reaction is that between NO and O_3

$$NO + O_3 \rightarrow NO_2{}^* + O_2(^1O_2?) \tag{27}$$

The reaction is highly exothermic and leads to electronically excited NO_2. Furthermore, production of $O_2(^1\Delta_g)$ as well as $NO_2{}^*$ seems reasonable because it leads to conservation of spins. Alternatively, in the presence of molecular oxygen an energy transfer process could occur. While these arguments

$$NO_2{}^* + O_2 \rightarrow NO_2 + {}^1O_2 \tag{28}$$

seem plausible, to date our preliminary studies of the emission from the NO-O_3 system (reaction 27) give negative results as far as $^1O_2$ production is concerned *(66)*.

Ozone might also react in a manner similar to reaction 27 with a variety of other atmospheric contaminants (such as sulfides) ultimately to yield singlet molecular oxygen as a product. Processes of this type are known to lead to $^1O_2$ formation in condensed phases, and Murray and Kaplan have noted the possible significance of such processes to air pollution *(19, 37)*.

Finally, Stephens had reported that the alkaline hydrolysis of PAN gives molecular oxygen *(67)*. To us it was intriguing from the point of view of

$$CH_3C \underset{OONO_2}{\overset{O}{\diagdown}} + 2OH^- \rightarrow CH_3C \underset{O}{\overset{O^-}{\diagup}} + H_2O + NO_2^- + O_2 \tag{29}$$

photochemical oxidant to speculate that it may be produced in the excited singlet state.

Recently we studied this reaction in our laboratory, and Drs. Steer and Darnall observed the 1.27-μ emission characteristic of $O_2(^1\Delta)$ when 0.4 M KOH in benzene-methanol (9:1) was added to dilute solutions of PAN in benzene *(68)*.

The great reactivity of PAN in chemical systems and in biological *in vitro* and *in vivo* systems is well documented, but little understood. Thus PAN is an important cause of eye irritation and plant damage in polluted urban atmospheres *(69, 70)*, and studies with simpler systems have shown that it can act as both an acetylating and an oxidizing agent *(71)*. Our results suggest that singlet molecular oxygen may have to be considered not only as a possible environmental oxidant but also in the elucidation of the mechanism(s) of chemical and biological oxidation by PAN.

Environmental Implications of Singlet Molecular Oxygen

Let me conclude by alluding briefly to several environmental implications of the possible presence of singlet molecular oxygen in urban atmospheres.* First, there is the possible role of $O_2(^1\Delta)$ in the photoconversion of nitric oxide to nitrogen dioxide, which we discussed at the beginning of this lecture. As we stated, the photoconversion of NO to NO_2 remains one of the perplexing problems of photochemical air pollution. We have proposed the possible involvement of $^1O_2$ as one part of a very complex mechanism for this conversion *(14, 15)*. It is based on the idea that singlet oxygen formed by energy transfer from the donor organic molecules will react with olefinic hydrocarbons to give hydroperoxides. These hydroperoxides are thermally unstable and sensitive to surface catalysis as well as photochemically reactive (reaction 30). Thus they could

$$RCOOH + h\nu \rightarrow RCO + OH \qquad (30)$$

decompose to give free radicals of the same type as those formed in the direct attack of atomic oxygen on olefins and aldehydes (for example, OH radicals). From this point on, the reactions resemble those of the NO_x-olefin-air system and could occur simultaneously. Thus the involvement of $^1O_2$ would be a concurrent process, admittedly possibly minor, to the overall reaction.

Singlet molecular oxygen may also play a significant role in the pathology of man, animals, and plants. In this connection, Foote has mentioned the implications of the production of skin cancer by photosensitizing dyes and polycyclic hydrocarbons *(20, 21)*. Furthermore, the possible effects of singlet oxygen on plants are worth serious consideration. To date there has been no direct evidence that singlet oxygen is a phytotoxicant, but there are some suggestions from studies on ozone damage that it may be implicated. We are currently exposing plants in our laboratories to atmospheres containing singlet oxygen and with the collaboration of Dr. O. C. Taylor hope to be able to evaluate its potential as a phytotoxicant. Finally, singlet molecular oxygen may well be involved in the degradation in polluted atmospheres of susceptible natural and synthetic substances with consequent economic loss.

---

*For detailed discussions, see the reviews of Foote *(20, 21)* and Pitts *(16)*.

Acknowledgment

I should like to express my great appreciation to the members of my research group and to visiting senior research scholars Drs. E. Whittle and R. P. Wayne for their many and varied contributions to our program of research on singlet oxygen and photochemical air pollution; to the National Air Pollution Control Administration who funded our work through Grants AP 00109 and 00771; and to my secretary Mrs. Constance Bennett who prepared this manuscript.

References

1. P. A. Leighton, "Photochemistry of Air Pollution," Academic Press, New York, 1961.

2. A.P. Altshuller and J.J. Bufalini, *Photochem. Photobiol.,* **4,** 97 (1965).

3. R.J. Cvetanovic, *Advan. Photochem.,* **1,** 115 (1963); *J. Air Pollution Control Assoc.,* **14,** 208 (1964).

4. E.R. Stephens, *Intern. J. Air Water Pollution,* **10,** 649 (1966).

5. E.R. Stephens, *Advan. Environ. Sci.,* **1,** 119 (1969).

6. A.J. Haagen-Smit and L.G. Wayne, in "Air Pollution," Vol. 1, 2nd ed. (A.C. Stern, ed.), Academic Press, New York, 1968, p. 149.

7. E.A. Schuck and E.R. Stephens, *Advan. Environ. Sci.,* **1,** 73 (1969).

8. A.P. Altshuller, *Intern. J. Air Water Pollution,* **10,** 713 (1966).

9. J.N. Pitts, Jr., *J. Air Pollution Control Assoc.,* **19,** 658 (1969).

10. "Air Quality Criteria for Photochemical Oxidants," NAPCA Publication No. AP-63, U.S. Department of Health, Education and Welfare, Public Health Service, Consumer Protection and Environmental Health Service, National Air Pollution Control Administration, Washington, D.C., March 1970.

11. "Air Quality Criteria for Sulfur Oxides," NAPCA Publication No. AP-50, U.S. Department of Health, Education and Welfare, Public Health Service, Consumer Protection and Environmental Health Service, National Air Pollution Control Administration, Washington, D.C., January 1969.

12. "Air Quality Criteria for Particulate Matter," NAPCA Publication No. AP-49, U. S. Department of Health, Education and Welfare, Public Health Service, Consumer Protection and Environmental Health Service, National Air Pollution Control Administration, Washington, D.C., January 1969.

13. *(a)* A.M. Winer and K.D. Bayes, *J. Phys. Chem.,* **70,** 302 (1966); *(b)* K.D. Bayes, Sixth Informal Photochemistry Conference, University of California, Davis, June 1964.

14. A.U. Khan, J.N. Pitts, Jr., and E.B. Smith, *Environ. Sci. Technol.,* **1,** 656 (1967); J.N. Pitts, Jr., AAAS Divisional Symposium on Air Pollution, University of California, Los Angeles, June 1967.

15. J.N. Pitts, Jr., A.U. Kahn, E.B. Smith, and R.P. Wayne, *Environ. Sci. Technol.,* **3,** 241 (1969).

16. J.N. Pitts, Jr., *Advan. Environ. Sci.,* **1,** 289 (1969).

17. R.H. Kummler, M.H. Bortner, and T. Baurer, *Environ. Sci. Technol.,* **3,** 248 (1969).

18. R.H. Kummler and M.H. Bortner, private communication, 1968; *Environ. Sci. Technol.,* **3,** 944 (1969).

19. R.W. Murray and M. L. Kaplan, *J. Am. Chem. Soc.,* **90,** 4161 (1968); see also later papers by Murray *et al.*

20. C.S. Foote, *Science,* **162,** 963 (1968).
21. C.S. Foote, *Accounts Chem. Res.,* **1,** 104 (1968).
22. K. Gollnick, *Advan. Photochem.,* **6,** 2 (1968).
23. K. Gollnick, *Advan. Chem. Ser.,* **77,** 78 (1968).
24. K. Gollnick and G.O. Schenck, in "1,4-Cycloaddition Reactions" (J. Hamer, ed.), Academic Press, New York, 1967, p. 255.
25. S.J. Arnold, M. Kubo, and E.A. Ogryzlo, *Advan. Chem. Ser.,* **77,** 133 (1968).
26. R.P. Wayne, *Advan. Photochem.,* **7,** 311 (1969).
27. R.P. Wayne, *Quart. J. Roy. Meteorol. Soc.,* **93,** 395 (1967).
28. G. Herzberg, "Spectra of Diatomic Molecules," 2nd ed., Van Nostrand, Princeton, New Jersey, 1950.
29. J.G. Calvert and J.N. Pitts, Jr., "Photochemistry," Wiley, New York, 1966.
30. R.M. Badger, A.C. Wright, and R.F. Whitlock, *J. Chem. Phys.,* **43,** 4345 (1965).
31. A.M. Falick and B.H. Mahan, *J. Chem. Phys.,* **47,** 4778 (1967).
32. W.S. Gleason, A.D. Broadbent, E. Whittle and J.N. Pitts, Jr., *J. Am. Chem. Soc.,* **92,** 2068 (1970).
33. E.J. Bowen and R.A. Lloyd, *Proc. Roy Soc.,* **A275,** 465 (1963); *Proc. Chem. Soc.,* 305 (1963); E.J. Bowen, *Nature,* **201,** 180 (1964).
34. A.U. Khan and M. Kasha, *J. Chem. Phys.,* **39,** 2105 (1963); **40,** 605 (1964); *Nature,* **204,** 241 (1964).
35. R.J. Browne and E.A. Ogryzlo, *Proc. Chem. Soc.,* 117 (1964); J.S. Arnold, R.J. Browne, and E.A. Ogryzlo, *Photochem. Photobiol.,* **4,** 963 (1965).
36. C.S. Foote and S. Wexler, *J. Am. Chem. Soc.,* **86,** 3879 (1964); **86,** 3880 (1964).
37. R.W. Murray and M. L. Kaplan, *J. Am. Chem. Soc.,* **91,** 5358 (1969).
38. H. Kautsky, *Biochem. Z.,* **291,** 271 (1937); *Trans. Faraday Soc.,* **35,** 216 (1939).
39. E.J. Bowen, *Advan. Photochem.,* **1,** 23 (1963).
40. R. Livingston, in "Autooxidation and Antioxidants," Vol. 1 (W.O. Lundberg, ed.), Interscience, New York, 1961, p. 249.
41. C.S. Foote, S. Wexler, W. Ando and R. Higgins, *J. Am. Chem. Soc.,* **90,** 975 (1968).
42. R.P. Steer, J.L. Sprung, and J.N. Pitts, Jr., *Environ. Sci. Technol.,* **3,** 946 (1969).
43. D.R. Snelling, *Chem. Phys. Letters,* **2,** 346 (1968).
44. R.P. Wayne and J.N. Pitts, Jr., *J. Chem. Phys.,* **50,** 3644 (1969).
45. R.P. Steer, R.A. Ackerman and J.N. Pitts, Jr., *J. Chem. Phys.,* **51,** 843 (1969).
46. R.A. Ackerman, J.N. Pitts, Jr. and R.P. Steer, *J. Chem. Phys.,* **52,** 1603 (1970).
47. A.M. Falick, B.H. Mahan and R.J. Myers, *J. Chem. Phys.,* **42,** 1837 (1965).
48. D.R. Kearns, A.U. Khan, C.K. Duncan and A.H. Maki, *J. Am. Chem. Soc.,* **91,** 1039 (1969).
49. E. Wasserman, V.J. Kuck, W.M. Delevan and W.A. Yager, *J. Am. Chem. Soc.,* **91,** 1040 (1969).
50. A.D. Broadbent, W.S. Gleason, J.N. Pitts, Jr., and E. Whittle, *Chem. Commun.,* 1315 (1968).
51. F.D. Findlay, C.J. Fortin and D.R. Snelling, *Chem. Phys. Letters,* **3,** 204 (1969).
52. T.P.J. Izod and R.P. Wayne, *Proc. Roy. Soc.,* **A308,** 81 (1968).
53. R.A. Young and G. Black, *J. Chem. Phys.,* **42,** 3740 (1965).
54. C.S. Foote and R. Denny, *J. Am. Chem. Soc.,* **90,** 6233 (1968).
55. S.J. Arnold, N. Finlayson and E.A. Ogryzlo, *J. Chem. Phys.,* **44,** 2529 (1965).
56. R.H. Kummler and M.H. Bortner, G.E. Report R67SD20, G.E. Space Sciences Laboratory, Philadelphia, Pa. (1967).
57. H.S. Johnston and H.J. Crosby, *J. Chem. Phys.,* **22,** 689 (1954).
58. E.J. Corey and W.C. Taylor, *J. Am. Chem. Soc.,* **86,** 3881 (1964).
59. J.W. Coomber and J.N. Pitts, Jr., *Environ. Sci. Technol.,* **4,** 506 (1970).

60. J.W. Coomber, D.M. Hebert, D.G. Marsh and J.N. Pitts, Jr., *Environ. Sci. Technol.*, in press.
61. D.F. Evans, *J. Chem. Soc.*, 345 (1953) (see references *60, 62*, and *63* for later papers).
62. H. Tsubomura and R.S. Mulliken, *J. Am. Chem. Soc.*, **82**, 5966 (1960).
63. G.J. Hoytink, *Accounts Chem. Res.*, **2**, 114 (1969).
64. R.L. Daubendiek, H. Magid and G.R. McMillan, *Chem. Commun.*, 218 (1968).
65. W.B. DeMore and O.F. Raper, *J. Chem. Phys.*, **44**, 1780 (1966).
66. R.P. Wayne, R.P. Steer, and J.N. Pitts, Jr., unpublished results.
67. E.R. Stephens, *Atmos. Environ.*, **1**, 19 (1967).
68. R.P. Steer, K.R. Darnall and J.N. Pitts, Jr., *Tetrahedron Letters*, **43**, 3765 (1969).
69. E.R. Stephens, E.F. Darley, O.C. Taylor and W.E. Scott, *Intern. J. Air Water Pollution*, **4**, 79 (1961).
70. W.M. Dugger, Jr., and I.P. Ting, *Phytopathology*, **58**, 1102 (1968), and references cited therein.
71. J.B. Mudd, *J. Biol. Chem.*, **241**, 4077 (1966); J.B. Mudd and W.M. Dugger, Jr., *Arch. Biochem. Biophys.*, **102**, 52 (1963).

Discussion

J.T. HERRON: R.E. Huie and I have carried out some rate measurements for the reactions of $O_2(^1\Delta_g)$ with olefins and some other organic reactants. Singlet oxygen was prepared by electrical discharge as described by Arnold *et al.** The reactions were followed continuously by means of a mass spectrometer.

Our approach has been to work under conditions where the $O_2(^1\Delta_g)$ concentration greatly exceeds that of the organic reactant. If $O_2(^1\Delta_g)$ is not appreciably consumed by reaction, then the rate constant can be found from the rate of loss of organic reactant and the $O_2(^1\Delta_g)$ concentration. The latter was measured by a titration method with 2,5-dimethylfuran as a titrant.

Our results are listed in Table IV, along with data for the comparable atomic oxygen reactions. It can be seen that, unless the concentration of $O_2(^1\Delta_g)$ in the atmosphere is of the order of 10^5 times as great as that of atomic oxygen, it cannot play a major role in the degradation of unsaturated hydrocarbons in the atmosphere. It should be noted in this context that atomic oxygen reactions are themselves less important than the comparable ozone reactions.

J.N. PITTS, JR.: We agree that $O_2(^1\Delta_g)$ is probably not responsible for the degradation of a significant fraction of the hydrocarbons present in polluted atmospheres (see references *45* and *46* of our preceding paper). This conclusion has been confirmed recently in our laboratories by obtaining the following additional rate constants for the removal of $O_2(^1\Delta_g)$ by olefins in the gas phase.

---

*S.J. Arnold, M. Kubo, and E.A. Ogryzlo, *Advan. Chem. Ser.*, **77**, 133 (1968).

Olefin	k_q (liters mole^{-1} sec^{-1})
2-Methyl-2-butene	$(1.4 \pm 0.2) \times 10^4$
2-Methyl-2-pentene	$(1.0 \pm 0.3) \times 10^4$
1,3-Butadiene	$(7.8 \pm 0.6) \times 10^3$
1,3-Pentadiene	$(6.3 \pm 0.9) \times 10^4$
Benzene	$(1.3 \pm 0.2) \times 10^3$

Table IV

Rate Constants for Some Reactions of O^3P and $O_2(^1\Delta_g)$

Reactant	k (cm^3 mole^{-1} sec^{-1})		$k(O^3P)/k[O_2(^1\Delta_g)]$
	O^3P	$O_2(^1\Delta_g)^a$	
Ethylene	4×10^{11} [b-d]	$\leqslant 1 \times 10^7$	4×10^4
Propene	2×10^{12} [e-g]	$\leqslant 1 \times 10^7$	$\geqslant 2 \times 10^5$
1-Butene	2.5×10^{12} [b,f,g]	$\leqslant 1 \times 10^7$	$\geqslant 2.5 \times 10^5$
Isobutene	1×10^{13} [b,f,h]	$-$	$-$
2-Butene	1×10^{13} [b,f]	$\leqslant 1 \times 10^7$	$\geqslant 1 \times 10^6$
2-Methyl-2-butene	4×10^{13} [i]	$\leqslant 1 \times 10^7$	$\geqslant 4 \times 10^6$
2,3-Dimethyl-2-butene	5×10^{13} [i]	1.0×10^9	$\geqslant 5 \times 10^4$
2,3-Dimethyl-2-pentene	$-$	7.0×10^8	$-$
3-Hexyne	$-$	$\leqslant 1 \times 10^7$	$-$
1,3-Pentadiene	$-$	$\leqslant 1 \times 10^7$	$-$
1-Methylcyclopentene	$-$	1.5×10^7	$-$
1,2-Dimethylcyclopentene	$-$	4×10^8	$-$
1,2-Dimethylcyclohexene	$-$	4×10^8	$-$
1,3-Cyclohexadiene	$-$	9×10^7	$-$
1,4-Cyclohexadiene	$-$	$\leqslant 1 \times 10^7$	$-$
Benzene	4×10^{10} [j]	$\leqslant 1 \times 10^7$	$> 4 \times 10^3$
o-Xylene	7×10^{11} [j]	$\leqslant 1 \times 10^7$	$\geqslant 7 \times 10^4$
2,5-Dimethylfuran	$\leqslant 10^{14}$ [k]	1.6×10^{10}	$\leqslant 6 \times 10^3$

[a] J.T. Herron and R.E. Huie, *J. Chem. Phys.*, **51**, 4164 (1969).
[b] L. Elias, *J. Chem. Phys.*, **38**, 989 (1963).
[c] A.A. Westenberg and N. de Haas, "Twelfth Symposium (International) on Combustion," The Combustion Institute, 1969, p. 289.
[d] H. Niki, E.E. Daby, and B. Weinstock, "Twelfth Symposium (International) on Combustion," The Combustion Institute, 1969, p. 277.
[e] S.J. Moss and K.R. Jennings, *Trans. Faraday Soc.*, **64**, 686 (1968).
[f] R.J. Cvetanovic, *J. Chem. Phys.*, **30**, 19 (1959).
[g] D. Saunders and J. Heicklen, *J. Phys. Chem.*, **70**, 1950 (1966).
[h] I.W.M. Smith, *Trans. Faraday Soc.*, **64**, 378 (1968).
[i] R.J. Cvetanovic, *J. Chem. Phys.*, **33**, 1063 (1960).
[j] J. Mani and M.C. Sauer, Jr., *Advan. Chem. Ser.*, **82**, 142 (1968).
[k] Estimated.

These results were obtained by monitoring the 1.27-μ emission from $O_2(^1\Delta_g)$ in a discharge flow system as previously described. This technique does not rely on knowledge of the absolute concentration of $O_2(^1\Delta_g)$, a quantity which is not trivial to obtain. (See reference *32* of preceding paper.)

The Photolysis and Photooxidation of Alkyl Nitrites

G. R. McMillan, Jalaj Kumari, and D. L. Snyder
Department of Chemistry
Case Western Reserve University
Cleveland, Ohio

Abstract

The photochemistry of alkyl nitrites is of interest to workers in the air pollution field because of (1) the appreciable absorption of solar radiation by these compounds, (2) the likelihood that they are formed in oxidizing atmospheres, and (3) their formation of ozone and PAN on photooxidation. The present state of knowledge of the photochemistry of various C_2 to C_5 alkyl nitrites is reviewed. The discussion includes the primary photochemical dissociation, subsequent reactions of the alkoxy radicals formed by the dissociation, the importance of vibrationally excited alkoxy radicals, and the suitability of nitrites as radical sources in air pollution studies.

Introduction

The photochemistry of alkyl nitrites has attracted the interest of workers in the air pollution field for several years. The absorption coefficients are appreciable in the wavelength region 3200 to 4000 Å (Fig. 1); the photooxidation of these compounds produces ozone and peroxyacetyl nitrate (PAN). Small amounts of nitrites are detected in laboratory experiments on NO_2-photosensitized oxida-

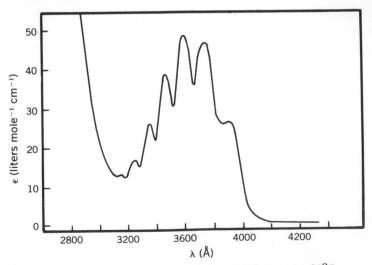

Fig. 1. Ultraviolet absorption spectrum of isopropyl nitrite vapor at 25°C.

References, p. 43

tion of olefins *(1)*, presumably through combination of alkoxy radicals with nitric oxide. Whether reaction 1,

$$RO + NO \rightarrow RONO, \tag{1}$$

is to be expected in real oxidizing atmospheres depends on uncertain values of rate constants of other reactions of alkoxy radicals. In any case, the concentration of alkyl nitrites in the atmosphere would remain very low because of rapid photolysis *(2)*. The aspects of nitrite photochemistry to be discussed here include the primary process, the importance of vibrationally excited alkoxy radicals, and the suitibility of nitrites as radical sources in laboratory studies related to air pollution.

Nature and Efficiency of Primary Dissociation

When the gas phase photochemistry of alkyl nitrites was reviewed in 1966 *(3)*, it seemed that the sole primary process in the near-ultraviolet region of the spectrum could be represented

$$RONO + h\nu \rightarrow aRO* + [1-a]RO + NO \tag{2}$$

A part of the alkoxy radicals (*) are supposed to be vibrationally excited and decompose rapidly. The primary quantum yield for dissociation, ϕ_2, has been assumed to be unity *(4)*; however, published reports *(5, 6)* and new results reported in this paper show that a primary yield of unity is unusual. The excited radical fraction, a, is usually evaluated from the quantum yield of decomposition products of excited alkoxy radicals, measured in experiments with added NO to scavenge unexcited alkoxy radicals. It seems that vibrationally excited radicals decompose only to a carbonyl compound and an alkyl radical, as do the unexcited radicals formed in thermal decompositions.

In the following sections are summarized published findings on photolysis at 3660 Å of tertiary and secondary alkyl nitrites, together with new results on primary alkyl nitrites.

tert-*Butyl Nitrite (7)*

In the presence of added NO the main reactions are:

$$(CH_3)_3CONO + h\nu \rightarrow a(CH_3)_3CO* + [1-a](CH_3)_3CO + NO \tag{3}$$

$$(CH_3)_3CO* \rightarrow CH_3COCH_3 + CH_3 \tag{4}$$

$$(CH_3)_3CO + NO \rightarrow (CH_3)_3CONO \tag{5}$$

$$CH_3 + NO \rightarrow CH_3NO \tag{6}$$

The CH_3COCH_3 quantum yield is 0.04, independent of NO pressure up to 44 torr. If the photolysis is carried out in the presence of ^{15}NO, the yield of incorporation of ^{15}N leads to a primary yield of dissociation of about 0.98 at $25^{\circ}C$.

Isopropyl Nitrite (6)

The principal reactions when NO is present are:

$$(CH_3)_2CHONO + h\nu \rightarrow a(CH_3)_2CHO^* + [1 - a] \, (CH_3)_2CHO + NO \qquad (7)$$

$$(CH_3)_2CHO^* \rightarrow CH_3CHO + CH_3 \qquad (8)$$

$$(CH_3)_2CHO + NO \rightarrow CH_3COCH_3 + HNO \qquad (9)$$

$$(CH_3)_2CHO + NO \rightarrow (CH_3)_2CHONO \qquad (10)$$

$$CH_3 + NO \rightarrow CH_3NO \qquad (6)$$

Alkoxy radicals react with NO by disproportionation (reaction 9) and combination (reaction 10). These processes have been discussed in detail by Heicklen and Cohen *(8)*. For nitrites with an a-hydrogen, the following type of primary process has been considered *(9)*.

$$(CH_3)_2CHONO + h\nu \rightarrow CH_3COCH_3 + HNO \qquad (11)$$

The evidence interpreted in terms of this type of reaction will not be discussed here, but it seems that such evidence may be interpreted in terms of the well-established step shown in reaction 9. The CH_3COCH_3 quantum yield places the primary yield of reaction 11 as < 0.06 at $26^{\circ}C$.

The quantum yields of CH_3CHO and CH_3COCH_3 are found to be independent of $(CH_3)_2CHONO$ pressure over the range investigated, 4 to 18 torr, and independent of NO pressure over the range investigated, 12 to 45 torr. This constancy suggests that reactions 8, 9, and 10 are the only fates of isopropoxy radicals. If so, the following equations apply:

$$\phi I_a = k_8[(CH_3)_2CHO^*] + (k_9 + k_{10})[(CH_3)_2CHO] \, [NO]$$

$$\phi = \phi_{CH_3CHO} + \left(1 + \frac{k_{10}}{k_9}\right) \phi_{CH_3COCH_3}$$

Taking the value of $k_{10}/k_9 = 4.55$ from results reported by Hughes and Phillips *(10)*, we calculate ϕ to be 0.35 ± 0.01 at $26^{\circ}C$, 0.44 ± 0.01 at $85^{\circ}C$, and 0.46 ± 0.01 at $125^{\circ}C$. The primary dissociative yield is found not to vary with wavelength over the banded region (Fig. 1).

Ethyl Nitrite

The main reactions in the presence of NO are assumed to be:

$$CH_3CH_2ONO + h\nu \rightarrow aCH_3CH_2O^* + [1-a]CH_3CH_2O + NO \quad (12)$$
$$CH_3CH_2O^* \rightarrow CH_3 + CH_2O \quad (13)$$
$$CH_3CH_2O + NO \rightarrow CH_3CHO + HNO \quad (14)$$
$$\rightarrow CH_3CH_2ONO \quad (15)$$
$$CH_3 + NO \rightarrow CH_3NO \quad (6)$$

The quantum yield of CH_3CHO is independent of nitrite pressure over the range investigated, 3 to 12 torr, and independent of NO pressure over the range investigated, 7 to 30 torr. Analysis for CH_2O in this system has not yet been carried out in the present experiments. Schuck and Stephens report no CH_2O *(5)*. There is some evidence that excited radical effects are less important for ethoxy than for isopropoxy or *tert*-butoxy *(11)*. The excited alkoxy contribution to the primary yield of $(CH_3)_2CHONO$ is only about 9% at 26°C and 18% at 85°C, so probably no great error is introduced by assuming a to be zero in the CH_3CH_2ONO system. The expression for the primary dissociative yield follows:

$$\phi = \left(1 + \frac{k_{15}}{k_{14}}\right)\phi_{CH_3CHO}$$

With $k_{15}/k_{14} = 3.3$ as reported by Arden *et al. (12)*, the primary yield is calculated to be 0.59 ± 0.01 at 23°C and 0.58 ± 0.01 at 50°C. The primary yield at higher temperatures could not be determined because of interference from an irreproducible thermal reaction producing CH_3CHO. Homogeneous pyrolysis of the nitrite is negligible at temperatures below about 120°C. Furthermore, experiments in aged and freshly cleaned vessels suggest that the surface is involved in the thermal process. An upper limit for the primary dissociative yield at 75°C may be set at about 0.8.

Schuck and Stephens recently employed long-path infrared spectrophotometry to study photolysis of CH_3CH_2ONO vapor in the ppm range *(5)*. The uncertain scavenging efficiency and third-body effects in the experiments at low pressure prevent direct comparison with the high-pressure results. At the highest pressure of NO ($\sim 10^4$ ppm) used by Schuck and Stephens, the high-pressure mechanism may apply. The treatment discussed above leads to a primary yield of 0.71, compared with 0.59 calculated from our data for pressures in the torr range.

n-Propyl Nitrite

The main reactions in the presence of NO are assumed to be:

$$CH_3CH_2CH_2ONO + h\nu \rightarrow aCH_3CH_2CH_2O^* + [1-a]CH_3CH_2CH_2O + NO \qquad (16)$$

$$CH_3CH_2CH_2O^* \rightarrow CH_3CH_2 + CH_2O \qquad (17)$$

$$CH_3CH_2CH_2O + NO \rightarrow CH_3CH_2CHO + HNO \qquad (18)$$

$$CH_3CH_2CH_2O + NO \rightarrow CH_3CH_2CH_2ONO \qquad (19)$$

$$CH_3CH_2 + NO \rightarrow CH_3CH_2NO \qquad (20)$$

The CH_3CH_2CHO yield is independent of pressures of nitrite and NO. If a is again taken to be zero, the primary yield is given by the following equation:

$$\phi = \left(1 + \frac{k_{19}}{k_{18}}\right) \phi_{CH_3CH_2CHO}$$

No value of k_{19}/k_{18} is available. If this ratio is assumed to be 3.3, the same as for the corresponding reactions of CH_3CH_2O, the primary yield is calculated to be 0.37 ± 0.01 at $23^\circ C$ and 0.36 ± 0.01 at $50^\circ C$.

Excited Alkoxy Radicals in Nitrite Photolysis

Leighton *(2)* noted that, even if small amounts of nitrites were produced and photolyzed in polluted air, smog formation might not be affected, since the probable fate of alkoxy radicals produced in photolysis might be the recombination with NO to regenerate the nitrite. It was further noted that a promotional effect on smog formation might occur if the alkoxy radicals bear excess energy which might permit other reactions. It seems on the basis of evidence now available that several reactions of alkoxy radicals of thermal energies can compete with recombination at atmospheric NO levels.

In any case, the excited radical effects expected by Leighton are observed. Table I presents for different nitrites the fraction of excited alkoxy radicals, a, evaluated as described on p. 36. At 2537 Å, excited radical production predominates, with the a values generally correlating with the enthalpies of decomposition of the various alkoxy species *(16)*. At 3660 Å no simple correlation is found, but the excited radical effect is so small that intrusion of minor side reactions producing carbonyl compounds would introduce considerable error in a. It appears that excited radical processes are relatively unimportant in the banded region of the spectrum. The result on $(CH_3)_2CHONO$ at 3270 Å shows, however, that a may be quite large in the relatively weak bands at shorter wavelengths. Certainly if alkyl nitrites are to be used in laboratory experiments as photochemical sources of alkoxy radicals, the incident radiation must be confined to $\lambda \geqslant 3660$ Å if complications due to excited alkoxy are to be avoided.

Reactions of Alkoxy Radicals with Nitric Oxide

$$RO + NO \rightarrow RONO \tag{1}$$

$$RO + NO \rightarrow R'O + HNO \tag{21}$$

These disproportionation and combination reactions are important in many laboratory systems of interest for air pollution. There is considerable uncertainty in the values of k_{21}/k_1, since these ratios are calculated from results in systems whose reaction mechanisms are far from being completely understood. The values of k_{21}/k_1 have usually been determined in high-temperature thermolysis. The temperature dependence of the ratio has been a point of controversy *(8, 12, 17, 18)*. In the CH_3CH_2O case the disproportionation-to-combination ratio at $25^\circ C$ has been estimated to be ~0 by Knight and Gunning *(17)* and > 0.2 by East *et al. (18)*. Our calculated primary quantum yields for CH_3CH_2ONO depend critically on this ratio (k_{15}/k_{14}). If the mechanism for CH_3CH_2ONO photolysis is correct, k_{15}/k_{14} must be at least 0.16, corresponding to a primary quantum efficiency of unity. The primary efficiency actually calculated was the same at $23^\circ C$ and $50^\circ C$, so no appreciable temperature dependence is indicated. This conclusion obviously depends on the assumption that the primary efficiency itself is temperature-independent, or nearly so.

Table I

Excited Radical Fraction in Photolysis of Several Nitrites

Alkyl Nitrite	*a*		References
	3660 Å	2537 Å	
$C_2H_5(CH_3)_2CONO$	0.05	1.0	*13*
$(CH_3)_3CONO$	0.04	0.87	*7, 14*
$(CH_3)_2CHONO^a$	0.08	0.86	*6, 15*
CH_3CH_2ONO	0.00 ?	–	*5*

[a] $a = 0.37$ (3270 Å), 0.04 (3910 Å).

In calculation of the primary yields, it is tacitly assumed that the unexcited radicals formed in the primary process are truly unexcited so that k_{21}/k_1 values obtained from studies of the thermally equilibrated radicals are appropriate. Two considerations support this assumption: (1) Two-thirds of the isopropoxy radicals formed in photolysis of $(CH_3)_2CHOOCH(CH_3)_2$ vapor are excited *(19)*, but the k_{21}/k_1 describing the unexcited fraction is in the range of values determined in pyrolysis experiments. (2) Apparently a bimodal energy distribution describes the *tert*-pentoxy radicals formed in photolysis of $C_2H_5(CH_3)_2CONO$ — the radicals are either excited or truly unexcited *(13)*.

Photooxidation

A preliminary study was made of photolysis of *tert*-amyl nitrite-O_2 mixtures. The mechanism in this case is far too complicated to be discussed in detail. The major interest in the present work bears on the suitability of nitrites in laboratory experiments as radical sources in oxidizing atmospheres. Some experiments with $C_2H_5(CH_3)_2CONO$ — NO mixtures were done for comparison. All experiments were carried out at 25°C with $C_2H_5(CH_3)_2CONO$ pressures of 10 to 30 torr. The only products analyzed were CH_3COCH_3 and $CH_3COC_2H_5$. The main results are summarized below.

1. With incident radiation of wavelength 2537 Å, the quantum yield of total ketones is 1.0, unaffected by addition of ^{13}NO or O_2, at least up to pressures of 50 torr. The ratio of ketone yields, $Y_{CH_3COCH_3}/Y_{CH_3COC_2H_5}$, is 11 ± 1, unaffected by added O_2 at least up to pressures of 50 torr. At 114°C and probably at 25°C also, the ratio of ketone yields is unaffected by added NO over the range 0 to 85 torr *(13)*.

2. With incident radiation of wavelength 3660 Å, the quantum yield of total ketones is about 0.1 when $C_2H_5(CH_3)_2CONO$ alone is photolyzed, but is reduced to about 0.05 on addition of NO or O_2. The ratio of ketone yields, $Y_{CH_3COCH_3}/Y_{CH_3COC_2H_5}$, is about 63 in pure nitrite, but falls to 30 to 35 at high pressures of added NO or O_2 (Fig. 2).

The important reactions are:

$$C_2H_5(CH_3)_2CONO + h\nu \rightarrow aC_2H_5(CH_3)_2CO^* + [1-a]C_2H_5(CH_3)_2CO + NO \qquad (22)$$

$$C_2H_5(CH_3)_2CO^* \rightarrow C_2H_5 + CH_3COCH_3 \qquad (23)$$

$$C_2H_5(CH_3)_2CO^* \rightarrow CH_3 + CH_3COC_2H_5 \qquad (24)$$

$$C_2H_5(CH_3)_2CO \rightarrow C_2H_5 + CH_3COCH_3 \qquad (25)$$

$$C_2H_5(CH_3)_2CO \rightarrow CH_3 + CH_3COC_2H_5 \qquad (26)$$

At 2537 Å, $a = 1$. Steps 23 and 24 are so fast that scavenging processes cannot

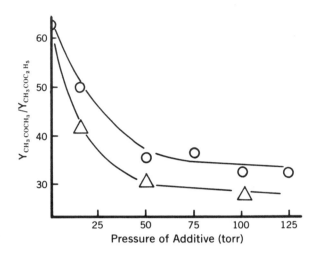

Fig. 2. Effect of added NO (Δ) and O_2 (O) on ratio of ketone yields in photolysis of *tert*-amyl nitrite at 3660 Å.

usually compete. There is no indication that NO or O_2 destroys excited nitrite molecules. In view of these facts and the high absorption coefficient at 2537 Å, *tert*-amyl nitrite may have some advantages as a photochemical source of alkyl radicals for quantitative studies.

The mechanism is much more complicated at 3660 Å. The fraction a is about 0.05. In the absence of added NO, probably both $C_2H_5(CH_3)_2CO^*$ and $C_2H_5(CH_3)_2CO$ decompose. At pressures of NO greater than about 20 torr, decomposition of $C_2H_5(CH_3)_2CO$ is suppressed. The variation of $Y_{CH_3COCH_3}/Y_{CH_3COC_2H_5}$ with NO pressure is thus explained, because k_{23}/k_{24} is considerably smaller than k_{25}/k_{26} *(13)*.

We can only speculate about the effect of O_2 at 3660 Å. At high O_2 pressure the ratio $Y_{CH_3COCH_3}/Y_{CH_3COC_2H_5}$ approaches the value found at high NO pressure. The primary dissociation leading to excited radicals is therefore probably unaffected by O_2. The primary dissociation leading to unexcited radicals may or may not be affected by O_2. No answer to this question can be given until a complete product and kinetic analysis is carried out.

Conclusions

The principal primary dissociative process in photolysis of alkyl nitrites at 3660 Å forms alkoxy radicals and NO. The efficiency of the process is considerably less than unity for certain nitrites. In some cases the primary efficiencies are calculated on the basis of questionable rate constants. Photodetachment of HNO does not occur to a significant extent. Alkyl nitrites are preferred photochemical sources of alkoxy radicals because excited radical formation is relatively unimportant, at least at wavelengths 3660 Å and longer. Photolysis of *tert*-amyl nitrite at 2537 Å forms excited *tert*-pentoxy radicals with a yield of unity even in the presence of NO or O_2. Decomposition of these excited radicals to ketones and alkyl radicals is complete; this suggests that the system might see use as an alkyl radical source in certain laboratory experiments on oxidizing atmospheres. The use of nitrite photolysis for generation of alkoxy radicals in systems containing oxygen is open to question at the present state of understanding.

References

1. E. A. Schuck, G. J. Doyle, and N. Endow, Air Pollution Foundation (Los Angeles) Rept. No. 31 (1960).
2. P. A. Leighton, "Photochemistry of Air Pollution," Academic Press, New York, 1961, pp. 70-71.
3. J. G. Calvert and J. N. Pitts, Jr., "Photochemistry," Wiley, New York, 1966, p. 480.
4. P. Kabasakalian and E. R. Townley, *J. Am. Chem. Soc.,* **84,** 2711 (1962); M. Akhtar, *Advan. Photochem.,* **2,** 263 (1964); R. O. Kan, "Organic Photochemistry," McGraw-Hill, New York, 1966, p. 236; J. G. Calvert and J. N. Pitts, Jr., "Photochemistry," Wiley, New York, 1966, p. 481.
5. E. A. Schuck and E. R. Stephens, *Environ. Sci. Technol.,* **1,** 138 (1967).
6. B. E. Ludwig and G. R. McMillan, *J. Am. Chem. Soc.,* **91,** 1085 (1969).
7. G. R. McMillan, *J. Phys. Chem.,* **67,** 931 (1963).
8. J. Heicklen and N. Cohen, *Advan. Photochem.,* **5,** 289 (1968).
9. J. G. Calvert and J. N. Pitts, Jr., "Photochemistry," Wiley, New York, 1966, p. 482.
10. G. A. Hughes and L. Phillips, *J. Chem. Soc.,* **A,** 894 (1967).
11. G. R. McMillan, *J. Am. Chem. Soc.,* **84,** 2514 (1962).
12. E. A. Arden, L. Phillips, and R. Shaw, *J. Chem. Soc.,* 5126 (1964).
13. D. Durant and G. R. McMillan, *J. Phys. Chem.,* 70, 2709 (1966).
14. G. R. McMillan, *J. Am. Chem. Soc.,* **84,** 4007 (1962).
15. J. G. Calvert and J. N. Pitts, Jr., "Photochemistry," Wiley, New York, 1966, p. 483.
16. P. Gray and A. Williams, *Chem. Rev.,* **59,** 239 (1959).
17. A. R. Knight and H. E. Gunning, *Can. J. Chem.,* **39,** 2466 (1961).
18. R. L. East, J. R. Gilbert, and L. Phillips, *J. Chem. Soc.,* **A,** 1673 (1968).
19. G. R. McMillan, *J. Am. Chem. Soc.,* **83,** 3018 (1961).

Discussion

G. S. HAMMOND: You indicated that it may be the primary process itself which is affected by oxygen. Have you done a "Pitts experiment" where you put in some tetramethylethylene?

G. R. McMILLAN: I have not yet looked to see if we are getting energy transfer to oxygen. This is something we propose to do but have not yet done. If we are not getting complete dissociation in the primary process, where are the other excited nitrite molecules going? We have no idea where they are going. We cannot find any other reaction products that seem to be derived from the carbon skeleton and we have not seen any luminescence. As a result, we fall back on the ignorance argument; that is, somehow the excited nitrite molecules are returning to the ground state by possibly radiationless processes. We did think that perhaps if we added oxygen we might get some energy transfer to oxygen and produce singlet oxygen. We have not tried the experiment which Professor Hammond mentions as yet.

I. C. HISATSUNE: Does isotopic NO exchange with your nitrite in the dark?

G. R. McMILLAN: Not if the alkyl nitrites are pure. There is no dark exchange. Unfortunately, no one ever had a pure alkyl nitrite, and consequently a small amount of dark exchange must be corrected for if you really want to get careful quantum yields. I did not mean to treat your question in a jocular fashion, but if you have a little water present in the system, you are going to have hydrolysis of the nitrite. Then you will have some alcohol, nitrous acid, and probably oxides of nitrogen. Furthermore, the surface of, say, a quartz or Pyrex vessel contains hydroxyl groups, and these may transesterify with RONO, giving again nitrous acid plus a little ROH. So the exchange experiments do require a small dark correction, but I believe it is due to impurity problems such as this rather than any direct reaction between the nitrite and nitric oxide.

P. A. LEIGHTON: Do you have any idea what HNO does in air?

G. R. McMILLAN: No, it would react with oxygen; perhaps some others can correct me here. Obviously, it will react very rapidly with any free radical. It will react quite rapidly with nitric oxide, and probably also NO_2.

P. A. LEIGHTON: It does react; it disappears. There is no question about this.

G. R. McMILLAN: Yes.

Hydrocarbon Reactivities and Nitric Oxide Conversion in Real Atmospheres

Edgar R. Stephens
Statewide Air Pollution Research Center
University of California, Riverside, California

Abstract

Analysis and irradiation of ambient air give a view of atmospheric photochemistry which cannot be obtained in any other way, since they force the investigator to think in terms of the real atmosphere. Such studies indicate that reaction equivalent to eight or ten hours of irradiation can occur and that during such an interval even the saturated hydrocarbons, which are generally of low reactivity, can, because of their generally larger quantities, make a significant contribution to total reaction. Although attack by ozone might reasonably account for loss of the olefins, it cannot account for the observed loss rate of the paraffins. Attack by oxygen atoms cannot, on the basis of literature rate constants, account for the loss rate of either class of hydrocarbons.

During the past few years we have been using flame ionization gas chromatography to study the amounts of individual hydrocarbons in polluted air. A valuable adjunct to this study has been the irradiation of such samples with natural sunlight and with artificial ultraviolet while monitoring individual hydrocarbon concentrations. One purpose of these studies has been to provide a realistic comparison for laboratory simulation experiments and for theoretical studies of the mechanism. More specifically, an objective has been to estimate the degree to which various individual hydrocarbons react under realistic conditions.

These studies have revealed several interesting features not readily apparent from laboratory simulations. Hydrocarbon concentrations are extremely low compared to most laboratory simulations, and the amounts that react when photochemical smog is formed are correspondingly small. Comparison of ambient air samples with laboratory irradiations of such samples showed that all classes of hydrocarbons contribute significantly to the "total reacted." The lower reactivity of paraffins as compared to olefins and aromatics is offset at least partially by their presence in larger amounts.

The striking feature of irradiation of ambient air is the approximately first-order decrease of the hydrocarbons over intervals as long as eight hours. Comparison with literature rate constants indicates that the olefin reaction rate could be accounted for by the presence of a few tenths of a part per million of ozone. Similar comparisons indicate that oxygen atom reactions could not account for the observed rate of olefin disappearance. Neither of these reactive species can account for the disappearance of paraffins.

Another striking feature is the quite small amounts of "hydrocarbon reacted" necessary to cause conversion of the nitric oxide to nitrogen dioxide and the development of smog symptoms. Visually it appears that the time required to develop symptoms such as ozone and aerosols is a few hours at most. During such a short time interval the amounts of hydrocarbon oxidized must be measured in parts per hundred million rather than parts per million. To account for complete conversion of the nitric oxide to nitrogen dioxide by this small amount of hydrocarbon requires that the hydrocarbon oxidized be very effective in causing nitric oxide oxidation. A simplified mechanism based on initiation by oxygen atoms and ozone and assumed conversion efficiency factors was then tested. Simplified kinetic equations based on this scheme were integrated to give the time required to convert the nitric oxide. Applying this to the values derived from ambient air leads to conversion times which are at least twenty times as long as those in ambient air. It seems certain that the assumptions made need to be modified. Oxidation of the highly reactive olefins alone probably cannot account for the conversion. The moderately reactive aromatics and the paraffins must make a significant contribution to the conversion. As noted previously, paraffin oxidation cannot readily be accounted for by oxygen atom and ozone attack.

When nitrogen and oxygen combine in high-temperature combustion processes, they form primarily nitric oxide, a colorless, low-boiling gas with the formula NO. To produce such temperatures by burning organic fuels in air requires that the mixture be nearly stoichiometric, which in turn means that the combustion gases are low in oxygen (compared to air). Dilution of the combustion products with air simultaneously raises the concentration of oxygen and lowers that of the nitric oxide. Since the rate of oxidation of NO depends on the first power of the oxygen concentration and the square of the nitric oxide, dilution has to be carried out very slowly to permit significant oxidation of the nitric oxide to the thermodynamically favored nitrogen dioxide (NO_2). For auto exhaust this dilution is surely much too fast to permit much oxidation. Nitric oxide therefore predominates over nitrogen dioxide in the diluted exhaust.

It is well known that conversion of NO to NO_2 in such dilute mixtures in air is greatly accelerated by the simultaneous presence of hydrocarbon and exposure to sunlight, natural or artificial. It is apparent that this conversion is related to the oxidation of the hydrocarbon, since the latter disappears during the process. Generally speaking, hydrocarbons that disappear most rapidly are those that are most effective for the NO oxidation. Since most of the bad effects of photochemical smog do not develop until the oxidation of NO to NO_2 is complete, it is apparent that this process plays a crucial role and that reduction in hydrocarbon emissions should eventually produce a state in which not all the NO is converted.

The exact chemical mechanism by which hydrocarbon oxidation promotes NO oxidation has been the subject of much speculation and some experimental work. Easily the most reasonable suggestion involves oxidation of NO by peroxy radicals:

$$NO + ROO \cdot \rightarrow NO_2 + RO \cdot$$

Several indirect pieces of evidence make this reaction plausible:

1. One form of peroxy radicals, acyl peroxy, is demonstrated to be present by their reaction to form peroxyacyl nitrates (PANs).

$$NO_2 + R\overset{\overset{\text{O}}{\|}}{C}OO \cdot \rightarrow R\overset{\overset{\text{O}}{\|}}{C}OONO_2$$

Since NO and NO_2 are both odd electron molecules, the corresponding reaction with NO is plausible.

$$NO + R\overset{\overset{\text{O}}{\|}}{C}OO \cdot \rightarrow NO_2 + R\overset{\overset{\text{O}}{\|}}{C}O$$

2. Furthermore, formation of PAN does not proceed rapidly until the conversion of NO is nearly complete, which suggests that NO and NO_2 are in competition for the available peroxyacyl radicals and perhaps for other peroxy radicals as well.

It is also possible that several peroxy radicals could be generated in succession from one hydrocarbon molecule. The acyl radical may be oxidized:

$$R\overset{\overset{\text{O}}{\|}}{C}O \cdot + O_2 \rightarrow RO_2 \cdot + CO_2$$

This process cannot go on without limit, since the hydrocarbon is being continually degraded. But a six-carbon paraffin might go through six such steps. Regeneration of the original peroxyacyl radical seems likely to involve a highly endothermic and therefore slow reaction.

In any particular system, experimental or ambient, there are at least three quantities which can be compared to gain more information about the conversion process:

1. The observed rate at which the concentration of NO_2 increases. This can be taken to be equal to the rate of decrease of NO, since several studies have

shown that the maximum NO_2 is nearly equal to the initial total of NO plus
NO_2. Apparently processes leading to other nitrogen-containing products play
a minor role during this first stage of the reaction.

2. The observed rate at which the concentration of hydrocarbon decreases.
Depending on the system under discussion, this might be one hydrocarbon
or many.

3. Rates of reaction of hydrocarbon calculated on the basis of some theory.

The ratio of (1) the rate of NO_2 formation to (2) the rate of hydrocarbon
disappearance can be called the "conversion efficiency." Knowledge of this
efficiency pertains to the mechanism of hydrocarbon oxidation and has little
bearing on the mechanism of hydrocarbon initiation. Conversion efficiencies
reported in the literature vary from less than 2 to more than 10 (*1, 2*).

Comparison of (2) the observed rate of hydrocarbon disappearance with
(3) rates of hydrocarbon disappearance calculated on some theoretical basis is
related to the mechanism of initiation and can be considered separately from
the first comparison (*1, 3, 4*).

From a practical point of view it would be valuable to know how much reduction in hydrocarbon will be needed to prevent complete conversion of NO
to NO_2, for this is a crucial point at which major improvements in symptoms
may be expected. The twin comparisons, mentioned previously, for rate of
hydrocarbon oxidation and conversion efficiency need to be better understood
before reasonable estimates of the results of control can be made. Several attempts have been made to estimate conversion efficiency and to make hydrocarbon rate comparisons for laboratory mixtures. But the real atmosphere
differs substantially in two respects from this. There are dozens of hydrocarbons instead of just one, and concentrations are lower than those used in
most laboratory studies. Recent data on reactions in real atmospheres have
made it possible to examine these questions a little more closely. Ambient polluted air has been analyzed for individual hydrocarbons, and the disappearance
of these hydrocarbons under natural and artificial sunlight followed. Although
no measurements of nitrogen oxides were possible, the amounts present could
be estimated from the composition of exhaust gas, and it is known from other
experiments that conversion must be completed in an hour or two.

Actually the observed rate of NO_2 formation is a net rate; it is the difference
between the rate of formation and the rate of disappearance of NO_2. Both
these rates are large compared to the differences between them. By far the
fastest process which produces NO_2 is the reaction of NO with ozone:

$$NO + O_3 \rightarrow NO_2 + O_2 \quad k_4(NO)(O_3)$$

This reaction is often improperly neglected when either the ozone or the
NO is too small to measure. With $k_4 = 33$ ppm^{-1} min^{-1}, only 0.01 ppm of

either NO or O_3 will cause the other to react at $33 \times 0.01 \times 100\% = 33\%/\text{min}$. Of course 0.01 ppm would be quickly depleted if not replenished, but it always *is* replenished by the photolysis of NO_2 in any real system.

$$NO_2 \rightarrow NO + O \qquad\qquad \phi k_a(NO_2)$$

$$O + O_2 + M \rightarrow O_3 + M \qquad\qquad k_2\,(M)\,(O_2)\,(O)$$

The net rate of change of the NO_2 concentration is then

$$\frac{d(NO_2)}{dt} = [k_4(NO)(O_3) + R_{HC}] - [\phi k_a(NO_2) + R_{28}]$$

In this rate equation R_{HC} is the rate of NO_2 formation by way of hydrocarbon oxidation and R_{28} is the rate of NO_2 loss through the reaction

$$O + NO_2 \rightarrow NO + O_2 \qquad\qquad k_{28}(O)(NO_2) = R_{28}$$

In the rate equation R_{HC} is much smaller than $k_4(NO)(O_3)$ and R_{28} is much smaller than $\phi k_a(NO_2)$, but it can be shown that these two large terms nearly cancel. A steady-state equation for oxygen atoms can be written by equating their rate of formation with the sum of the rates of consumption.

$$\phi k_a(NO_2) \cong k_2(M)(O_2)(O) + k_{28}(NO_2)(O) + k_1(HC)(O)$$

The last term refers to the reaction with hydrocarbon:

$$O + HC \rightarrow \qquad\qquad k_1(HC)(O)$$

The steady-state equation for ozone is

$$k_2(M)(O_2)(O) \cong k_4(NO)(O_3) + k_3(HC)(O_3)$$

in which the last term refers to the reaction of hydrocarbon with ozone. Combining these two equations gives

$$\phi k_a(NO_2) = k_4(NO)(O_3) + k_3(HC)(O_3) + k_{28}(NO_2)(O) + k_1(HC)(O)$$

When this is inserted into the rate equation the two biggest terms cancel to give

$$\frac{d(NO_2)}{dt} = R_{HC} - k_3(HC)(O_3) - k_1(HC)(O) - 2k_{28}(NO_2)(O)$$

Clearly the NO_2 can increase only if R_{HC} exceeds the three negative terms in the equation. If the steady-state equation for oxygen atoms is inserted, it is seen that the last term depends on the square of the NO_2 concentration.

$$\frac{2k_{28}\,\phi k_a(NO_2)^2}{k_2(M)(O_2) + k_{28}(NO_2) + k_1(HC)}$$

This square dependence makes this term very small at realistic ambient air levels. At 0.3 ppm of NO_2 this term is estimated to be 0.004 ppm/hour. It will be neglected in the rest of this discussion. The R_{HC} term is related to hydrocarbon oxidation, and for test purposes it can be broken into two parts proportional to the rate of hydrocarbon reaction with ozone and oxygen atoms.

$$\frac{d(NO_2)}{dt} = (F_3 - 1)k_3(HC)(O_3) + (F_1 - 1)\,k_1(HC)(O)$$

$$= G_3 k_3(HC)(O_3) + G_1 k_1(HC)(O)$$

In this equation G_1 and G_3 are the net conversion efficiencies for the two initiation processes. The steady-state equations for oxygen atoms and ozone can be simplified by neglecting small terms and then inserted into the rate equation:

$$\frac{d(NO_2)}{dt} = \frac{G_3 k_3(HC)\,\phi k_a(NO_2)}{k_4\,[(NO_x) - (NO_2)]} + \frac{G_1 k_1(HC)\,\phi k_a(NO_2)}{k_2(M)(O_2)}$$

In this equation NO_x is taken to be the total of NO and NO_2, which is assumed to be constant. This equation can be integrated to produce the following expressions:

$$T = \frac{(NO_x)}{A(NO_x) + B}\,\ell n\,\frac{(NO_2)}{(NO_2)_0} - \frac{B}{A\,[A(NO_x) + B]}\,\ell n\,\frac{(NO_x) - (NO_2)_0 + B/A}{(NO_x) - (NO_2) + B/A}$$

where

$$A = \frac{\phi k_a}{k_2(M)(O_2)}\;\; G_1 k_1(HC)$$

$$B = \frac{\phi k_a}{k_4}\;\; G_3 k_3(HC)$$

For oxygen atom reaction only,

$$T = \frac{1}{A} \ln \frac{(NO_2)}{(NO_2)_0}$$

For ozone reaction only,

$$T = \frac{(NO_x)}{B} \ln \frac{(NO_2)}{(NO_2)_0} - \frac{[(NO_2) - (NO_2)_0]}{B}$$

For $\phi k_a = 0.33$ min^{-1} :

$$k_2(M)(O_2) = 4.25 \times 10^6 \text{ min}^{-1}$$

$$k_4 = 33 \text{ ppm}^{-1} \text{ min}^{-1}$$

$$k_1 = 5.0 \times 10^3 \text{ ppm}^{-1} \text{ min}^{-1}$$

$$k_3 = 1.2 \times 10^{-2} \text{ ppm}^{-1} \text{ min}^{-1}$$

These equations were tested using data for ambient air in Riverside, California, on October 24, 1968 *(5)*. The total hydrocarbon in this sample was estimated to be 0.67 ppm (less CH_4). It was estimated that, if unreacted, this sample would have contained 0.05 ppm of acetylene. Auto exhaust analyses *(6, 7)* suggest that the NO_x is about six times the acetylene (1500 ppm versus 250 ppm), so calculations were based on 0.3 ppm of NO_x of which 0.03 was NO_2 initially. The conversion efficiencies were taken to be $G_1 = G_3 = 2$. The result of this calculation is plotted in Fig. 1. Even with both initiating processes the time calculated for complete conversion is about 26 hours. This is, of course, about ten or twenty times too large. Because NO_2 is the light absorber, the first portion of the conversion is much slower than the latter stages. If the initial NO_2 were 0.15 ppm, the conversion time would be reduced to four hours. This might sometimes be the case if NO_2 were carried over from one day to the next, but it can hardly account for conversion observed in fresh exhaust gas. The conversion time as plotted in Fig. 1 is inversely dependent on the conversion efficiency, the rate constants for hydrocarbon initiation, and the hydrocarbon concentration. Increasing the product of these three factors by 10 is required to account for the conversion in a reasonable time.

Samples of ambient air have also been irradiated with natural and artificial sunlight, and the disappearance of individual hydrocarbons followed *(8)*. Over an eight-hour period substantial loss of olefins was observed and also a smaller loss of paraffins. Within this range of observations the disappearance was approximately first-order. The equations developed above were used to estimate the importance of the two postulated initiating mechanisms. Rather than

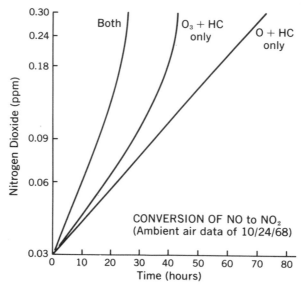

Fig. 1. Formation of NO_2, calculated on the basis of theory using ambient air data with conversion efficiency of 2 and literature rate constants.

calculate theoretical rates of hydrocarbon disappearance, the amounts of ozone or of nitrogen dioxide necessary to account for the observed hydrocarbon loss rate were estimated. These are given in Table I. For the olefins the necessary ozone concentrations are of the order of a few tenths of a part per million. This system was too small to permit measurement of ozone, but the presence of this amount of ozone is entirely reasonable and it could be nearly constant for eight hours to produce the observed first-order loss of the olefin hydrocarbons. Ozone cannot, of course, account for the loss of paraffins. The amounts of NO_2 which would be required to generate the oxygen atom concentration necessary to produce the observed rate of hydrocarbon loss are much too large (see Table I) to be reasonable. This is particularly true of the paraffins, which must therefore be initiated by some other species. It would also be surprising if the NO_2 were nearly constant for eight hours as would be required to account for a first-order loss of hydrocarbons.

   Another approach involves comparison of the total amount of hydrocarbon lost with the amount of nitric oxide converted. The ambient air data used for the rate calculation illustrated in Fig. 1 was examined from this point of view. It was estimated that about 0.2 ppm of hydrocarbon had been reacted in this well-reacted sample and about 0.3 ppm of NO was converted. Since reaction equivalent to about ten hours of irradiation had occurred *(5)*, whereas only about two hours are required for NO conversion, the ratio of NO oxidized to hydrocarbon reacted must have been nearly 10 to 1. Olefinic hydrocarbons

Table I

Hydrocarbon Loss in an Ambient Air Sample under Ultraviolet Irradiation

Hydrocarbon	Observed Rate $(1/t)\ln_e(HC)_0/(HC)_t$ $(\text{min}^{-1} \times 10^3)$	$k(O + HC)$ $(\text{ppm}^{-1} \text{ min}^{-1} \times 10^{-3})$	NO_2 Calculated (ppm)	$k(O_3 + HC)$ $(\text{ppm}^{-1} \text{ min}^{-1} \times 10^{-3})$	O_3 Calculated (ppm)
Ethene	1.04	0.78	17	2.0	0.52
Propene	3.92	4.7	10.6	12.0	0.33
1-Butene	3.96	4.9	10.3	–	–
Isobutene	3.20	20.7	2.0	9.0	0.36
1,3-Butadiene	8.60	–	–	12.0	0.72
trans-2-Pentene	20.2	18.3	14.2	240.	0.085
n-Butane	0.46	0.034	173	~ 0	Inf
n-Hexane	0.63	0.39	20.6	~ 0	Inf

constitute a very small portion of the total hydrocarbon and are quite inadequate to account for NO conversion by themselves.

The experiments with ambient air seem to require that paraffins play a significant role in the conversion process and that the average conversion efficiency (moles of NO_2 formed per mole of hydrocarbon oxidized) must be 5 or 10. The fact that hydrocarbons of all types are capable of promoting the oxidation of NO is clear from the work of Glasson and Tuesday *(9)* as well as earlier studies.

References

1. E.R. Stephens, *Intern. J. Air Water Pollution,* **10,** 793-803 (1966).
2. A.P. Altshuller and I.R. Cohen, *Intern. J. Air Water Pollution,* **8,** 611-632 (1964).
3. P.A. Leighton, "Photochemistry of Air Pollution," Academic Press, New York, 1961, p. 264.
4. A.P. Altshuller and J.J. Bufalini, *Photochem. Photobiol.,* **4,** 97-146 (1965).
5. E.R. Stephens and F.R. Burleson, *J. Air Pollution Control Assoc.,* **19,** 929 (1969).
6. F. Bonnamassa, R.J. Gordon, and H. Mayrsohn, Exhaust Composition of Pre-1966 California Automobiles, presented at the 155th Meeting, ACS, San Francisco, California, April, 1968.
7. J.N. Pattison and E.R. Stephens, Composition of Automotive Blowby Gases, Proc. 3rd Technical Meeting APCA West Coast Section, September 1963.
8. E.R. Stephens, E.F. Darley, and F. R. Burleson, *Proc. Am. Petrol. Inst. Sec. III,* **47,** 466-483 (1967).
9. W.A. Glasson and C.S. Tuesday, Hydrocarbon Reactivities in the Atmospheric Photo-oxidation of Nitric Oxide. General Motors Research Publication GMR-584, GM Research Laboratories, Warren, Michigan.

Discussion

B. WEINSTOCK: I should like to mention an analysis that was made by Eric Daby, Joe Niki, and myself. It was made possible by the kind generosity of Paul Altshuller, who gave us some data on the photooxidation of propylene.

I want to stress the initial part of the photochemical smog reaction, the conversion of NO to NO_2, which we call stage 1 of the analysis. As others have done, we calculated the concentration of oxygen atoms and ozone in the first stage from steady-state assumptions. They only account for a very small fraction of the loss of the propylene in this initial stage, leaving the so-called "excess rate." What drives the NO to NO_2 if it isn't oxygen atoms and ozone? It must involve a chain reaction, and the oxygen atoms are simply the initiators of the chain. Dr. Cvetanovic's work showed that about 30% of the oxygen atoms that react with propylene result in the formation of radicals, while about 70% result in the formation of addition products. We postulate that the reaction of oxygen atoms with propylene in the presence of NO eventually forms hydroxyl radicals or HO_2 radicals, and this is the chain reaction that drives the system.

We have solved this system quantitatively and get the following expression for the conversion of NO to NO_2.

$$NO_2 = (NO_2)_0 \frac{(NO_x)_0 - (NO_2)}{(NO_x)_0 - (NO_2)_0} \exp [AC(NO_x)_0 (\overline{P})t]$$

where $A = k/(O_2)(M) = 4.13 \times 10^{-4}$ ppm^{-1} sec^{-1}; $C = 2\lambda K'/K(wall) = 84$ ppm^{-1}; $(NO_x)_0 = (NO_2)_0 + (NO)_0$, the initial NO_x concentration; $\overline{P}$ is the average propylene concentration; and t is time. K is a collection of rate constants, all of which are known; $\lambda = 0.3$, which we derive from Cvetanovic's work; K' is the rate constant for the reaction $HO_2 + NO \rightarrow HO + NO_2$, which is not well known; and $K(wall)$ is some termination step.

We have derived a value of this parameter C from Altshuller's experimental data. It turns out to be 84 ppm^{-1}. From this we can estimate the chain length to be about 280 and the lifetime of the OH radical in the system to be 56 seconds, both of which are reasonable numbers.

If you go beyond the first stage, the loss of propylene becomes much more rapid. In the well-known work of Glasson and Tuesday* on the inhibiting effect of NO, they define the propylene oxidation rate as the average rate for converting half of the propylene. This depends not only on stage 1 but also on the much more rapid rate that occurs after the NO_2 maximum.

Another feature of this is, as Dr. Stephens has suggested, the initial NO_2 concentration. We compared Glasson and Tuesday's* and Altshuller's† results in the 2 ppm propylene - 1 ppm NO system and found that, if you correct for the differences in initial NO_2 concentration, the disagreement between laboratories becomes much less. I should like to suggest that we should perhaps start rethinking this question about NO inhibition in terms of these effects.

J. HEICKLEN: I should like to present some work on the conversion of NO to NO_2 in polluted atmospheres which was carried out with Carl Westberg and Norm Cohen of the Aerospace Corporation.

The most important unresolved problem in air pollution is the mechanism of the conversion of NO to NO_2. The well-known termolecular reaction‡

$$2NO + O_2 \rightarrow 2NO_2 \tag{1}$$

_____

*W.A. Glasson and C.S. Tuesday, *Environ. Sci. Technol.,* **4,** 37 (1970).

†A.P. Altshuller, S.L. Kopczynski, W.A. Lonneman, T.L. Becker, and R. Slater, *Environ. Sci. Technol.,* **1,** 899 (1967)

‡J. Heicklen and N. Cohen, *Advan. Photochem.,* **5,** 157 (1968)

has a room-temperature rate constant of 7.0×10^3 liters mole^{-1} sec^{-1} and is much too slow to be of any importance; typically the half-life of conversion of NO to NO_2 via this step is about 100 days. Another mechanism was proposed by Heicklen and Cohen,[*] which they pointed out could be as much as 10^5 as fast as reaction 1:

$$NO + O_2 \;\rightarrow\; NO_3 \tag{2}$$

$$NO_3 + h\nu \;\rightarrow\; NO_3^* \;\xrightarrow{O_2}\; NO_2 + O_3 \tag{3}$$

However, the rate they calculated for this sequence was based on an equilibrium constant for reaction 2 which has since been revised so as to reduce the effectiveness of this route.[*] Furthermore, results of Bufalini and Stephens[†] indicate that this route is probably no more than ten times as fast as reaction 1 and therefore not fast enough to be significant.

The purpose of this presentation is to suggest a mechanism which we think adequately explains the NO oxidation—namely, a free radical chain mechanism with HO as the chain carrier. Since HO is an expected intermediate in the polluted air oxidation of hydrocarbons,[¶][△] Leighton[¶] has also discussed an HO chain for the NO-to-NO_2 conversion. Our mechanism consists of three interrelated chains.

The first chain (I) for the conversion of NO to NO_2 develops from the HO radical attack on carbon monoxide:

$$HO\cdot + CO \;\rightarrow\; H\cdot + CO_2 \tag{4}$$

$$H\cdot + O_2 + M \;\rightarrow\; HO_2\cdot + M \tag{5}$$

$$HO_2\cdot + NO \;\rightarrow\; NO_2 + HO\cdot \tag{6}$$

The overall reaction is

$$CO + NO + O_2 \;\rightarrow\; CO_2 + NO_2 \tag{7}$$

The second chain (II) develops from the HO attack on alkenes. For example, for isobutene (2-methylpropene) the reactions are

[*]J. Heicklen and N. Cohen, *Advan. Photochem.*, **5**, 157 (1968)
[†]S.D. Morris, Jr., and H.S. Johnston, *J. Chem. Phys.*, **47**, 4282 (1967).
[‡]J.J. Bufalini and E.R. Stephens, *Intern. J. Air Water Pollution*, **9**, 123 (1965).
[¶]P.A. Leighton, "Photochemistry of Air Pollution," Academic Press, New York, 1961, p.269.
[△]K. Westberg and N. Cohen, Aerospace Report ATR-70 (8107)-1, December, 1969, The Aerospace Corporation, El Segundo, California.

$$C_4H_8 + HO\cdot \rightarrow \dot{C}_4H_8OH \tag{8}$$

$$\dot{C}_4H_8OH + O_2 \rightarrow C_4H_8(OH)O_2\cdot \tag{9}$$

$$C_4H_8(OH)O_2\cdot + NO \rightarrow C_4H_8(OH)O\cdot + NO_2 \tag{10}$$

$$C_4H_8(OH)O\cdot \rightarrow C_3H_6O + \dot{C}H_2OH \tag{11}$$

$$\dot{C}H_2OH + O_2 \rightarrow CH_2(OH)O_2\cdot \tag{12}$$

$$CH_2(OH)O_2\cdot + NO \rightarrow CH_2(OH)O\cdot + NO_2 \tag{13}$$

$$CH_2(OH)O\cdot \rightarrow CH_2O + HO\cdot \tag{14}$$

The overall reaction is

$$C_4H_8 + 2NO + 2O_2 \rightarrow C_3H_6O + CH_2O + 2NO_2 \tag{15}$$

The third chain (III) develops from the HO attack on alkanes. For example, for butane the sequence is

$$C_4H_{10} + HO\cdot \rightarrow C_4H_9\cdot + H_2O \tag{16}$$

$$C_4H_9\cdot + O_2 \rightarrow C_4H_9O_2\cdot \tag{17}$$

$$C_4H_9O_2\cdot + NO \rightarrow C_4H_9O\cdot + NO_2 \tag{18}$$

$$C_4H_9O\cdot + O_2 \rightarrow C_4H_8O + HO_2\cdot \tag{19}$$

$$HO_2\cdot + NO \rightarrow NO_2 + HO\cdot \tag{6}$$

The overall reaction is

$$C_4H_{10} + 2NO + 2O_2 \rightarrow C_4H_8O + H_2O + 2NO_2 \tag{20}$$

All reactions in each chain are consistent with current chemical knowledge. As the examples illustrate, both branched and straight-chain hydrocarbons can be degraded by an HO radical chain. Note that in each chain NO is converted to NO_2 by reactions of the form

$$HO_2\cdot + NO \rightarrow HO\cdot + NO_2 \tag{6}$$

$$RO_2 \cdot + NO \rightarrow RO \cdot + NO_2 \tag{21}$$

Although no hydrocarbons appear in reaction 6 and chain I, they are still necessary for the NO-to-NO_2 conversion because it is from hydrocarbons that HO is initially produced.

The relative importance of each chain will depend largely on the relative rates of reactions 4, 8, and 16. We estimate the rate constant for reaction 8 to be 10^{10} liters mole^{-1} sec^{-1}. The rate constant for the reaction of HO with methane[*] is 6.5×10^6 liters mole^{-1} sec^{-1} at 300°K; the rate constant for the analogous reaction with butane and with branched hydrocarbons should be higher because of weaker hydrogen bonds in these molecules. Recent measurements[†] give k_4 as about 8×10^7 liters mole^{-1} sec^{-1}. In polluted air, the CO concentration is typically a hundred times as great as the hydrocarbon concentration. Thus, reactions 4 and 8 and, possibly, 16 will be competitive, which means that carbon monoxide as well as hydrocarbons may play a role in NO oxidation.

A thorough analysis of the chemistry of the polluted air, of course, involves more than merely comparing the rates of reactions 4, 8, and 16. Chain-terminating reactions, secondary reactions, reactions which produce HO, reactions of ozone with hydrocarbons, and so forth must be considered. Such a complete analysis can be done only on a computer. We have modified the Aerospace nonequilibrium chemical kinetics computer program which was previously used to analyze shock wave measurements,[‡] so that it can now be used to analyze smog chemistry. Using a complete set of chemical reactions of which chain II is a part, we have quantitatively reproduced[¶] with the computer the results of the smog chamber experiments of Schuck and Doyle,[◊] in which smog was produced from 1 ppm NO_2 and 2.8 ppm isobutene. We are now beginning to examine both experimentally and with the computer the effect of CO on photochemical smog production. Our goal is a better estimate of the relative contributions of chains I and II. This is especially important because, according to current beliefs, the chief danger of CO in the air is its own toxicity and not its role in the conversion of NO to NO_2 and hence as an agent in ozone production. If these proposals are correct, controls on CO emission from automobiles may be more important than was previously believed.

[*]W.E. Wilson and A.A. Westenberg, "Eleventh Symposium (International) on Combustion," The Combusiton Institute, 1967, p. 1143.

[†]"High Temperature Reaction Rate Data," Department of Physical Chemistry, The University, Leeds, England, No. 1 (1968).

[‡]See, for example, T.A. Jacobs, N. Cohen, and R.R. Giedt, *J. Chem. Phys.*, **46**, 1958 (1966).

[¶]K. Westberg and N. Cohen, Aerospace Report ATR-70 (8107)-1, December, 1969, The Aerospace Corporation, El Segundo, California.

[◊]E.A. Schuck and G.J. Doyle, Air Pollution Foundation Report No. 29, Stanford Research Institute, South Pasadena, California, 1959.

Professor Calvert and George Jackson have another mechanism which might be important. They have permitted me to mention their results. This is the possibility that RO could react with CO to give R plus CO_2. Then the R could react with O_2 to give RO_2. Then this could react with NO. The chains could be carried on this way to get high conversions of NO with low olefin consumption.

J.G. CALVERT: The only difference is that R replaces H in your mechanism, Dr. Heicklen. The unusual thing is oxygen being lost from R, but actually, energetically, this is more favorable than H losing it to CO. Furthermore, the pre-exponential factor is theoretically only lower by about a factor of 3 than in the case of hydrogen. Although this reaction does occur, we have not measured the rate constant for it because it is a bit faster than we expected.

W.A. GLASSON: Dr. Heicklen, with regard to your CO cycle, we did some exploratory work a while back on the effect of CO on NO-to-NO_2 conversions. In the system 2 ppm ethylene plus 1 ppm NO, the addition of 400 ppm CO only doubled the rate of NO_2 formation.

J. HEICKLEN: You have two hundred times as much CO as ethylene in that system, and you doubled the rate. That's a pretty good fit according to my numbers. I would have expected a threefold increase.

B. DIMITRIADES: We added $C^{14}O$ and measured the rate of CO oxidation in photochemical systems of this type. Of course, the rate was very slow. About 0.1% per hour of CO was oxidized to CO_2.

J.J. BUFALINI: This would lead you to believe that the CO cycle is not important.

J. HEICKLEN: Not necessarily. You see, you oxidize hardly any of the CO in this cycle. The CO concentration is about one hundred times that of NO. You can oxidize all the NO while only converting 1% of the CO.

E.R. STEPHENS: I should say a 20-to-1 ratio of CO to NO would be more representative of real atmospheres.

A.P. ALTSHULLER: Yes, Dr. Heicklen, I think your ratios are a little high if you actually look at aerometric data, either at Riverside or downtown Los Angeles.

SESSION II

Reactions of O(^{3}P) with Aldehydes in Photochemical Smog

R. D. Cadle and E. R. Allen
National Center for Atmospheric Research*
Boulder, Colorado

Abstract

A laboratory study has been made of the kinetics and products of the reaction of O(^{3}P) with acetaldehyde, propionaldehyde, and acrolein using both fast-flow and static methods. A comparison of the rate constants with the effectiveness of the aldehydes in accelerating the oxidation of nitric oxide to nitrogen dioxide suggests that the aldehydes are much,more effective as producers of smog than the rates of reaction with atomic oxygen might indicate. This in turn suggests that their role in smog formation is much more involved than merely to produce highly reactive species by reaction with atomic oxygen. When nitrogen dioxide-acetaldehyde mixtures were photolyzed at 3660 Å, oxygen, nitric oxide, carbon dioxide, methyl nitrate, and nitromethane were produced. When oxygen was added to the mixture, these compounds plus peroxyacetyl nitrate were produced.

Introduction

The role that hydrocarbons play in the chemistry of photochemical smog has, quite properly, been studied very extensively, but relatively little attention has been given to the involvement of other types of organic compounds. One of these other types that may play an important role because of its relatively great reactivity and fairly high concentration is aldehydes. Concentrations as high as 1.98 ppm have been observed in Los Angeles *(1)*, and much higher concentrations may occur for short time periods. Furthermore, if concentrations of hydrocarbons and of nitrogen oxides are greatly reduced without decreasing those of aldehydes, the importance of the latter will be greatly increased.

Altshuller and Cohen *(2)* have found that aldehydes behave like hydrocarbons in photochemical smog in that they accelerate the oxidation of nitric oxide to nitrogen dioxide. Of the organic compounds studied, only internally double-bonded olefins were more effective. Furthermore, Altshuller *et al. (3)* have shown that the photooxidation of aliphatic aldehydes at wavelengths below

---

*The National Center for Atmospheric Research is sponsored by the National Science Foundation.

3400 Å produces intermediate products that react with olefinic and aromatic hydrocarbons. Although the rates of photooxidation are slower than those induced by nitrogen oxides, they are significant with respect to photochemical smog.

We have been undertaking laboratory investigations of the kinetics and products of the reactions of atomic oxygen in the electronic ground state (^{3}P) with several aldehydes for two main reasons. One is that the reactions occur in photochemical smog and by initiating free radical chain reactions may be of considerably greater importance than the initial reaction rate alone would indicate. The second reason is the greater insight the results of such investigations give into the general chemical behavior of gas-phase aldehydes, insight which may help in understanding the role aldehydes play in photochemical smog.

This paper describes and discusses results obtained for three aldehydes: acetaldehyde, propionaldehyde, and acrolein. Two methods have been used to study the reactions. One employs a fast-flow system, using concentrations of the aldehydes and the atomic oxygen of the same order of magnitude. It provides absolute determinations of rate constants, but only relatively unreactive products can be identified. The other (only applied to acetaldehyde) uses a static system, producing atomic oxygen at much lower concentrations than those of the aldehyde, by the photolysis of nitrogen dioxide. By utilizing wavelengths at and exceeding 3660 Å, only nitrogen dioxide absorbs to produce nitric oxide and atomic oxygen. Only relative rate constants can be determined, but intermediate products can be observed.

The results of studies of the kinetics and products of the reactions of O(^{3}P) with formaldehyde and with acetaldehyde have been published *(4-12)*. The results obtained in our own and in other laboratories indicate that the results and conclusions of Avramenko and his co-workers *(8-11)* are largely incorrect. It also seems unlikely that similar results obtained by Avramenko *et al.(13)* for the reaction of propionaldehyde with O(^{3}P) could be correct.

Experimental Procedure

The fast-flow system was a modification of that used by Elias and Schiff *(14)* and is shown schematically in Fig. 1. Molecular nitrogen was passed through a microwave discharge produced in an Evenson-type cavity with 2450-MHz radiation. The small percentage of atomic nitrogen which resulted was converted to atomic oxygen by introducing nitric oxide:

$$N + NO \rightarrow N_2 + O \tag{1}$$

As the flow rate of nitric oxide is gradually increased, the orange Lewis-Rayleigh afterglow, resulting from the recombination of nitrogen atoms, is replaced by the blue afterglow resulting from the reaction

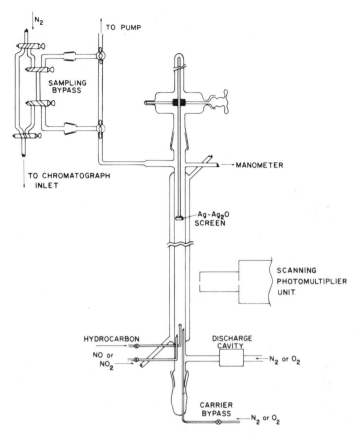

Fig. 1. Schematic of fast-flow system used for this and similar studies. O_2 and NO_2 were not used in the current work, nor was the carrier bypass.

$$N + O + M \rightarrow NO^* + M \tag{2}$$

When stoichiometric amounts of N and NO are entering the reaction chamber, no glow is observed and the flow rate of NO, which is easily measured, equals that of the atomic oxygen. The addition of slightly more NO results in the greenish "air afterglow," produced by

$$O + NO\,(+ M) \rightarrow NO_2^*\,(+ M) \tag{3}$$

Reaction 3 is slow, removing little atomic oxygen as the gases flow up to the reaction tube.

The nitric oxide (Matheson) was purified by passing it through a bed of

Ascarite to remove N_2O_3. It was stored in a 6-liter flask, and its flow, like that of the other gases and vapors, was controlled with a stainless-steel, 20-turn needle valve. The flow rate of the nitric oxide was determined from the rate of pressure drop in the flask by using a manometer filled with Fluorolube FS-5.

The acetaldehyde was from Matheson, while the propionaldehyde and acrolein were from the Eastman Kodak Co. They were purified by trap-to-trap distillation, stored in a 6-liter flask, and the flow rates determined from the pressure drop, again with a Fluorolube manometer. The nitrogen was from National Cylinder Gas, specified to be typically 99.98% nitrogen.

The admission of the organic reactant into the reaction tube produced a decrease in the air afterglow as the result of reaction with atomic oxygen. The intensity of this afterglow along the tube was proportional to the atomic oxygen concentration, the flow was laminar, and the distance along the tube from the point of injection of the organic reactant was proportional to the reaction time. Thus a scan of the reaction tube with a photomultiplier tube produced a record on a chart which was essentially a plot of reaction time versus atomic oxygen remaining.

A schematic diagram of the scanner is shown in Fig. 2. It was described in detail by Allen *et al.* *(15)*. The drive for the photomultiplier unit used a 0.9-rpm, 7.5-watt Bodine KC 1-22 RM reversible motor E, which could deliver a torque of 120 in.-oz. A Voland ball chain 20-socket sprocket was attached to the shaft of the motor, and a Voland stainless-steel bead chain, 3/32 inch in diameter, was used to support and drive the photomultiplier unit. The micro-switches automatically turned off the motor at the top and bottom of the scan. The two horizontal slits limited the region of the reaction tube from which light was transmitted to the photomultiplier tube. The output of the photomultiplier tube was sent to a millivolt recorder. In a later model of the scanner, the photomultiplier housing and base were replaced by a commercial model sold by Pacific Photometric Instruments of Berkeley, California. In this arrangement, the photomultiplier could scan up or down the vertical reactor at a constant speed of 5.7 cm min^{-1}. The linear flow rate through the 16-mm reaction tube varied with the pressure of nitrogen in the system, but the average was about 550 cm sec^{-1}. Thus 1 minute of scan time was the equivalent of about 10 msec of reaction time.

The reaction tube was surrounded by a jacket. The vapor from each of a series of boiling liquids could be passed between this jacket and the reaction tube to permit measuring the reaction rates at various temperatures and thus to calculate the activation energies. By utilizing very clean jacket and tube walls, a uniform film of condensate flowed down and did not interfere with the photomultiplier signals. Liquids found to be useful included ethanol, water, cyclohexanol, dodecane, and hexadecane. Temperatures in the reaction zone were determined with a thermocouple in a well during operation of the system (including the admission of the organic reactant) and were found to be within a few degrees of the boiling point of the liquid.

In addition to determining the reaction rates by scanning the air afterglow, they could be determined by stopping the reaction at one or more levels in the reaction tube and analyzing the effluent gases for the organic reactant. Products could also be determined for various degrees of reaction. The quenching was achieved by lowering a disk of silver screen, mounted on a rod as shown in Fig. 1, to the desired location. The disk quickly became coated with silver oxide, which is an excellent catalyst for the recombination of atomic oxygen. The rod could be raised or lowered along the reaction tube by rotation of the gum-rubber-covered rod which pressed against it.

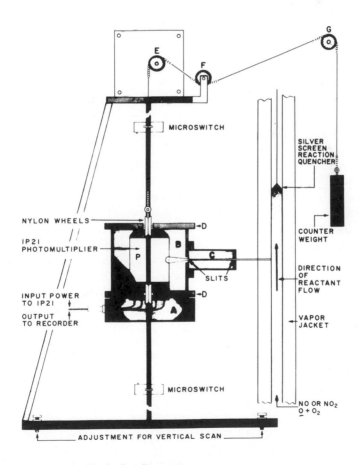

Fig. 2. Scanner used with the fast-flow system.

Gas chromatography was used to analyze for the unreacted aldehyde, and several techniques were employed to analyze for products. The sampling system for gas chromatography is shown in the upper left portion of Fig. 1. The sample to be analyzed was isolated between the two central stopcocks and then swept by the carrier gas (N_2 in the figure) into the chromatograph column. A flame ionization detector was used for all this work, but a number of types of columns were employed. Concentrations of acetaldehyde in the effluent gases were determined by using a dinonyl phthalate column at 80°C. Methane was detected and identified with a molecular sieve column, a dinonyl phthalate column, and a silica gel column — all calibrated with known amounts of methane. Concentrations of propionaldehyde and ethane were determined with a Carbowax 600 column at 50°C. The Carbowax column was also effective for acrolein, but the detector was insufficiently sensitive to acrolein to permit quantitative analyses at the low concentrations involved.

Samples for analysis by infrared and mass spectroscopy and for formaldehyde were collected by passing all the gases from the reaction tube through a trap cooled with liquid nitrogen. It replaced the sampler for chromatography. This trap was found to collect about 99% of known amounts of carbon dioxide under conditions that might be expected during an actual run. The analysis for the carbon dioxide was by infrared spectroscopy. The above trap did not collect methane, ethane, or carbon monoxide. These and carbon dioxide were detected and their yields determined semiquantitatively in the following manner. The gases flowing from the reaction tube were passed through a U-tube of 1-cm o.d. Pyrex tubing containing about 0.75 gram of silica gel. The gel was from Sargent, 8-20 mesh, and was heated overnight at 100°C before being placed in the tube. Larger amounts of silica gel produced such a large pressure drop that the system could not be effectively operated. The U-tube was cooled with liquid nitrogen while the gases were passed over the silica gel for one hour. The adsorbed gases were then desorbed into a micro gas cell (22-ml capacity, 60-cm path length), and the infrared spectrum was obtained. The technique was calibrated by substituting carbon monoxide, ethane, methane, and carbon dioxide, at known flow rates, for the reaction products passing over the silica gel. Formaldehyde was determined from the blue color it produces on reaction with chromotropic acid in sulfuric acid solution *(16)*. At this wavelength, other aldehydes did not interfere. Mass spectra were also obtained for a number of samples using an E A1 Model 250 quadrupole residual gas analyzer equipped with a specially built Ultek ion pump vacuum system to convert it to a mass spectrometer.

Rate constants were calculated in two ways. One involved calculations from the rates of atomic oxygen decrease at zero time, corrected for the slight decrease in the absence of aldehyde. The other involved calculations from the decrease in aldehyde concentration during a time determined by the position of the silver oxide-coated screen using the equation *(14)*

$$\ln \frac{[\mathrm{H_3CCHO}]_1}{[\mathrm{H_3CCHO}]_2} = k \int_{t_1}^{t_2} [\mathrm{O}]\, dt$$

The values of the integral were determined graphically from the scans of the airglow.

The total pressure in the reaction tube was varied from 1.2 to 4.4 mm. Concentrations of atomic oxygen were varied from about 4×10^{-11} to 6×10^{-9} mole cm^{-3}. Concentrations of aldehyde were varied from about 5×10^{-11} to 2.0×10^{-9} mole cm^{-3}.

The static experiments were performed in a conventional mercury-free high-vacuum system using oil (Dow Corning Silicone DC-704) diffusion pumping (Fig. 3). All stopcocks were lubricated with Dow Corning Silicone high-vacuum

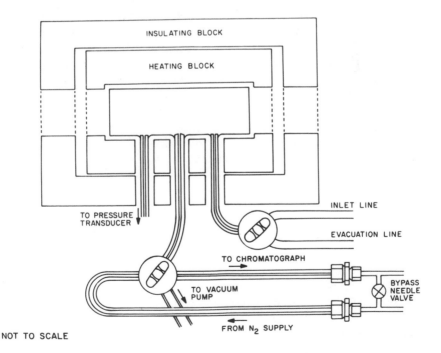

Fig. 3. Schematic of static system.

grease, which is relatively stable to attack by the oxides of nitrogen and organic vapors. Radiation at 3660 Å was obtained by filtering (Corning CS-7-83) the emission of a Hanovia type SH, medium-pressure mercury arc lamp. The radiation transmitted by the cylindrical (5-cm o.d. × 15-cm) Pyrex reaction vessel was detected by an RCA 935 phototube and monitored on a Pacific Photometric Model 10 photometer. Pressure in the reaction vessel was measured as the electrical output from a Statham PA 707 TC-5-350 absolute-pressure transducer capable of detecting pressure changes of 0.1 torr.

The progress of reaction was followed by repeatedly extracting small aliquots (0.05%) of the gaseous reaction mixture at regular intervals and immediately injecting these samples onto various chromatographic columns. This procedure eliminates the necessity of terminating a reaction in order to analyze the products. In addition, it is not necessary to perform a large number of experiments with the same parameters except for the time variable, nor is it necessary to use the questionable technique of handling and separating reactive reaction products by low-temperature fractional distillation. Using the procedure described, we have been able to isolate and measure unstable products — for example, nitrosomethane and peroxyacetyl nitrate. These products would normally be difficult, if not impossible, to observe by other techniques. Extraction and injection of samples for gas chromatographic analysis was accomplished using either a four-way stopcock described in the literature *(17)* or a combination three-way stopcock and Carle Model 2014 purged microvalve. The sample volumes use less than 100 μl in either case. Depletion of material in the 300-cm^3 reactor by these repeated extractions was less than 1% over a six-hour experiment and was therefore considered to be negligible.

Quantitative analyses were made on previously calibrated chromatographic systems. The permanent and inorganic gases O_2, N_2, NO, CO, CO_2, and N_2O were separated on a 6-foot × 1/2-inch Porapak S column at 0°C and measured by a Beckman helium ionization detector. Organic compounds were separated on an 8-foot × 1/2-inch 10% β,β'-oxydipropionitrile column at 25°C and measured by a Varian Aerograph flame ionization or electron capture detector. Columns of Porapak Q and Carbowax 1000 have been employed as well to separate the organic products in addition to looking for new products. A detailed discussion of these techniques is published elsewhere *(18)*.

At the completion of an experiment, the remaining reactants and products could be collected in a low-temperature trap (-215°C). The condensate could be subjected either to low-temperature fractional distillation or to bulk injection onto a 10-foot × 1/4-inch β,β'-oxydipropionitrile column with detector splitting incorporated. The components separated by these techniques were quantitatively analyzed by their gas phase infrared absorption spectra and their mass spectral cracking patterns. Final confirmation was obtained by reproducing the gas chromatographic retention time with a known sample of the deduced product.

Eastman Organic Chemicals acetaldehyde was purified by trap-to-trap distillation at reduced temperature. Matheson nitrogen dioxide (99.5% min) was oxidized by bubbling oxygen through the liquefied NO_2 at $O^\circ C$, dried with P_2O_5, and distilled into a blackened storage reservoir. Actinometry was by the potassium ferrioxalate method of Hatchard and Parker *(19)*.

Results

Acetaldehyde in the Fast-Flow System. The chromatogram of the partially reacted gases when a dinonyl phthalate column was used exhibited only two peaks, even when only a few percent of the acetaldehyde had reacted. Methane, as confirmed by further studies, produced one, and acetaldehyde produced the other. Biacetyl and acetic acid were not detected, although chromatograms prepared from these substances showed that they would have been detected if produced to an appreciable extent.

The production of methane was confirmed by using a silica gel column and a molecular sieve column. The former was found to effectively separate methane from ethane, and a peak was produced by the products having a retention time corresponding to methane but not to ethane. The molecular sieve column would be expected to retain most organic substances. Again, the only peak produced corresponded in retention time to that produced by methane. The yield of methane accounted for an average of about 9% of the acetaldehyde reacted. The flame ionization detector does not respond to carbon monoxide and carbon dioxide.

The products collected at the temperature of liquid nitrogen in the absence of silica gel were identified from the infrared and mass spectra as carbon dioxide and water. The yield of carbon dioxide varied from 32 to 62% of the acetaldehyde carbon. The products desorbed from silica gel were shown by infrared spectroscopy to be carbon monoxide, carbon dioxide, methane, water, and traces of formaldehyde. Yields calculated from the spectra showed that the acetaldehyde was oxidized almost entirely to these compounds (Table I). The chemical analyses for formaldehyde showed that small amounts were formed, about 0.1 to 1.5% of the acetaldehyde reacted.

The mole ratio of atomic oxygen reacted to acetaldehyde reacted varied with the ratios of the initial concentrations of the reactants, increasing from 0.31 to 6.5 as $[O]_0/[H_3CCHO]_0$ increased from 0.12 to 5.6. Varying these ratios had little effect on the yield of methane (Table II).

Reaction orders were determined by maintaining the initial concentration and the total pressure constant while varying the concentration of the other reactant and measuring initial reaction rates. The rates were essentially first-order in acetaldehyde and in atomic oxygen, and were independent of the pressure over the range investigated.

Table I

Yields of Carbon Dioxide, Carbon Monoxide,
and Methane Calculated from the Infrared Spectra
of the Products Collected on and Then Desorbed
from Silica Gel[a]

	Yield (moles per mole of CH$_3$CHO reacted)		
Run	CO$_2$	CO	CH$_4$
1	0.72	1.12	0.19
2	0.81	1.23	0.15

[a]All the acetaldehyde had been allowed to react. The two runs were essentially duplicates, at about 299°K.

Second-order rate constants calculated from the atomic oxygen concentrations (k_0) could be represented by the rate equation:

$$k_O = 1.1 \; (\pm \; 0.3) \times 10^{13} \; \exp(-2300/RT) \; cm^3 \; mole^{-1} \; sec^{-1}$$

The rate constants calculated from the acetaldehyde concentrations (k_a) exhibited more scatter than those for k_O. The ratio k_a/k_O was greater than unity for every run, varying from 1.4 to 6.3 with an average of about 2. Further results obtained during the study of this reaction are given by Cadle and Powers *(5)*.

Propionaldehyde. The chromatograms for the partially reacted propionaldehyde also had two peaks, in this case corresponding to ethane and propionaldehyde. The presence of ethane, indicated by the retention time, was confirmed with the infrared and mass spectra of the gases desorbed from the silica gel.

The infrared spectra showed that the products were almost entirely ethane, carbon monoxide, carbon dioxide, and water. The molar proportions of the first three were appropriately 0.1:1:2, respectively.

As was true for acetaldehyde, the mole ratio of atomic oxygen reacted to propionaldehyde reacted varied with the ratios of the initial concentrations of the reactants, increasing with increasing [0]/[H$_3$CCH$_2$CHO]$_0$ as shown in Table III. Variations in these ratios had no observable effect on the yield of ethane.

Reaction orders were determined in the same manner as for the O-acetaldehyde reaction and were found to be essentially unity in each reactant. The rates were independent of the pressure over the range investigated (Table IV).

The Arrhenius plot of the rate constants calculated from the atomic oxygen concentrations (k_O), Fig. 4, could be represented by the rate equation:

Table II

The Effect of the Initial Ratio of the Concentrations of Atomic Oxygen to Those of Acetaldehyde on Various Parameters of the Reaction at 298°K

$[O]_0 \times 10^{10}$ (moles cm^{-3})	$[CH_3CHO]_0 \times 10^{10}$ (moles cm^{-3})	CH_4 Yield $\times 10^2$ (moles of CH$_4$ per mole of CH$_3$CHO reacted)	$\Delta[O]/\Delta[CH_3CHO]$	$k_O \times 10^{-11}$ (cm^3 mole^{-1} sec^{-1})	$k_a \times 10^{-11}$ (cm^3 mole^{-1} sec^{-1})
2.0	17	13	0.31	2.8	–
6.1	20	9.4	0.76	3.0	5.1
5.8	9.4	13	1.0	3.5	8.1
6.2	10	15	1.0	3.2	5.6
8.1	6.7	12	1.4	3.8	9.5
5.8	3.1	–	2.5	2.4	9.2
12	5.1	19	2.6	3.5	7.4
13	2.3	–	6.5	2.0	4.3

Table III

Effect of the Initial Ratio of the Concentrations of Atomic
Oxygen to Those of Propionaldehyde on Various Parameters of the Reaction at 300°K

$[O]_0 \times 10^{10}$ (moles cm^{-3})	$[\text{Prop.}]_0 \times 10^{10}$ (moles cm^{-3})	$k_O \times 10^{-11}$ (cm^3 mole^{-1} sec^{-1})	$k_p \times 10^{-11}$ (cm^3 mole^{-1} sec^{-1})	$\dfrac{\Delta[O]}{\Delta[\text{Prop.}]}$	$\dfrac{[\text{Ethane}]}{\Delta[\text{Prop.}]}$
17.5	6.1	1.2	1.1	3.3	0.10
7.4	12.8	0.68	1.0	0.82	0.10
5.6	9.0	1.1	1.2	0.89	0.14
5.8	14.2	0.62	1.8	0.61	0.09
8.8	10.0	0.84	0.9	2.1	0.17
8.7	8.0	1.2	1.9	2.8	0.14

Table IV

Effect of Total Pressure on the Rate Constant
for the Reaction of Atomic Oxygen with Propionaldehyde

Total Pressure (torr)	$k_O \times 10^{-11}$ (cm^3 mole^{-1} sec^{-1})
2.7	1.1
2.7	0.9
2.2	1.4
1.3	1.1
0.5	0.9

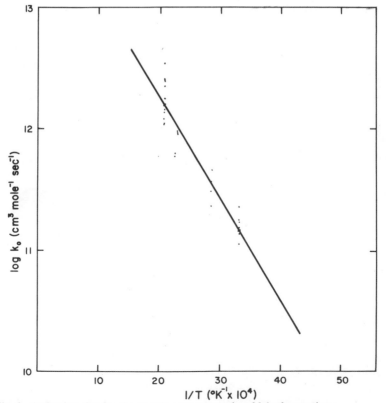

Fig. 4. Arrhenius plot for the atomic oxygen-propionaldehyde reaction.

$$k_O = 8.5 \times 10^{13} \exp(-3800/RT) \text{ cm}^3 \text{ mole}^{-1} \text{ sec}^{-1}$$

fitted to the data by the usual least-squares technique. The rate constants calculated from the propionaldehyde concentrations (k_p) were slightly larger than the values for k_O, but by hardly enough to be significant (Table III).

Acrolein. We are still studying the atomic oxygen-acrolein reaction, and the products have not yet been identified. Attempts to determine rate constants from the decrease in acrolein concentrations resulting from the reaction have been unsuccessful so far because of the relatively low sensitivity of the flame ionization detector to acrolein.

Holding one reactant constant while varying the other to determine reaction orders is difficult with this fast-flow system. Therefore, a different approach was used for the atomic oxygen-acrolein reaction. The equation

$$d[O]/dt = k[O]^A [\text{acrolein}]^B$$

is of the form

$$z = f(x, y; a_1, a_2, a_3)$$

where x and y are independent variables, z is the dependent variable, and the a_K's are parameters. A surface of this form can be fitted to a set of data (x_i, y_i, z_i) by a least-squares technique by minimizing a function of the sort

$$Q(a_1, a_2, a_3) = \sum_{i=1}^{n} [z_i - f(x_i, y_i; a_1, a_2, a_3)]^2$$

A necessary condition that Q have a minimum is that $\partial Q/\partial a_K = 0$ for all K. A computer technique was developed to determine the values of k, A, and B that satisfied this condition for a large number of sets of data. The results demonstrated that the orders were essentially unity in both atomic oxygen and acrolein.

The Arrhenius-type plot is shown in Fig. 5. The rate equation, fitted by the usual least-squares technique, is

$$k_O = 4.7 \times 10^{12} \exp(-2000/RT) \text{ cm}^3 \text{ mole}^{-1} \text{ sec}^{-1}$$

Acetaldehyde in the Static System. There was no measurable dark reaction observed between nitrogen dioxide and acetaldehyde during static experiments over the period of a typical experiment, six hours.

The following products were observed in the early stages of photolysis. The concentrations could be extrapolated to the origin of the concentration-versus-time graphs, indicating that the products were primary products of reaction: oxygen, nitric oxide, carbon dioxide, methyl nitrate, and nitromethane. Secondary products not extrapolating to the origin but delayed to some time after commencing irradiation, suggesting that they were produced by some reaction involving the accumulation of primary products, were nitrous oxide, nitrosomethane, and methyl acetate. The results confirmed previously published data on the rate of photolysis of nitrogen dioxide in the absence of additives, and support the observation of Christie and Collins *(12)* that the rate of consumption of nitrogen dioxide increases with increasing aldehyde concentration. The effect was not large; for example, a ratio of $[CH_3CHO]/[NO_2] \approx 30$ was necessary to double the rate of removal of NO_2 in the absence of aldehyde.

Addition of molecular oxygen did not alter the rate of consumption of nitrogen dioxide to any great extent nor did it markedly suppress nitrogen compound formation. In fact, the major effect of the addition of oxygen was the formation of one new product, peroxyacetyl nitrate (PAN).

Discussion

As indicated above, the only products detected from the atomic oxygen-acetaldehyde reaction in the flow system were water, methane, carbon dioxide, carbon monoxide, and a trace of formaldehyde. Intermediate products, such as the biacetyl observed by Cvetanović, were not detected presumably because of the difference in the relative acetaldehyde and oxygen atom concentrations. The ratios of atomic oxygen to acetaldehyde were much higher in the present study, with a result that intermediate products reacted with atomic oxygen. The rate constant and activation energy agreed very well with those obtained by others except for those obtained by Avramenko *et al.* (Table V).

The following sequence of reactions was proposed by Cadle and Powers *(5)* to explain the formation of methane, and, if reaction 5 is fast, the fact that k_a/k_o exceeded 1:

$$CH_3CHO + O \;\rightarrow\; CH_3CO + OH \tag{4}$$

$$CH_3CHO + OH \;\rightarrow\; CH_3CO + H_2O \tag{5}$$

$$CH_3CO + O \;\rightarrow\; CH_3CO_2 \tag{6}$$

$$CH_3CO_2 \;\rightarrow\; CH_3 + CO_2 \tag{7}$$

$$CH_3 + CH_3CHO \;\rightarrow\; CH_4 + CH_3CO \tag{8}$$

Table V

Comparison of Rate Constants for Atomic Oxygen–Organic Compound Reactions with Effectiveness
of the Organic Compound in Promoting the Oxidation of NO

Rate Constants for O(^{3}P)–Organic Molecule Reactions				Time to Maximum NO$_2$ Concentration[a] (min)	
k at ~300°K (cm^3 mole^{-1} sec^{-1})	E (cal mole^{-1})	Ref.	Organic Molecule	FEP	Mylar
2.1×10^{10}	< 5500	b	Formaldehyde	25	200
2.7×10^{11}	2300	c	Acetaldehyde	30	140
3.2×10^{11}	~3000	d	Acetaldehyde	–	–
$\sim 10^{11}$	–	e	Acetaldehyde	–	–
1.4×10^{11}	3800		Propionaldehyde	15	80
1.6×10^{11}	2000		Acrolein	45	180
7.2×10^{11}	1600	f	Ethylene	60	240
9.6×10^{12}	400	g	Isobutene	23	50

6.5×10^{10}	—	h	3-Methylheptane	80	—
1.1×10^{13}	—	h	cis-2-Pentene	—	—
8.5×10^{7}	7300	i	Methane	—	—

[a] A.P. Altshuller and I.R. Cohen, *Intern. J. Air Water Pollution*, **7**, 787 (1963).
[b] H. Niki, *J. Chem. Phys.*, **45**, 2330 (1966).
[c] R.D. Cadle and J.W. Powers, *J. Phys. Chem.*, **71**, 1702 (1967).
[d] R.J. Cvetanović, *Can. J. Chem.*, **34**, 775 (1956).
[e] M.I. Christie and B.M. Collins, *Nature*, **218**, 1245 (1968).
[f] L. Elias and H.I. Schiff, *Can. J. Chem.*, **38**, 1657 (1960).
[g] L. Elias, *J. Chem. Phys.*, **38**, 989 (1963).
[h] H.W. Ford and N. Endow, *J. Chem. Phys.*, **27**, 1277 (1957).
[i] R.D. Cadle and E.R. Allen, *J. Phys. Chem.*, **69**, 1611 (1965).

This reaction sequence is essentially that proposed by Cvetanović. In addition, the following reactions must be occurring:

$$CH_3CO \rightarrow CH_3 + CO \tag{9}$$

$$OH + CO \rightarrow CO_2 + H \tag{10}$$

$$CH_3 + O \rightarrow products \tag{11}$$

The methyl radical must undergo reactions such as reaction 11 in addition to hydrogen abstraction, since the yield of carbon dioxide plus carbon monoxide is much greater than that of methane. The above equations do not constitute a complete mechanism, and the reason for the relative lack of dependence of methane yield on the $[CH_3CHO]_0/[O]_0$ ratio (Table II) is not obvious.

The increasing ratio of atomic oxygen reacted to acetaldehyde reacted with increasing $[O]_0/[H_3CCHO]_0$ (Table II), together with the fact that the former ratios varied from fractional values to severalfold, agrees with the concept that both atomic oxygen and acetaldehyde are involved in secondary reactions. Such secondary reactions may have a much greater effect on k_a than on k_o, since the latter is calculated from initial rates when the concentrations of intermediate products are small. This, of course, will be true only if the rate constants for the reaction of atomic oxygen with the intermediate products are not markedly greater than that for the primary reaction of atomic oxygen with acetaldehyde.

This mechanism predicts that the reaction of atomic oxygen with propionaldehyde produces ethane, as was found to occur.

As would be expected, no great difference was observed between the rate constants for acetaldehyde and propionaldehyde, although both the activation energy and the pre-exponential factor were higher for propionaldehyde than for acetaldehyde. The activation energy and the pre-exponential factor for the acrolein were much lower than for the propionaldehyde. At room temperature, the rate constant for the reaction of acrolein is almost identical with that for propionaldehyde, but at higher temperatures it is much lower. The reaction involving acrolein is complicated by the fact that the atomic oxygen may abstract hydrogen or add to the double bond. Until the products are studied, the mechanism (or mechanisms) of attack cannot be resolved, and an explanation of the low pre-exponential factor cannot be suggested. Attack of the atomic oxygen on the double bond may be decreased by the fact that the atomic oxygen is electrophilic and the carbonyl group attracts electrons. Stabilization of acrolein by resonance may also play a role.*

Note added in proof: The main products of the reaction of atomic oxygen with acrolein have been found by infrared spectroscopy to be ethylene, acetylene, CO, CO_2, and H_2O.

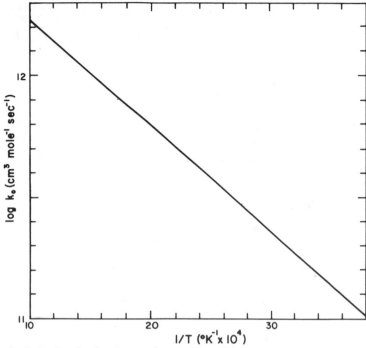

Fig. 5. Arrhenius plot for the atomic oxygen-acrolein reaction.

A comparison of the rate constants at room temperature for atomic oxygen-organic compound reactions with some measure of the effectiveness of the organic compounds in producing photochemical smog is desirable. Although a number of methods for making ratings of this effectiveness have been developed, the only one which has been applied to several aldehydes is that based on the rate at which NO is oxidized to NO_2 during the irradiation of NO-organic vapor-air mixtures [2]. The irradiations were conducted in plastic containers made of Mylar or of FEP (fluorinated ethylene propylene copolymer) films. The light transmission of the FEP containers was greater than that of the Mylar containers, especially in the < 3300-Å region where the aldehydes strongly absorb. Both the rate constants and the time to achieve the maximum NO_2 concentration (which was essentially proportional to the rate of NO oxidation) are shown in Table V. Olefins such as isobutene have long been recognized as being very effective in promoting the development of photochemical smog [20]. Judging from the data of Table V, the aldehydes are much more effective as producers of smog than the rates of reaction with atomic oxygen might suggest. This in turn suggests that their role in smog formation is much more involved than merely to produce highly reactive species by reaction with atomic oxygen. This is indicated by the work of Altshuller *et al.* [3] mentioned above. The aldehydes may serve to excite $O_2(^3\Sigma)$ to $O_2(^1\Delta)$, as suggested by Pitts *et al. (21)*, which in turn ultimately leads to the oxidation of NO to NO_2.

The following scheme may be used to describe the formation of the products observed during the static experiments with acetaldehyde.

Primary Reactions

$$NO_2 + h\nu \ (\lambda < 3660 \ \text{Å}) \ \rightarrow \ NO + O \tag{12}$$

$$O + NO_2 \ \rightarrow \ O_2 + NO \tag{13}$$

$$O + CH_3CHO \ \rightarrow \ CH_3CO + OH \tag{4}$$

$$OH + CH_3CHO \ \rightarrow \ CH_3CO + H_2O \tag{5}$$

$$CH_3CO + NO_2 \ \rightarrow \ CH_3CO_2 + NO \tag{14}$$

$$CH_3CO_2 \ \rightarrow \ CH_3 + CO_2 \tag{7}$$

$$CH_3 + NO_2 \ \rightarrow \ CH_3NO_2 \tag{15}$$

$$CH_3 + NO_2 \ \rightarrow \ CH_3O + NO \tag{16}$$

$$CH_3O + NO_2 \ \rightarrow \ CH_3ONO_2 \tag{17}$$

Secondary Reactions

$$CH_3 + NO + (M) \rightarrow \ CH_3NO + (M) \tag{18}$$

$$CH_3NO + NO \ \rightarrow \ CH_3O + N_2O \tag{19}$$

$$CH_3CO + NO \ \rightarrow \ CH_3CONO \tag{20}$$

$$CH_3CO + O_2 \ \rightarrow \ CH_3CO_3 \tag{21}$$

$$CH_3NO + NO \ \rightarrow \ CH_3O_2 + (M) \tag{22}$$

$$CH_3CONO + CH_3O_2 \ \rightarrow \ CH_3COOCH_3 + NO_2 \tag{23}$$

$$CH_3CO_3 + CH_3NO \ \rightarrow \ CH_3COOCH_3 + NO_2 \tag{24}$$

$$CH_3O_2 + NO \rightarrow CH_3O + NO_2 \qquad (25)$$

$$CH_3CO_3 + NO \rightarrow CH_3CO_2 + NO_2 \qquad (26)$$

$$O + NO + (M) \rightarrow NO_2^* + (M) \qquad (3)$$

$$O + O_2 + (M) \rightarrow O_3 + (M) \qquad (27)$$

$$O_3 + NO \rightarrow NO_2 + O_2 \qquad (28)$$

This scheme is obviously complex, owing to the many competing reactions. For the purpose of this article, we shall confine our discussion to the early stages of reaction caused by the first nine steps.

Carbon monoxide was not observed as a product of the reaction, suggesting that all the acetyl radicals react rapidly with nitrogen dioxide via steps 14 and 7. If this is the case, then CO_2 production is a measure of the methyl radicals formed and available to react with nitrogen dioxide. The absence of ethane, biacetyl, and acetone suggests that radical recombination reactions are not important in this system; they are, therefore, not included in this scheme. To determine whether we have completely described the system and accounted for the majority of the products, two material balances were checked. First, [NO] should equal $2[O_2] + [CO_2] + [CH_3ONO_2]$; and second, $[CO_2]$ should equal $[CH_3NO_2] + [CH_3ONO_2]$. Both agreed to within 5% in the early stages of reaction. The formation of methyl nitrite has not been observed. This substantiates Gray's conclusion *(22)* that addition of nitrogen dioxide to a methyl radical to form a C—O bond has energy in excess (20 kcal mole^{-1}) of that required to rupture the O—N bond and the molecule CH_3ONO will immediately fly apart as in step 16. This is also supported by the observation of methyl nitrate which presumably is a product of the resulting methoxy radical-NO_2 reaction.

The competition of methyl radicals for nitrogen dioxide forming nitromethane via step 15 or methyl nitrate via steps 16 and 17 may be estimated from the production of nitromethane and methyl nitrate. Thus,

$$\frac{d(CH_3NO_2)}{dt} = k_{15} \, (CH_3)(NO_2)$$

$$\frac{d(CH_3ONO_2)}{dt} = k_{17} \, (CH_3O)(NO_2) = k_{16}(CH_3)(NO_2)$$

and

$$\frac{[CH_3NO_2]_t}{[CH_3ONO_2]_t} = \frac{k_{15}}{k_{16}}$$

using the steady-state approximation.

We find that $k_{15}/k_{16} = 0.61$ at $25°C$, which is essentially in agreement with the value of 0.5 at $90°C$ obtained by Phillips and Shaw *(23)* and an estimated value of 0.55 from the data of Avery and Cvetanović *(7)*. An unfortunate error shows the reciprocal of this value in a previous publication *(18)*. As mentioned above, the rate of consumption of nitrogen dioxide increases with increasing acetaldehyde concentration. The effect is not large, which suggests that the presence of aldehydes in smog does not have a marked effect on the rate of nitrogen dioxide consumption. On the other hand, the formation of organic nitro compounds may be very important from a practical standpoint, since they are very toxic. The lack of information regarding the formation of such compounds and their stability is indicative that much more effort should be applied to the identification of organic nitrogen compounds in smog and to the study of their physiological action.

Photolysis of nitrogen dioxide-acetaldehyde mixtures at 3660 Å in the presence of excess oxygen resulted in the observation of one new major product, peroxyacetyl nitrate. The formation of other products was suppressed, but not by as much as expected. This would indicate that radical-nitrogen oxide reactions may successfully compete with radical-oxygen reactions in urban air or that the peroxy radicals may react with nitrogen oxides producing nitro and nitrated organics by different routes.

References

1. B.D. Tebbens, in "Air Pollution," Vol. I, 2nd ed. (A.C. Stern, ed.), Academic Press, New York, 1968.

2. A.P. Altshuller and I.R. Cohen, *Intern. J. Air Water Pollution,* 7, 787 (1963).

3. A.P. Altshuller, I.R. Cohen, and T.C. Purcell, *Science,* 156, 937 (1967).

4. H. Niki, *J. Chem. Phys.,* 45, 2330 (1966).

5. R.D. Cadle and J.W. Powers, *J. Phys. Chem.,* 71, 1702 (1967).

6. R.J. Cvetanović, *Can. J. Chem.,* 34, 775 (1956).

7. H.E. Avery and R.J. Cvetanović, *J. Chem. Phys.,* 43, 3727 (1965).

8. L.I. Avramenko and R.V. Lorentso, *Zh. Fiz. Khim.,* 26, 1084 (1952).

9. L.I. Avramenko and R.V. Kolesnikova, *Izv. Akad. Nauk SSSR Otd. Khim. Nauk,* 1231 (1961).

10. L.I. Avramenko, R.V. Kolesnikova, and M.F. Sorokima, *Izv. Akad. Nauk SSSR Otd. Khim. Nauk,* 1005 (1961).

11. L.I. Avramenko and R.V. Kolesnikova, *Advan. Photochem.,* 2, 25 (1964).

12. M.I. Christie and B.M. Collins, *Nature,* 218, 1245 (1968).

13. L.I. Avramenko, R.V. Kolesnikova, and G.I. Savinova, *Izv. Akad. Nauk SSSR Ser. Khim.,* 22(1967).

14. L. Elias, and H.I. Schiff, *Can. J. Chem.,* **38**, 1657 (1960).
15. E.R. Allen, F.E.Grahek,and R.D. Cadle, *Rev. Sci. Instr.,* **36**, 35 (1965).
16. A.P. Altshuller, L.J. Land,and A.F. Wartburg, *Intern. J. Air Water Pollution,* **6**, 381 (1962).
17. E.R. Allen, *Anal. Chem.,* **38**, 527 (1966).
18. E.R. Allen and K.W. Bagley, *Ber. Bunsenges. Physik. Chem.,* **72**, 227 (1968).
19. C.G. Hatchard and D.A. Parker, *Proc. Roy. Soc.,* **A235**, 518 (1956).
20. P.A. Leighton, "Photochemistry of Air Pollution," Academic Press, New York, 1961.
21. J.N. Pitts, Jr., A.U. Khan, E.B.Smith,and R.P. Wayne, *Environ. Sci. Technol.,* **3**, 241 (1969).
22. P. Gray, *Trans. Faraday Soc.,* **51**, 1367 (1955).
23. L. Phillips and R. Shaw, in "Tenth Symposium (International) on Combustion," The Combustion Institute (1965), p. 453.

Discussion

J. T. HERRON: In your mechanism for the acetaldehyde reaction you omit the very important reaction of hydroxyl radicals with atomic oxygen, $OH + O \rightarrow O_2 + H$. The hydrogen atoms formed in this way may play a significant role in the overall reaction. It has been observed that methane is a major product of the hydrogen atom-acetaldehyde reaction as studied by the discharge-flow method,* and it could be argued that this is the source of methane in the present case rather than the reaction $CH_3 + CH_3CHO \rightarrow CH_4 + CH_3CO$, which has a rate constant of about 10^6 cm^3 mole^{-1} sec^{-1} at $300°K$.† In terms of a flow system this is an extremely slow reaction. Furthermore, atomic oxygen reacts very rapidly with methyl radicals to give formaldehyde.‡◊ However, formaldehyde is not found as a major product. This implies that either methyl radicals play a minor role in the reactions, or the product analyses are for experimental conditions under which the formaldehyde is almost completely consumed. In either case it does not lend much support to the overall mechanism given here.

Any overall mechanism must include the following reactions:

$$O + CH_3CHO \rightarrow CH_3CO + OH$$

$$O + OH \rightarrow O_2 + H$$

$$OH + CH_3CHO \rightarrow CH_3CO + H_2O$$

$$H + CH_3CHO \rightarrow CH_3CO + H_2$$

*W.R. Trost, B. deB. Darwent, and E.W.R. Steacie, *J. Chem. Phys.,* **16**, 353 (1948).
†A.F. Trotman-Dickenson and G.S. Milne, "Tables of Bimolecular Gas Reactions," NBS

Natl. Std. Ref. Data Series 9, 1967.
‡H. Niki, E.E. Daby, and B. Weinstock, *J. Chem. Phys.,* **48**, 5729 (1968).
◊J.T. Herron and R.D. Penzhorn, *J. Phys. Chem.,* **73**, 191 (1969).

The significance of the reported rate measurements is also open to criticism.

Since secondary reactions are almost certainly faster than the primary reactions, rate constants based on loss of atomic oxygen at zero time will include contributions from subsequent rapid atomic oxygen reactions. The true rate will be the measured rate divided by some stoichiometry factor.

Rate measurements based on the use of the integrated rate expression:

$$k = \ln \left[(CH_3CHO)_a / (CH_3CHO)_b \right] / \int_a^b (O)dt$$

are valid only if acetaldehyde is consumed solely through reaction with atomic oxygen, which is clearly not the case here.

R.D. CADLE: We looked at rates in two different ways. In the case of the atomic oxygen reactions, we attempted to measure initial rates. In the case of the rate constants measured from the acetaldehyde reactions, we measured the rates after the reactions had progressed to a considerable extent. So there is a difference, and hopefully — we cannot guarantee this, obviously — by looking at initial rates, we eliminated the OH-acetaldehyde reaction. As a matter of fact, we eliminated it in two ways. First, we just looked at the atomic oxygen decrease rather than the acetaldehyde decrease, and second, we looked at initial rates before appreciable amounts of OH may have built up.

On another system (the atomic oxygen-*n*-butane system*), we measured the stoichiometry at various reaction stages. At very early times, the stoichiometry was essentially unity, but as the reaction progressed increasingly large deviations occurred. This does not necessarily prove that going to zero times gives initial rate constants, but it increases one's confidence in the results.

B. WEINSTOCK: We did some work on the reaction of acetaldehyde with atomic oxygen and atomic hydrogen several years ago. In the discharge flow the stoichiometry — that is, the ratio of reactants — has a profound influence on the products. Dr. Cvetanović has a polemic with Avramenko about this because in his system — where you photolyze N_2O, I believe — he found only biacetyl, and Avramenko and the Russians had never seen biacetyl. They were getting things like acetic acid and so on. In Cvetanović's system, where you have very tiny amounts of oxygen atoms, the acetyl radicals that are formed in the primary step could do nothing but recombine and form biacetyl.

The point about OH plus O is significant, because the system with oxygen atoms soon becomes a system with hydrogen atoms in it. The way we are able to get reliable rate constants in an oxygen atom system is to use a very large excess of oxygen atoms.

R.D. CADLE: Our rate constants for the atomic oxygen-acetaldehyde reaction agreed within a factor of 1.2 or 1.5. They were essentially the same.

---

*E.R. Allen and R.D. Cadle, *Photochem. Photobiol.*, **4**, 979 (1965).

B. WEINSTOCK: The methane comes from the ketene reaction. We were able to demonstrate this in a hydrogen atom system, because the methane we got depended on the character of the hydrogen. That is, if we started with protonated acetaldehyde and dueterium atoms, the methane would mostly be completely deuterated, because one makes the methyl radical which exchanges many times with hydrogen atoms before it settles on the wall.

R.D. CADLE: I might add that several other people have determined rate constants for the atomic oxygen-acetaldehyde reaction. They all agree remarkably well, considering the differences in the techniques that were used. Ours agreed very well with Cvetanović's relative rates, applying various absolute rates in making the calculation. They agreed very well with the paper that was presented by Niki; however, their technique has not been published. Christie and Collins (reference *12* of preceding paper) also have a rate constant. I think they are all within a factor of about 1½, except for the data by Avramenko. His differs from that of any of these others by about two orders of magnitude.

A.P. ALTSHULLER: Apropos of your explaining the relationship between the rates of reactions of the oxygen atoms with the various aldehydes and hydrocarbons versus using the time to formation of peak NO_2, you suggested two possibilities. One of these was the possible role of singlet oxygen. I think it is appropriate to ask Dr. Kummler: In the work you published fairly recently on benzaldehyde, didn't you have difficulty in observing singlet oxygen when formaldehyde and acetaldehyde were the aldehydes available for energy exchange?

R.H. KUMMLER: Yes. We only observed emission at 1.27 microns in the presence of benzaldehyde. We did not observe it in the case of acetaldehyde or formaldehyde. But since our signal-to-noise ratio even in the case of benzaldehyde was probably not as good as Pitts has shown recently, I am not sure it is significant. For example, in pure oxygen after irradiation in the ultraviolet, we never saw any emission at 1.27 microns. So I am not sure that it is significant that we did not observe it. Just a small increase in concentration might have allowed us to observe it. We cannot say.

A.P. ALTSHULLER: So it would be desirable to have additional evidence at a better signal-to-noise ratio in this situation.

Aldehyde-Olefin Interaction in the Nitrogen Oxide-Sensitized Photooxidation of Aliphatic Olefins

B. Dimitriades* and M.L. Whisman†
Bartlesville Petroleum Research Center
Bureau of Mines, U.S. Department of the Interior
Bartlesville, Oklahoma

Abstract

To predict photochemical smog potential of mixtures of hydrocarbon and hydrocarbon derivatives, it is necessary to establish whether component interactions affect behavior of individual components in the reaction system. This report covers work done at the Bureau of Mines, Bartlesville (Oklahoma) Petroleum Research Center, for the purpose of investigating olefin-aldehyde interactions possibly occurring in NO_x-sensitized photooxidation of 1-butene-aldehyde mixtures.

First results showed that in such mixtures consumption of 1-butene is affected by the presence and nature of other hydrocarbons and/or aldehydes. Further investigation revealed that the effects of aldehydes on butene consumption could be explained in terms of effects on oxygen atom and ozone concentrations only during the later reaction stage following photooxidation of NO into NO_2. In the earlier stages, the aldehyde effects can be explained only if olefin-radical reactions occur in parallel with the olefin-oxygen atom reaction.

Introduction

Information reported in this paper was generated at the Bartlesville Petroleum Research Center of the Bureau of Mines in the course of studying reactivities of mixtures of hydrocarbons and hydrocarbon derivatives in photochemical smog reaction systems. The objective of such studies was to obtain experimental evidence that would reveal interactions that might exist in multiple hydrocarbon component systems. Ultimately, such evidence is expected to provide a valid method for predicting the reactivity of a hydrocarbon mixture from reactivities manifested in single component systems.

In current practice, reactivity of a hydrocarbon mixture is taken to be the weighted average of the individual component reactivities,

---

*Project Leader, Fuels Combustion Research Group.
†Project Leader, Petroleum Chemistry & Refining Research Group.

References, pp. 98-99

$$R = \Sigma x_i r_i \qquad\qquad (1)$$

where x_i and r_i designate mole fraction and specific reactivity of the ith component. In using equation 1, it is assumed that each component's reactivity, r_i, and associated reactions are unaffected by the presence and nature of other components; in other words, component interactions do not occur.

To check the validity of equation 1, simple (binary) hydrocarbon mixtures as well as the complex hydrocarbon mixtures present in automotive emissions were irradiated in gas phase with simulated sunlight. Results from such tests with automotive emissions have been discussed elsewhere *(1)*. Results from tests with simple hydrocarbon mixtures are discussed here.

The work described and discussed in this paper consisted of a series of tests in which air samples containing fixed concentrations of hydrocarbons and nitrogen oxides, at near atmospheric levels, were irradiated with artificial sunlight. Irradiation tests were conducted both in a 50-liter Pyrex* glass reactor and in a 64-cu-ft aluminum and Pyrex irradiation chamber.

The specific objective in the glass reactor program was to obtain stoichiometric data on NO_x-sensitized photooxidation of butene in the presence of one other hydrocarbon or aldehyde. The results of interest in the present discussion are those pertaining to butene consumption as affected by organic reactant composition. These results, given in Table I, show clearly that the

Table I

Extent-of-Reaction Data from NO_x-Sensitized Photooxidation of 1-Butene in the Presence of Added Aldehydes or Hydrocarbons

Organic Reactant[a]	Extent of 1-Butene Reaction (%)[b]
1-Butene	33.6 ± 0.4
1-Butene + 1-butene	75.6 ± 1.1
1-Butene + formaldehyde	58.8 ± 1.6
1-Butene + acetaldehyde	23.8 ± 0.5
1-Butene + propionaldehyde	22.8 ± 0.9
1-Butene + propylene	77.5 ± 0.3
1-Butene + *trans*-2-butene	79.4 ± 0.3
1-Butene + *m*-xylene	46.1 ± 0.6
1-Butene + mesitylene	55.8 ± 0.5

[a] Initial reactant charge consisted of purified air containing the designated hydrocarbons or aldehydes, each at 1 ppm, and NO_2 at 1 ppm.
[b] Range is also given for values obtained from three to five replicated irradiation tests.

*Trademarks are used in this report for identification only and do not imply endorsement by the Bureau of Mines.

hydrocarbons and formaldehyde cause acceleration of butene consumption, whereas acetaldehyde and propionaldehyde inhibit the butene reaction. Such accelerative and inhibitive effects can be caused either by effects on oxygen atom and ozone concentrations in the reaction system or by interactions involving organic radicals or by both. To further investigate the nature of such effects, reactant mixtures similar to the ones shown in Table I were irradiated in the 64-cu-ft chamber *(2)* where more complete analyses of reaction mixtures could be made.

Experimental Procedures and Results from Chamber Program

The irradiation chamber is a 64-cu-ft chamber with a 92-sq-ft surface, of which 68% is aluminum and the remainder is Pyrex glass. Radiation is provided by 80 fluorescent lamps (blacklight, bluelamps, sunlamps) and three 400-watt mercury vapor lamps (GE-H400RST-33-1). Light intensity in terms of the NO_2 photolysis constant, k_D *(3)*, is 0.40 min^{-1} for 2-min irradiation and 0.47 min^{-1} for 1-min irradiation. Chamber temperature was $93° \pm 2°F$, and relative humidity was about 27%. Mixing of chamber content is accomplished with a pair of fans capable of moving the chamber air at a velocity of 3 chamber volumes per minute, approximately. Nitrogen dioxide was measured continuously by the Saltzman method. A Mast ozone meter, calibrated with standardized O_3 blends, was used to measure photochemical oxidant; these Mast data were taken to represent ozone levels. Butene-1 was measured chromatographically.

The specific objective in the irradiation chamber program was to generate evidence indicative of the extent to which organic component interactions — in the form of radicals-hydrocarbon or radicals-aldehyde reactions — affect butene consumption. To this end, each of the reactant mixtures studied was irradiated in the chamber for 4 to 6 hours, and concentrations of 1-butene, NO_2, and ozone were followed with time.

In one experiment, the chamber fans were switched off during irradiation in order to lessen the effect of chamber walls — if such effect is present — on the reacting system.

Resultant data were analyzed in a manner similar to that described by Stephens *(4)*. Consumption of 1-butene was assumed to be caused by second-order reactions with oxygen atoms and with ozone only. Further, it was assumed that, under the experimental conditions of the study, concentration of oxygen atoms is proportional to concentration of NO_2. On the basis of these assumptions it can be shown *(4)* that concentration of 1-butene is related to that of NO_2 and of O_3 through equation 2,

$$\log \frac{[B]_1}{[B]_2} = k_O \int_{t_1}^{t_2} [NO_2]\, dt + k_{O_3} \int_{t_1}^{t_2} [O_3]\, dt \qquad (2)$$

where $[B]_1$ and $[B]_2$ represent concentrations of butene at times t_1 and t_2, respectively, and k_O and k_{O_3} are constants. Using equation 2 and experimental data for NO_2 and O_3, values for k_O and k_{O_3} were obtained for each of the reaction systems of the study.

Results

The constant k_{O_3} was computed from experimental data taken during the later stages of the irradiation test when butene is consumed mainly in reaction with ozone. In some cases, however, butene levels in this stage of reaction were extremely low and experimental measurement was of questionable accuracy. In these cases additional butene was injected at the end of the normal run as shown in Fig. 1, and k_{O_3} was determined again from subsequent butene and ozone

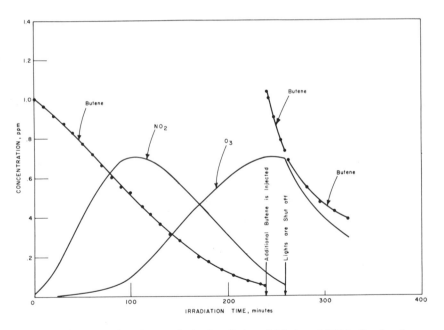

Fig. 1. Concentration changes during irradiation of 1-butene + NO in the chamber.

measurements. Also, k_{O_3} values were obtained from experimental data taken after the lights were shut off, as shown in Fig. 1. The constant k_O was calculated from data taken during the 0-to-peak-NO_2 time interval when olefin is consumed almost entirely in reaction with oxygen atoms.

In the systems where the initial nitrogen oxide reactant was NO_2, k_{O_3} was calculated first, as described in the previous paragraph; k_O was calculated subsequently using equation 2, the experimental data, and the k_{O_3} value. For these systems, the described method of calculating k_O is valid if k_{O_3} is independent of length of the time interval within which k_{O_3} was computed. The dependency of k_{O_3} value on length of time interval was checked for each and every reaction system. For example, with data from one system, k_{O_3} values were obtained for different time intervals; they are shown in Table II. Similar calculations for the

Table II

Values of k_{O_3} for Different Reaction Time Intervals[a] in Photooxidation of 1 ppm Butene in the Presence of 1 ppm NO

Time Interval (min)	k_{O_3} $(ppm^{-1} min^{-1})$
160 – 180	0.0117
160 – 200	0.0118
160 – 220	0.0123
160 – 240	0.0120
	Average 0.0120
	Range ± 0.0003 or $\pm 2.5\%$

[a]Defined as time intervals (t_1, t_2) in equation 2.

other reaction systems gave range values from ± 2.5 to $\pm 5\%$ and in one case $\pm 14\%$. These results suggest that k_{O_3} is independent of length of time interval and that k_{O_3} values can be used to calculate k_O. Results from all determinations of the k_{O_3} constant are given in Tables III and IV.

Unlike k_{O_3}, k_O was found to depend on the length of time interval within which k_O was computed; consequently, computed k_O values are reported in Tables V and VI along with corresponding time intervals.

Discussion

The experimentally obtained values for k_O and k_{O_3} were compared with those calculated with data from the literature as follows:

By definition:

$$k_O \equiv \frac{k_D k_1}{2.3\, k_2\, [O_2]\, [M]}$$

Table III

Values of k_{O_3} for Various Reaction Systems

Reactant[a]	k_{O_3} (ppm^{-1} min^{-1})	Length of Time Interval Used to Calculate k_{O_3} (min)
1-Butene + NO	0.0120	60
1-Butene + NO[b]	0.0127	60
1-Butene + NO (fans off)	0.0115	60
1-Butene + 1-butene + NO	0.0099	60
1-Butene + propionaldehyde + NO	0.0119	80
1-Butene + propionaldehyde + NO[b]	0.0102	80
1-Butene + formaldehyde + NO	0.0130	80
1-Butene + NO_2	0.0102	120
1-Butene + propylene + NO_2	0.0099	100
1-Butene + propionaldehyde + NO_2	0.0112	120
1-Butene + formaldehyde + NO_2	0.0111	80
1-Butene + acrolein + NO_2	0.0105	80

[a] Initial reactant charge consisted of purified air containing the designated hydrocarbons or aldehydes, each at 1 ppm, and NO_2 or NO at 1 ppm.
[b] Replicated runs.

Table IV

Values of the Ozone-Butene Reaction Constant, k_{O_3}, Obtained by Different Experimental Methods

Reaction System	k_{O_3} (ppm^{-1} min^{-1})		
	Method A[a]	Method B[b]	Method C[c]
Butene + NO	0.0120	0.0116	0.0093
Butene + NO[d]	0.0127	–	–
Butene + NO (fans off)	0.0115	0.0112	0.0101
Butene + butene + NO	0.0099	0.0087	0.0085
Butene + propionaldehyde + NO	0.0102	0.0095	0.0084

[a] k_{O_3} was calculated by using experimental data from last 60 or 80 minutes preceding the injection of additional butene (see Fig. 1).
[b] k_{O_3} was calculated by using experimental data from time period following butene injection and until lights were shut off (see Fig. 1).
[c] k_{O_3} was calculated by using experimental data obtained after lights were shut off (see Fig. 1).
[d] Replicated runs.

Table V

Values of k_0 for Different Reaction Time Intervals[a] and for Reaction Systems in Which Initial Nitrogen Oxide Reactant is NO

Reactant[b]	k_0 (ppm^{-1} min^{-1})			
	$0 - t_m/4$[c]	$0 - t_m/3$[c]	$0 - t_m$[c]	t_m[c] $- 1.5 t_m$[c]
1-Butene + NO	0.0148	0.0106	0.0066	0.0043
1-Butene + NO[d]	0.0145	0.0106	0.0073	0.0044
1-Butene + NO (fans off)	0.0148	0.0105	0.0064	0.0040
1-Butene + 1-butene + NO	0.0106	0.0073	0.0057	0.0044
1-Butene + propionaldehyde + NO	0.0101	0.0078	0.0058	0.0027
1-Butene + propionaldehyde + NO[d]	0.0097	0.0075	0.0054	0.0033
1-Butene + formaldehyde + NO	0.0214	0.0154	0.0085	0.0041

[a]Defined as time intervals (t_1, t_2) in equation 2.
[b]Initial reactant charge consisted of purified air containing the designated hydrocarbons or aldehydes, each at 1 ppm, and NO at 1 ppm.
[c]t_m designates time to maximum NO_2 level.
[d]Replicated runs.

Table VI

Values of k_0 for Different Reaction Time Intervals[a] and for Systems in Which Initial Nitrogen Oxide Reactant is NO_2

Reactant[b]	k_0 (ppm^{-1} min^{-1})	
	$0 - t_{0.5}$[c]	$0 - t_{0.9}$[d]
1-Butene + NO_2	0.0050	0.0064
1-Butene + propylene + NO_2	0.0053	0.0075
1-Butene + propionaldehyde + NO_2	0.0042	0.0040
1-Butene + formaldehyde + NO_2	0.0060	0.0067
1-Butene + acrolein + NO_2	0.0044	0.0053

[a]Defined as time intervals (t_1, t_2) in equation 2.
[b]Initial reactant charge consisted of purified air containing the designated hydrocarbons or aldehydes, each at 1 ppm, and NO_2 at 1 ppm.
[c]Designates time required for consumption of 50% of initially present butene.
[d]Designates time required for consumption of 90% of initially present butene.

$$k_{O_3} \equiv \frac{k_3}{2.3}$$

where k_D, k_1, k_2, and k_3 are rate constants for the following reaction steps:

$$NO_2 \xrightarrow[\text{light}]{k_D} NO + O$$

$$O + 1\text{-butene} \xrightarrow{k_1} \text{products}$$

$$O + O_2 + M \xrightarrow{k_2} O_3 + M$$

$$O_3 + 1\text{-butene} \xrightarrow{k_3} \text{products}$$

The NO_2 photolysis constant, k_D, was determined experimentally by irradiating 1 ppm of NO_2 in N_2 for 1 min. From irradiation data, k_D was calculated from equation 3, suggested by Tuesday *(3)*, and equation 4, suggested by Stephens *(5)*.

$$k_D \equiv \frac{1}{t} \ln \frac{[NO_2]_i}{[NO_2]_f} \tag{3}$$

$$k_D' \equiv \frac{0.6}{t} \ln \frac{[NO_2]_i}{[NO_2]_f} \tag{4}$$

where t = irradiation time, and $[NO_2]_i$ and $[NO_2]_f$ are NO_2 levels before and after irradiation. Results gave $k_D = 0.47$ min^{-1} and $k_D' = 0.28$ min^{-1}.

Literature values for k_1 range from 0.31×10^9 to 2.94×10^9 liters mole^{-1} sec^{-1} *(6)*. The value of k_2 has been established more reliably at 6.9×10^7 liters^2 mole^{-2} sec^{-1} *(6)*. With these values for k_1 and k_2, k_O is calculated to be 0.00011 to 0.00102 min^{-1} if $k_D = 0.47$ min^{-1} is used, and 0.00006 to 0.00001 min^{-1} if $k_D' = 0.28$ min^{-1} is used. Literature values of k_3 range from 3.2×10^3 liters mole^{-1} sec^{-1} *(6)* to 5.1×10^3 liters mole^{-1} sec^{-1} *(7)*; corresponding calculated values for k_{O_3} range from 0.0034 to 0.0054 ppm^{-1} min^{-1}.

Values for k_O and k_{O_3} obtained from this work are compared with those calculated from literature data in Table VII. Table VII also includes values for k_O obtained experimentally by Stephens *(4)*.* These comparisons led to the following observations:

1. Experimentally obtained k_{O_3} values (Table IV, method C) are higher than those calculated from literature data by a factor of 2.0. This represents good agreement, considering the uncertainty in measurement of O_3 by the Mast meter.

*Table VII, *see* p. 101.

2. Experimentally obtained k_O values are higher than those calculated from literature data by a factor of from 3 to 350, depending on specific literature data used and on the method used to calculate k_D and k_O from experimental data.

3. Experimentally obtained k_O values agree well with those obtained by Stephens *(4)*.

Before these results were examined for the presence of olefin-aldehyde interactions, the possibility was considered that results from this study reflect peculiarities of the experimental system rather than the chemistry of the observed reaction systems. In regard to this possibility, observations 1 and 3 are highly significant. Agreement of the experimentally obtained k_{O_3} value with the literature value (observation 1) underscores the appropriateness of the experimental system used in this study. Also, agreement of present results with those obtained with a considerably different experimental system (observation 3) lends credibility to any mechanistic implications of results of both studies. Further, the observed agreement in results between replicated runs as well as the agreement in k_{O_3} values obtained by various methods (Table IV) are also indicative of the high level of reliability of the generated experimental data.

Regarding the presence of olefin-aldehyde interaction, the data of Table III suggest that, when butene is consumed mainly in reaction with ozone, aldehydes do not interfere significantly. This suggestion is based on the investigators' belief that the variation in k_{O_3} value shown by the data of Table III is within the experimental uncertainty limits.

When butene is consumed mainly in reactions with oxygen atoms, the data of Tables V and VI indicate the presence of two effects: (1) The value of k_O is clearly dependent on the length of time interval that was used to calculate k_O; in general, k_O has higher values in reaction mixtures with lower NO_2/NO ratio. (2) The constant k_O has somewhat different values for different organic reactant mixtures; this indicates the presence of interaction effects. The data of Tables V and VI indicate further that these two effects are present only when butene is consumed mainly in converting NO into NO_2. For butene consumption following completion of NO conversion, k_O becomes independent of time interval and of the presence of other organic reactants, and its value more closely approaches those derived from literature data. Considering all these indications, it is concluded that butene reactions with ozone and oxygen atoms adequately account for butene consumption in the later stages of the reaction.

Results from the tests with the chamber circulation fans inoperative showed that the unstirred system had a somewhat higher NO_2 dosage* and comparably lower ozone dosage.* Both these effects probably result from the fact that NO_2

---

*Defined as $\int NO_2\, dt$ or $\int O_3\, dt$ over a period of 4 hours.

loss on chamber walls is lower in the unstirred system. However, values of k_O and k_{O_3} were the same in the stirred and unstirred systems (see Tables III, IV, and V); this fact suggests that, in our experimental system, the difference between the effective wall surface of the stirred system and that of the unstirred system had no effect on the relative importance of butene-consuming reaction steps. The overall significance of this experimental observation is obscure because it is recognized that the difference in effective wall surface between the stirred and unstirred systems may not be sufficiently large to produce a noticeable effect.

In conclusion, the results from this study suggest the following:

1. In photooxidation of butene in the presence of NO_2, the effect of aldehyde on butene consumption is adequately explained in terms of the aldehyde's effects on the ozone and the oxygen atom concentrations in the reacting system.

2. In photooxidation of butene in the presence of NO, the effect of aldehyde cannot be accounted for unless olefin-aldehyde interactions occur in parallel to the olefin-ozone and olefin-oxygen atom reactions. Such interactions are toward faster butene consumption in the presence of formaldehyde and toward slower butene consumption in the presence of propionaldehyde.

From the standpoint of reaction mechanisms, these results are significant in that they offer an explanation of the manner in which some aldehydes affect butene reaction; namely, aldehydes interfere with butene reaction both directly and indirectly by modifying the oxygen atom and ozone concentrations. However, in programs such as the one conducted by these investigators and in which the main objective is the characterization of emissions as smog precursors, the item of interest is not an explanation but rather the quantitative definition of such olefin-aldehyde interaction phenomena. Therefore, from a viewpoint appropriate to our program, results from this study are significant in that they reveal a problem and point the direction for additional work that is needed for more accurate reactivity characterization of emission mixtures. In line with these findings, this group is now engaged in a program to define quantitatively the effect of aldehydes on the various types of smog manifestations using reactant mixtures similar to those found in typical urban atmospheres.

Acknowledgment

This work was supported by the National Air Pollution Control Administration, U.S. Department of Health, Education, and Welfare.

References

1. Basil Dimitriades, B.H. Eccleston, and R.W. Hurn, An Evaluation of the Fuel Factor through Direct Measurement of Photochemical Reactivity of Emissions. APCA Preprint No. 69-153, presented at 62nd Annual Meeting Air Pollution Control Association, New York, June 22-26, 1969.
2. Basil Dimitriades, *J. Air Pollution Control Assoc.*, **17**, 460-466 (1967).
3. C.S. Tuesday, "Chemical Reactions in the Lower and Upper Atmosphere" (R.D. Cadle, ed.), Interscience, New York, 1961, pp. 15-49.

4. E.R. Stephens, *Intern. J. Air Water Pollution,* **10**, 793-803 (1966).
5. E.R. Stephens, *Intern. J. Air Water Pollution,* **10**, 649-663 (1966).
6. A.P. Altshuller and J.J. Bufalini, *Photochem. Photobiol.,* **4**, 97-146 (1965).
7. Philip A. Leighton, "Photochemistry of Air Pollution," Academic Press, New York, 1961.

Discussion

H.F. RICHARDS: Did you vary the light intensity to see what effect it has on k_O and k_{O_3}?

B. DIMITRIADES: No, we did not. Every time we change the light intensity, we have to remeasure it by the photolysis of NO_2 in nitrogen. This is difficult to do with a large chamber.

J.J. BUFALINI: Was the irradiation system a mixture of sunlamps and blacklights?

B. DIMITRIADES: Yes, sunlamps, blacklights, and bluelights similar to the irradiation systems used by HEW, GM, and others.

J.J. BUFALINI: With sunlamps, you would get some photodissociation of the aldehydes in the early stages of the reaction. If formaldehyde photodissociates faster than propionaldehyde, this would account for the effect you noted.

B. DIMITRIADES: I did not attempt to offer any explanation of this effect. Our interest was to quantify this effect, rather than to explain it. I think, however, that your suggestion is reasonable.

W.E. WILSON: When you measure a rate constant and it is not constant, this means that there are other reactions taking place that are not accounted for. I have measured k_{ozone} under similar conditions for 1-butene, as a function of the concentrations of water vapor and SO_2. It was measured in the latter part of the reaction, so oxygen atom reactions can be neglected. As shown in Fig. 2, in a dry system with no SO_2, we get 22 ppb^{-1} min^{-1}. This compares with Dr. Dimitriades' value of about 10 ppb^{-1} min^{-1}. With 65% relative humidity, the apparent ozone-1-butene rate constant increases to 36 or so. As SO_2 increased at 65% relative humidity, the apparent constant did not change. In a dry system, however, as the SO_2 increased, the k_{ozone} increased. I point this out as another example of the strange things that can happen, and the many different kinds of reaction that we do not know about and cannot account for.

J.J. BUFALINI: I believe a group at the Franklin Institute back in the late fifties studied water vapor effects. They studied ozone-olefin reactions, purposely added water vapor to the system, and observed no effects. This was without SO_2.

B. DIMITRIADES: In our study, the temperature was 90° to 92°F; the relative humidity was about 70%.

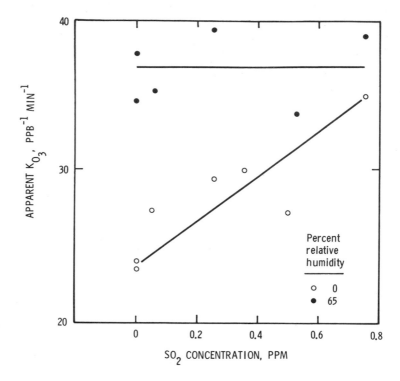

Fig. 2. Effect of relative humidity and SO_2 on the apparent rate constant for the 1-butene-ozone reaction.

E.R. STEPHENS: k_O should be linear in light intensity, and inversely proportional to the oxygen concentration. A very good test of this would be to change the oxygen concentration by a known amount and then measure k_O.

G.S. HAMMOND: I don't see how you can treat k_O as though it were a rate constant for an individual reaction. It is a collection of rate constants and concentrations. Seeing how k_O responds to a single variable is not very informative. It indicates that these systems interact with each other, but I don't think it tells anything beyond that.

P.A. LEIGHTON: It is a collection of constants in a complex rate equation.

G.S. HAMMOND: That's right.

A.P. ALTSHULLER: This study and several others have shown a discrepancy which may be accounted for by OH reaction, RO_2 reaction, or still other reactions. Each of these reactions is interwoven in this rate, so it is difficult to disentangle them.

R.J. CVETANOVIC: I believe that the rate constant for the oxygen atom-1-butene reaction is known very much better than the variation indicated in

Table VII. It is probably known within 20%. It has been determined by quite a few people. I don't think there is any justification now to use that wide variation. You have a variation of a factor of 10. We all like to choose data from the literature which come rather close to what we find. But in this particular case, I don't think this is justifiable any longer.

B. DIMITRIADES: I think the data listed in Table VII may be somewhat misleading. In addition to the variation in the literature values of k_O, I also included the variations in the values for k_D by photolysis of NO_2 in nitrogen. There are limitations to this method because it ignores the reaction of oxygen atoms with NO_2 in two different ways: first, to form O_2 and NO; and second, to form NO_3 which subsequently oxidizes the NO back to NO_2. If we assume that these latter reactions do occur, then the k_D value will be different. I included these two differently calculated values in this range. This may be why the range is wider than perhaps it should be.

Table VII

Values of k_0 and k_{0_3} from Present Work and from Literature Data

	k_0 (ppm^{-1} min^{-1})		k_{0_3} (ppm^{-1} min^{-1})
	Before NO_2 Peak	After NO_2 Peak	
From present work			
Organic reactant + NO	0.00540-0.02140[a]	0.00270-0.00440[a]	0.0099-0.0130[b] (0.0083-0.0110)[c]
Organic reactant + NO_2		0.00400-0.00750[a]	0.0099-0.0112[b] (0.0083-0.0094)[c]
From Stephens' work			
Organic reactant + NO	0.00280-0.00773[d] 0.00164-0.00392[e]		
From literature data			
Organic reactant + NO, NO_2	0.00011-0.00102[d] 0.00006-0.00061[e]		0.0034-0.0054

[a] Range of values for different reaction systems and different lengths of time interval within which k_0 was determined.
[b] Range of values for different reaction systems. Values were obtained by method A (see Table IV).
[c] Range of values for different reaction systems. Values were obtained by method C (see Table IV).
[d] Values were obtained using $k_D = 0.47$ min^{-1}.
[e] Values were obtained using $k_D = 0.28$ min^{-1}.

Some Reactions of Nitrogen Dioxide with Olefins

Sigmund Jaffe
California State College
Los Angeles, California

Abstract

Thermal and photochemical reaction rates were measured for C_2H_4, C_3H_6, $1-C_4H_8$, iso$-C_4H_8$, *trans*$-C_4H_8$, *cis*$-C_4H_8$, and $1-C_5H_{10}$. The thermal reactions were performed at temperatures from $25°$ to $100°C$, and Arrhenius parameters were determined. The activation energies ranged from 4.0 to 8.1 kcal mole^{-1}, decreasing for the 1-olefins as the molecular weight increased, and decreasing for the isomers of butene as the molecule became more unsymmetrical. This observation is consistent with the premise that the reaction proceeds more rapidly as the intermediate first formed is capable of increased stability.

Linear free energy correlations between NO_2 rate constants and O_3 and O rate constants for a selected set of olefins yield reasonably straight lines. They support the contention that the rate-controlling steps in the three systems have some common elements. The formation of the intermediate, especially in the case of O_3, should be similar to that in the case of NO_2. Some speculation on the geometry and stability of the intermediate first formed is included in the presentation.

The rate laws in all cases were first-order in both NO_2 and olefin. These results are not in agreement with those of Cottrell and Graham [1,2], although they are consistent with those of Cadle [3] and Ford and Endow [4].

A mechanism is presented in the case of ethylene to explain the experimental results. In this case, the rates of production of products were determined by gas chromatographic techniques. The essential features of the mechanism are that NO_2 adds to the ethylene, forming an intermediate that rearranges to yield excited acetaldehyde or ethylene oxide plus NO. The acetaldehyde is energetic enough (ΔH reaction = -38 kcal/mole) to react readily with NO_2. The ethylene oxide is less energetic ($\Delta H = -11$ kcal/mole) and reacts more slowly with NO_2. The reaction of the aldehyde or oxide with NO_2 gives rise to free radicals which may account for the products found upon further reaction with NO_2.

The rate law derived from this mechanism agrees with the second-order kinetics found experimentally. The mechanism also explains the formation of NO, CO_2, N_2O, H_2O, CH_3NO_2, CH_3ONO_2, C_2H_4O, and CH_3CHO, which were found by chromatographic analysis. Some rate constants have been estimated. The results of quantum yield measurements for the loss of NO_2 in the photooxidation of the representative set of olefins are presented. In addition, related thermal and photochemical reactions of NO_2 with ethylene oxide, acetaldehyde, acetone, and propionaldehyde are discussed.

References, p. 129

Introduction

The reactions of NO_2 are of paramount importance in the photochemistry of air pollution. The role of NO_2 in producing oxygen atoms has been studied extensively, and the subsequent reactions of the oxygen atoms with olefins and O_2 are well known. However, NO_2 reacts further with free radicals and with almost every one of the species that are formed in the primary process. A determination of the role of NO_2 in the secondary thermal reactions is therefore of considerable interest.

The direct reactions of NO_2 with olefins, oxides, aldehydes, and ketones are in general rather slow, with specific rate constants of the order of 10^{-3} liters mole^{-1} sec^{-1}. It would seem that they could not compete effectively with reactions of O atoms for which the rate constants are 10^8 to 10^9 liters mole^{-1} sec^{-1}, and reactions of O_3 for which the rate constants are about 10^3 liters mole^{-1} sec^{-1}. However, several of the products of the thermal reactions of NO_2 are the same as those derived in the photochemical processes. This indicates that intermediates and free radicals in these reactions may be similar. The determination of mechanisms and specific rate constants for the thermal reactions therefore serves as a means of determining the rates of several of the elementary steps that have been proposed for the photochemical schemes.

A second purpose in studying the thermal reactions of NO_2 with olefins and with the products of olefin oxidation is the determination of overall rates to be used as empirical corrections on photochemical processes that are carried out at appreciable concentrations. When reactions are run in the millimeter range rather than in the parts per million range, these corrections become important.

Some of the thermal reactions of NO_2 and low-molecular-weight olefins have been studied in the liquid state *(5-7)* at low temperatures, and in the gas phase at elevated temperatures and at relatively high concentrations. Only a few rates have been determined at room temperature *(3)*.

In the liquid state and in the absence of oxygen, the mechanism is described *(8)* by a two-step addition process:

$$\ce{\overset{\backslash}{\underset{/}{C}}{=}\overset{/}{\underset{\backslash}{C}} + NO_2 \rightarrow \overset{\backslash}{\underset{/}{\dot{C}}}{-}\overset{|}{\underset{|}{C}}{-}NO_2}$$

$$\ce{\overset{\backslash}{\underset{/}{\dot{C}}}{-}\overset{|}{\underset{|}{C}}{-}NO_2 + NO_2 \rightarrow -\overset{|}{\underset{NO_2}{C}}{-}\overset{|}{\underset{NO_2}{C}}{-} \ or \ -\overset{|}{\underset{NO_2}{C}}{-}\overset{|}{\underset{ONO}{C}}{-}}$$

Ethylene reacts slowly, giving 1,2-dinitroethane and 2-nitroethyl nitrite, which in turn yields the nitrate. Propylene and the butylenes react more rapidly, giving the 1,2-dinitro compounds and β-nitroisopropyl nitrate as well as nitro-*tert*-butyl nitrate.

The gas phase reactions of ethylene and propylene were studied by Cottrell and Graham *(1,2)* at 160° to 280°C and at pressures of 3 to 12 cm of Hg. They obtained third-order rate laws with rate constants, in units of liters^2 mole^{-2} sec^{-1}, reported as

$$k = 10^{8.5} \exp(-12,500/RT) \qquad 160°\text{-}220°\,C, \text{ethylene}$$

$$k = 10^{10.9} \exp(-18,000/RT) \qquad 220°\text{-}280°C, \text{ethylene}$$

$$k = 10^{9.7} \exp(-13,600/RT) \qquad 160°\text{-}260°C, \text{propylene}$$

Work by Cadle *et al. (3)* on the reactions of NO_2 with 1-hexene, cyclohexene, and 1,3-butadiene in O_2 and N_2 as carrier gases yielded second-order rate constants of 1.5×10^{-2}, 1.8, and 76 liters mole^{-1} sec^{-1}, respectively. Ford and Endow's *(4)* study of the reaction of NO_2 with 1-pentene gave a rate constant of 1.3×10^3 liters mole^{-1} sec^{-1}.

Recent work by Landgraf (personal communication) using electron spin resonance spectrometry has shown that the reactions proceed through the formation of a stable intermediate. In addition, Bielski and Gebicki *(9)* describe reactions 1 and 2 as taking place as a result of the formation of a π-complex intermediate which is an exothermic reaction. Their conclusions were also based on electron spin resonance evidence.

It is apparent from this brief review that further study of the thermal reactions is necessary if an understanding of the mechanisms and determination of the rate constants is to be obtained.

Experimental Procedure

The thermal reactions were carried out in two separate quartz cells each 10 cm long and about 2 cm in diameter. One cell was inserted in the sample compartment of a line-operated Beckman D.U. spectrophotometer which is equipped to record the output. This means was used to follow the rate of loss of NO_2 at 4350 Å where no photolysis of NO_2 takes place. Standard high-vacuum techniques were used for introducing the samples into the cells. The vacuum system is directly attached to a gas chromatograph where the samples that were transferred from the quartz cell after reaction were analyzed. Analyses were carried out on Porapak-Q and dibenzyl ether columns, after the removal of excess NO_2 by treatment with Hg.

The second cell was wrapped with ¼-inch-wide heating tape so that Arrhenius parameters could be determined. The cell had a thermocouple well just above the light path. The output of the thermocouple was fed to a Honeywell-Brown Pyr-o-vane temperature controller, and the temperature was controlled to about

$\pm 1^\circ$C. The rate of loss of NO_2 was measured photometrically by focusing light at 4350 Å, from a Bausch and Lomb monochromator using a Hanovia S-100 mercury arc as the light source, on a solid-state photocell. The output from the photocell was measured with a Fluke differential voltmeter.

The photochemical reactions were carried out in a quartz cell 4 feet long and 2 inches in diameter. The cell was silvered on the outside to prevent light leakage. It was also contained in a thermostated water jacket to control the temperature within $\pm 1^\circ$C. The light intensity was measured with two photomultiplier tubes, one of which sensed the light transmitted and the other the incident light. The outputs of the photomultiplier tubes opposed each other so that the difference in voltage was proportional to the fraction of light absorbed. The signal was amplified and recorded so that NO_2 changes could be followed as a function of irradiation time.

The products of the photochemical reactions were analyzed on a Loenco Model 15-B chromatograph which was modified to include a flame ionization detector in series with a thermal conductivity detector. Porapak-Q in a column 1/8 inch in diameter and 12 feet long was used to analyze the products. The column was kept at 110°C, and helium was used as the eluting gas.

All gases used in this program were chemically pure and were further purified by repeated trap-to-trap distillation. The oxygen and nitrogen were specially dried and purified and were delivered in prepurified tanks. The gases were introduced into the reaction cell after passing through Ascarite and $Mg(ClO_4)_2$ to remove CO_2 and H_2O.

Results and Discussion of the Thermal Reactions of NO_2 with Olefins.
Several series of reactions were run in which the initial concentrations of NO_2 and olefin were varied in a systematic manner. The initial rates of the reactions were obtained by the extrapolation to zero time of curves such as those shown in Fig. 1. Plots of the initial rates as a function of the products of the initial concentrations of NO_2 and olefin yielded straight lines like that shown in Fig. 2 for ethylene.

These results, along with the straight lines obtained from the conventional second-order function,

$$\frac{1}{[\text{olefin}]_0 - [NO_2]_0} \, \ell n \, \frac{[NO_2]_0 \, [\text{olefin}]}{[\text{olefin}]_0 \, [NO_2]} = kt \tag{3}$$

lend support to the assignment of

$$-\frac{d[NO_2]}{dt} = k[NO_2] \, [\text{olefin}] \tag{4}$$

as the rate law.

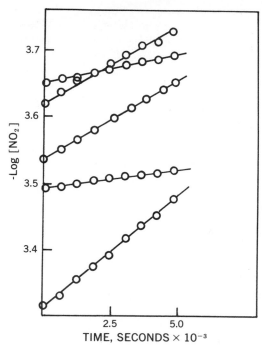

Fig. 1. Typical first-order rate curves for the loss of NO_2 in the C_2H_4-NO_2 system.

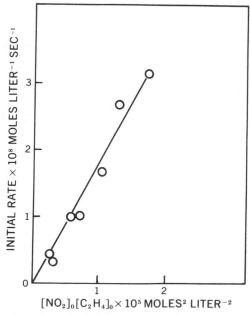

Fig. 2. Initial rate dependence in the NO_2-C_2H_4 system.

This rate law is not in agreement with the second-order dependence on $[NO_2]$ found by Cottrell and Graham *(1,2)* in their study of NO_2-ethylene and NO_2-propylene reactions. However, their work was carried out at relatively high concentrations of NO_2 (3 to 12 cm of Hg) and high temperatures. This rate law is consistent with the second-order dependence found by Cadle *et al. (3)* and by Ford and Endow *(4)* in their investigation of similar NO_2-olefin systems.

The rates of these reactions were determined as a function of temperature from 25° to 100°C. The results are given in Table I and are shown in Fig. 3. It

Table I

Least-Squares Arrhenius Relationships in Oxidation of Olefins by NO_2

Olefin	Equation of Line	E_a (kcal mole^{-1})
C_2H_4	$\log k = 3.3 - 1.8 \times 10^3 T^{-1}$	8.1
C_3H_6	$\log k = 3.5 - 1.7 \times 10^3 T^{-1}$	7.9
$1\text{-}C_4H_8$	$\log k = 3.4 - 1.6 \times 10^3 T^{-1}$	7.3
cis$-2-C_4H_8$	$\log k = 2.4 - 1.2 \times 10^3 T^{-1}$	5.4
trans$-2-C_4H_8$	$\log k = 3.2 - 1.4 \times 10^3 T^{-1}$	6.4
iso$-C_4H_8$	$\log k = 1.6 - 0.86 \times 10^3 T^{-1}$	4.0
$1-C_5H_{10}$	$\log k = 3.2 - 1.6 \times 10^3 T^{-1}$	7.2

is at first surprising that such slow reactions have relatively low activation energies. However, the pre-exponential factors are also relatively low, indicating that the slow rate of the reactions may be the result of a large negative entropy of activation. The 1-olefins show a regular decrease in activation energy with increasing molecular weight, while the butene isomers exhibit decreasing activation energies as the complexity of the molecule increases.

It is convenient to describe the NO_2-ethylene system in some detail in an effort to understand the processes taking place in the general olefin-NO_2 systems. For ethylene, as determined from the slope of the curve in Fig. 2, one obtains $1.9 \pm 0.1 \times 10^{-3}$ liter mole^{-1} sec^{-1} at 25°C for the specific rate constant. The value obtained from equation 3 is $1.85 \pm 0.06 \times 10^{-3}$ liter mole^{-1} sec^{-1}, which is a satisfactory agreement.

The rates of production of products in the ethylene-NO_2 system are presented in Figs. 4 through 6. They show that most products are formed rapidly at first but tend to reach a steady state after some time. This behavior suggests that the products, when they build up, all react further, probably with NO_2.

A mechanism that explains the observed behavior is the following:

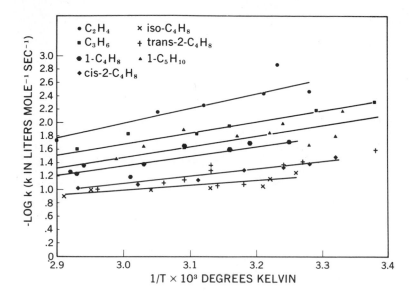

Fig. 3. Arrhenius relationships for the reactions of NO_2 with some olefins.

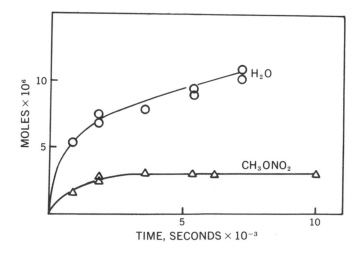

Fig. 4. The rates of production of H_2O and CH_3ONO_2 in the NO_2-C_2H_4 system.

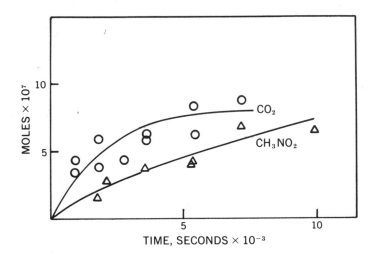

Fig. 5. The rates of production of CO_2 and CH_3NO_2 in the NO_2-C_2H_4 system.

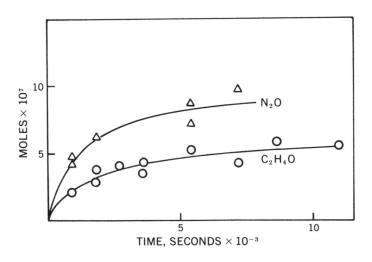

Fig. 6. The rates of production of N_2O and C_2H_4O in the NO_2-C_2H_4 system.

$$C_2H_4 + NO_2 \rightleftharpoons [int] \tag{5),(-5}$$

$$[int] \begin{array}{l} \rightarrow NO + CH_3CHO^* \\[6pt] \rightarrow NO + CH_2CH_2O^* \xrightarrow{M} CH_2CH_2O \end{array} \tag{6}$$

$$\tag{7),(7M)}$$

$$CH_3CHO^* + NO_2 \rightarrow CH_3CO + HONO \tag{8}$$

$$CH_3CO + NO_2 \rightarrow CH_3COO + NO \tag{9}$$

$$CH_3COO \rightarrow CH_3 + CO_2 \tag{10}$$

$$CH_3 + NO_2 \rightarrow CH_3O + NO \tag{11}$$

$$CH_3 + NO_2 \rightarrow CH_3NO_2 \tag{12}$$

$$CH_3O + NO_2 \rightarrow CH_3ONO_2 \tag{13}$$

$$CH_3O + NO \rightarrow CH_3ONO \tag{14}$$

$$CH_3O + NO \rightarrow H_2CO + HNO \tag{15}$$

$$2HONO \rightarrow H_2O + NO + NO_2 \tag{16}$$

$$2HNO \rightarrow H_2O + N_2O \tag{17}$$

Assuming the usual steady-state approximation on all intermediates, free radicals, and CH_3CHO, one obtains the rate law for the initial stages of reaction (when [NO] and [HONO] are small):

$$-\frac{d[NO_2]}{dt} = k_5\left[1 + \frac{k_6\left(3 + \dfrac{k_{11}}{k_{11}+k_{12}}\right) - k_{-5}}{(k_{-5}+k_6+k_7)}\right][C_2H_4][NO_2] \tag{18}$$

Equation 18 has the same form as equation 4, which was derived empirically.

It should be pointed out that, if NO and HONO are not assumed to be small as in equation 18, the rate law becomes

$$-\frac{d[NO_2]}{dt} = k_5\left\{1 + \frac{2k_6 - k_{-5} + \dfrac{k_6 k_{11} k_{13}[NO_2]}{(k_{11}+k_{12})[k_{13}[NO_2]+(k_{14}+k_{15})[NO]]}}{(k_{-5}+k_6+k_7)}\right\}[C_2H_4][NO_2] \tag{19}$$

Equation 19 has an $[NO_2]^2$ term in it. However, the rate curves remained nearly first-order in $[NO_2]$ for a considerable length of time. This indicates that the influence of the second-order term must be very small. It can be seen from equation 19 that it gets smaller with increasing reaction time. Thus, the first-order dependence on $[NO_2]$ is retained.

One can estimate the ratios of some of the constants from our data in Figs. 4 through 6:

$$\frac{d[C_2H_4O]_0}{d[CO_2]_0} = \frac{k_7}{k_6} = 0.8 \tag{20}$$

and

$$\frac{d[CH_3NO_2]_0}{d[CH_3ONO_2]_0} = \frac{k_{12}}{k_{11}} = 0.1 \tag{21}$$

Using these values one obtains $k_{-5} = 2.5k_6$. With Phillips and Shaw's *(10)* values of k_{11} and k_{12}, one obtains $3.7k_6$ as a minimum for k_{-5}. The maximum value of k_5 is 1.9×10^{-3} liter mole^{-1} sec^{-1}. It appears that the formation of the intermediate could be the slow step in the process.

The results suggest that the reaction is similar to that of O_3 with olefins. The parallel reactions are

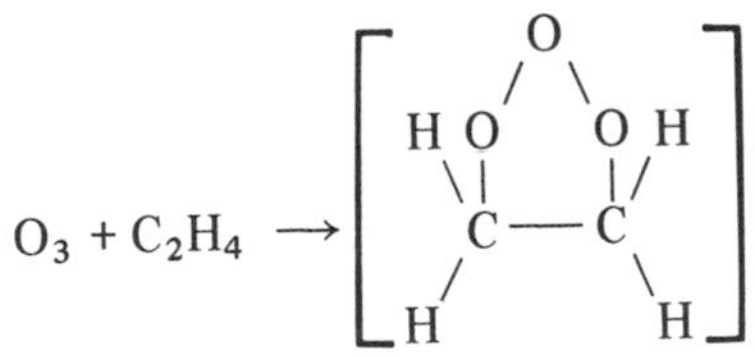

$$O_3 + C_2H_4 \rightarrow \left[\begin{array}{c} O \\ \diagup \diagdown \\ H\ O \qquad O\ H \\ \diagdown | \qquad |\diagup \\ C - C \\ \diagup \qquad \diagdown \\ H \qquad H \end{array} \right] \tag{22}$$

and

$$NO_2 + C_2H_4 \rightarrow \left[\begin{array}{c} N \\ \diagup \diagdown \\ O \qquad O \\ H\ | \qquad |\ H \\ \diagdown C - C \diagup \\ \diagup \qquad \diagdown \\ H \qquad H \end{array} \right] \tag{23}$$

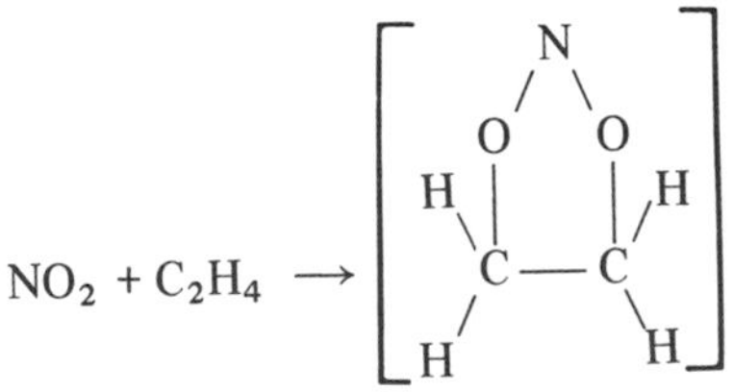

The formation of molozonide, reaction 22, has been suggested by several investigators and recently proposed by De More *(11)* as favored over as an intermediate. De More presents entropy of activation calculations to support his argument. If the intermediate is formed as shown in equation 23, its formation would be accompanied by a negative entropy change. From the relationship

$$k_{\text{rate}} = e^2 \, (RT) \frac{kT}{h} \, e^{\frac{\Delta S_p^{\ddagger}}{R}} \, e^{\frac{-Ea}{RT}} \tag{24}$$

one can see that a negative entropy change would lead to a small A factor and explain the slow rates of the reactions of NO_2 with olefins. The value of $\Delta S_p^{\ddagger}$ obtained from our data is -54.7 gibbs mole^{-1}. Using $S^{\circ}(C_2H_4) = 52.5$ gibbs mole^{-1} and $S^{\circ}(NO_2) = 57.5$ gibbs mole^{-1}, one obtains $S_{\ddagger}^{\circ} = 55.3$ gibbs mole^{-1}. Although this value seems low compared with analog compounds such as cyclopentane for which $S^{\circ} = 70$ gibbs mole^{-1}, it cannot be verified at present.

Free energy correlation plots were made from the data in Tables II, III, and IV. They are shown in Figs. 7 and 8. The logarithms of the rate constants for the O + olefin, and O_3 + olefin reactions, compared with those of the NO_2-olefin reactions, indicate that the mechanisms have some common elements. We suggest that the common factors include the formation of the intermediates in the O atom addition and O_3 molecule addition reactions with olefins.

It should be noted that similar curves presented by Vrbaski and Cvetanović *(12)* for the correlation of O and O_3 reactions showed isobutene to be an exception, as we do in Fig. 7. Either one of the isobutene rate constants is in error, or the intermediate formed in that case differs from those of the other olefins. A similar correlation with ionization potentials is shown in Fig. 9. This supports the contention that the reactions exhibit electrophilic behavior. The ionization potentials were taken from reference *12* and from the work of Collin and Lossing *(13)*.

Photochemical Reactions of NO_2 and Olefins. The quantum yields for NO_2 consumption were measured as a function of olefin concentration for a series of olefins at $25^{\circ}C$ using the mercury arc line at 3660 Å for irradiation. The NO_2 concentration was about 1×10^{-4} mole liter^{-1}, and the olefins were varied from zero to about 3×10^{-2} mole liter^{-1}. The total pressure was 1 atm using N_2

Table II

Rates of Oxygen Atom-Olefin Reactions at $25^\circ C$

Olefin	Rate Constant (liters mole^{-1} sec^{-1})	References
C_2H_4	3.1×10^8	*14, 15*
C_3H_6	1.7×10^9	a
$1-C_4H_8$	1.7×10^9	a
iso$-C_4H_8$	7.5×10^9	a
cis$-2-C_4H_8$	7.1×10^9	a
trans$-2-C_4H_8$	8.5×10^9	a
$1-C_5H_{10}$	3.1×10^9	*16*
cis$-2-C_5H_{10}$	6.8×10^9	a
$1-C_6H_{12}$	1.95×10^9	a

[a]Calculated from the relative rates of O + olefin versus O + iso$-C_4H_8$; NO_2 = 0.44 from reference *17*, where $k(0 + NO_2) = 3.3 \times 10^9$ liters mole^{-1} sec^{-1}.

Table III

Rates of Ozone-Olefin Reactions at $25^\circ C$

Olefin	Rate Constant (liters mole^{-1} sec^{-1})	References
C_2H_4	1.6×10^3	*18*
C_3H_6	5.1×10^3	*12*
$1-C_4H_8$	6.2×10^3	*18*
iso$-C_4H_8$	3.6×10^3	*12*
cis$-2-C_4H_8$	1.3×10^4	*12*
trans$-2-C_4H_8$	1.7×10^4	*12*
$1-C_5H_{10}$	3.9×10^3	*12*
cis$-2-C_5H_{10}$	1.0×10^4	*12*
$1-C_6H_{12}$	6.8×10^3	*18*

Table IV

Reactions of Olefins with NO_2 at 25°C

Olefin	Rate Constant (liters mole^{-1} sec^{-1})	
C_2H_4	1.8×10^{-3}	
C_3H_6	6.3×10^{-3}	
$1-C_4H_8$	1.2×10^{-2}	
$iso-C_4H_8$	5.1×10^{-2}	
$trans-2-C_4H_8$	3.2×10^{-2}	
$cis-2-C_4H_8$	2.3×10^{-2}	
$1-C_5H_{10}$	6.6×10^{-3}	
$1-C_5H_{10}$	1.3×10^{3}	Ref. *4*
$1-C_6H_{12}$	1.5×10^{-2}	Ref. *3*

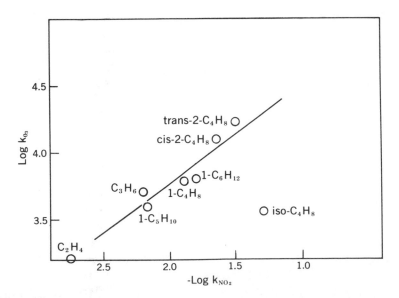

Fig. 7. Linear free energy correlations for reactions of olefins with O_3 and NO_2.

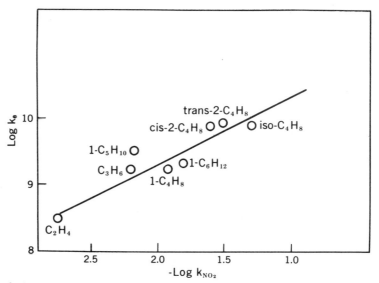

Fig. 8. Linear free energy correlations for reactions of olefins with O atoms and NO_2.

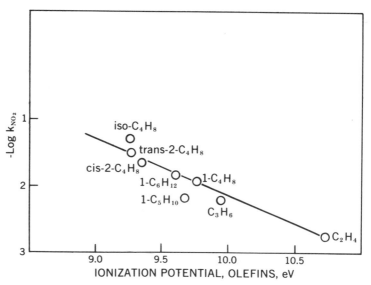

Fig. 9. Correlation of rates of olefin-NO_2 reactions with the ionization potentials of the olefins.

except for propylene, where the total pressure was 0.5 atm. The results conformed to the general relationship:

$$\Phi = A + \frac{Bx}{C + Dx} \tag{25}$$

in which A (the value of Φ for pure NO_2) is the intercept obtained on plotting Φ as a function of $x = (olefin)(NO_2)$ as in Fig. 10. Terms B, C, and D are combinations of rate constants related to mechanisms similar to those reported in references *19* and *20*. The essential features of the mechanisms are that $O(^3P)$ atoms produced in the photodissociation of NO_2 add to the olefin, yielding the

biradical, $R_1 R_2 \overset{\overset{\displaystyle O\cdot}{|}}{C} - \overset{\displaystyle .}{C} R_3 R_4$. The biradical rearranges to yield excited oxides, aldehydes, or ketones. These excited molecules may be stabilized by collisions or dissociate into free radicals that react rapidly with NO_2. The products of these photochemical reactions are similar to those for the thermal reactions mentioned before.

Equation 25 may be rearranged to

$$\frac{1}{\Phi - A} = \frac{D}{B} + \frac{C}{Bx} \tag{26}$$

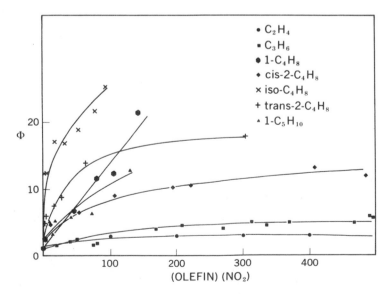

Fig. 10. Quantum yields as a function of olefin-NO_2.

which yields a straight line when $1/(\Phi - A)$ is plotted as a function of $1/x$. Table V summarizes the results of the quantum yield determinations by expressing linear least-squares relationships for equation 26.

Photochemical Reactions of NO_2, C_2H_4, and O_2. Several series of experiments were carried out in the photolysis at 3600Å of a mixture of NO_2, C_2H_4, O_2, and N_2. The oxygen concentration was varied from zero to 1 atm, and the nitrogen concentration was adjusted so that the total pressure remained constant at 1 atm. NO_2 and C_2H_4 ratios were kept at near 1 : 1 with concentrations which varied from 10^{-8} to 10^{-5} mole liter^{-1}.

Typical rate curves are shown in Fig. 11, where the logarithm of the NO_2 concentration is plotted as a function of time. It can be seen that the rate exhibits a first-order dependence on the NO_2 concentration. Differences in rates are a result, principally, of the effect of O_2 on the reaction, since $[NO_2]_0[C_2H_4]_0$ was kept nearly constant for several runs. A selected set of curves is shown in Fig. 12, where the log of $[NO_2]$ is divided by $[C_2H_4]_0$ to normalize the curves.

A convenient way of displaying the data is shown in Fig. 13, where the function $d \log[NO_2]/dt$ is plotted versus the product $[NO_2]_0[C_2H_4]_0[O_2]_0$, the initial concentrations of the reactants. The function $d \log[NO_2]/dt$ is proportional to the quantum yield for NO_2 loss, since

$$\frac{d \log[NO_2]}{dt} = \frac{1}{2.3[NO_2]} \frac{d[NO_2]}{dt} \tag{27}$$

Table V

Least-Squares Relationships in the Photooxidation of Olefins by NO_2

Olefin	A	C/B	D/B
C_2H_4	1.6	9.5	0.59
C_3H_6	1.2	35.3	0.19
$1-C_4H_8$	1.6	2.6	0.085
$1-C_5H_{10}$	1.6	1.1	0.30
$cis-2-C_4H_8$	1.6	2.1	0.10
$trans-2-C_4H_8$	1.6	1.3	0.058
$iso-C_4H_8$	1.6	0.36	0.049

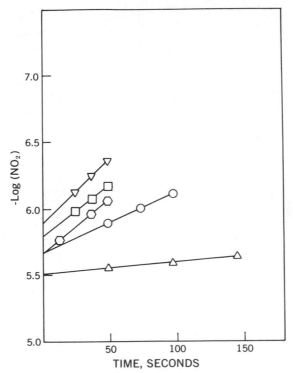

Fig. 11. First-order rates of NO_2 decomposition in the NO_2-C_2H_4-O_2 system.

and

$$\Phi = \frac{-d[NO_2]/dt}{kI[NO_2]} \tag{28}$$

in which k is proportional to the absorption cross section, and I is the incident light intensity. Fig. 13 shows that the addition of O_2 tends to slow down the rate of disappearance of NO_2, probably because of the competition between NO_2 and O_2 for free radical reactions, and the substitution of the slow O_3 oxidation processes for the more rapid O atom oxidation of olefins which predominates at low O_2 concentrations. Fig. 14 shows the fraction of C_2H_4 left as a function of $[NO_2]_0[C_2H_4]_0[O_2]_0$. There is a slight decrease in the amount of C_2H_4 that is oxidized as the oxygen is increased. This reflects the competition for O atoms by C_2H_4 and O_2 and the slower oxidation of C_2H_4 by O_3 which is gradually replacing the more rapid oxidation by O atoms.

The rate of production of products is presented in Figs. 15 through 17. The products include NO, CO_2, H_2O, N_2O, CH_2O, CH_3OH, C_2H_4O, CH_3CHO,

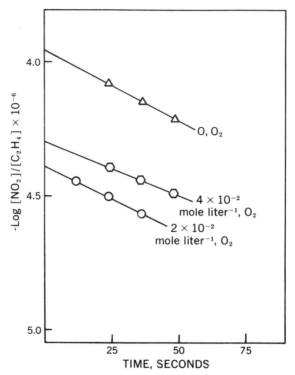

Fig. 12. The effect of O_2 concentration on the rate of decomposition of NO_2.

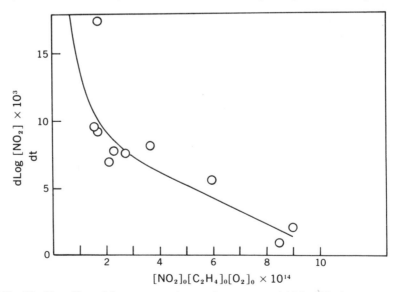

Fig. 13. The effect of O_2 concentration on the quantum yield for NO_2 loss.

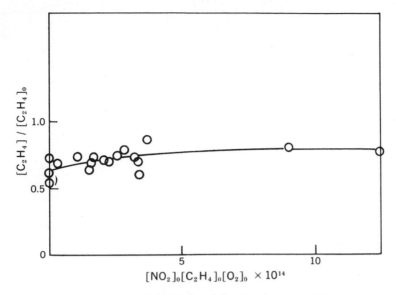

Fig. 14. The fraction of C_2H_4 left after irradiation as a function of O_2 concentration.

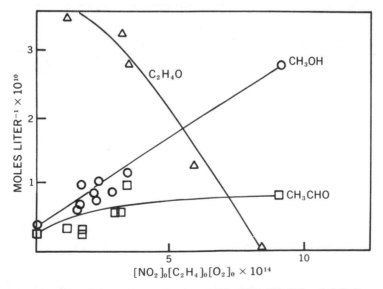

Fig. 15. The effect of O_2 on the production of CH_3CHO, CH_3OH, and C_2H_4O.

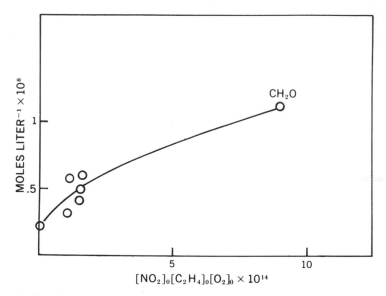

Fig. 16. The effect of O_2 on the production of CH_2O.

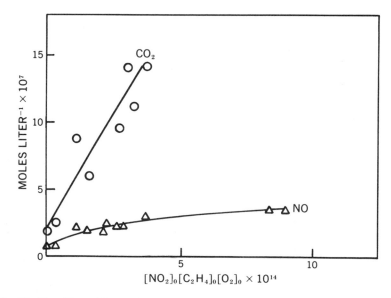

Fig. 17. The effect of O_2 on the production of CO_2 and NO.

CH_3NO_2, and CH_3ONO_2. It can be seen that the increase in O_2 favors the formation of CO_2, while the formation of NO tends to reach a steady level. Formaldehyde is also favored, but ethylene oxide production falls off with increasing O_2. The formation of H_2O was followed, but not measured quantitatively. Small quantities of CH_3CHO, CH_3NO_2, and CH_3ONO_2 were formed. It seems, from fragmentary evidence, that the CH_3NO_2 decreased while the CH_3ONO_2 increased as the O_2 increased. All these data were scattered, and further experiments are necessary to complete the estimation of the true effects of O_2 addition. These results should be considered as indicating trends in the behavior of the system as O_2 is increased. At present, they exhibit the trends reported by Tuesday *(21)*.

Photolytic Reaction of NO_2 with Propionaldehyde. A series of reactions was carried out with propionaldehyde and NO_2 at 3660 Å. The preliminary results shown in Figs. 18 and 19 indicate that the quantum yield for NO_2 loss is directly proportional to the ratio $[C_2H_5CHO]_0 / [NO_2]_0$.

If one assumes that the mechanism is similar to that for acetaldehyde, as presented by Avery and Cvetanovic *(22)*, with the addition of the NO_2 oxygen atom reactions, one has

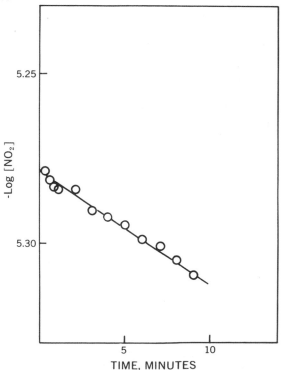

Fig. 18. First-order dependence of NO_2 decomposition in the C_2H_5CHO-NO_2 system.

$$NO_2 + h\nu \longrightarrow NO + O \qquad\qquad\qquad\qquad\text{I}$$

$$O + NO_2 \longrightarrow NO + O_2 \qquad\qquad\qquad\qquad (29)$$

$$C_2H_5CHO + O \longrightarrow C_2H_5CO + OH \qquad\qquad (30)$$

$$C_2H_5CHO + OH \longrightarrow C_2H_5CO + H_2O \qquad\qquad (31)$$

$$C_2H_5CO + NO_2 \longrightarrow C_2H_5CO_2 + NO \qquad\qquad (32)$$

$$C_2H_5CO_2 \longrightarrow C_2H_5\cdot + CO_2 \qquad\qquad\qquad (33)$$

$$C_2H_5\cdot + NO_2 \longrightarrow C_2H_5NO_2 \qquad\qquad\qquad (34)$$

$$C_2H_5\cdot + NO_2 \longrightarrow C_2H_5O + NO \qquad\qquad\qquad (35)$$

$$C_2H_5O + NO_2 \longrightarrow C_2H_5ONO_2 \qquad\qquad\qquad (36)$$

$$C_2H_5O + NO \longrightarrow C_2H_5ONO \qquad\qquad\qquad (37)$$

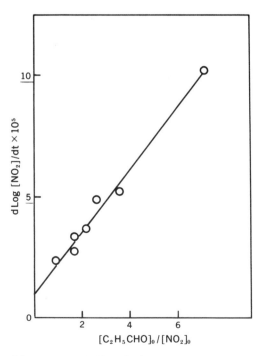

Fig. 19. Dependence of the quantum yield for NO_2 decomposition on the ratio $[C_2H_5CHO]_0/[NO_2]_0$.

The quantum yield expression derived from this mechanism, assuming steady-state on all radicals and intermediates and initial times so that reaction 37 is unimportant, is

$$\Phi = 1 + \frac{k_{29}[NO_2] + 4k_{30}[C_2H_5CHO]\left(1 + \dfrac{k_{35}}{k_{35} + k_{34}}\right)}{k_{29}[NO_2] + k_{30}[C_2H_5CHO]} \tag{38}$$

which would be in agreement with the results in Fig. 19 if $k_{29} \gg k_{30}$. The equation for the line is

$$\Phi' = (1 \times 10^{-5}) + (2.98 \times 10^{-5})\frac{[C_2H_5CHO]}{[NO_2]} \tag{39}$$

Now $\Phi = $ constant Φ'; therefore,

$$\Phi = 1 + 2.98\frac{[C_2H_5CHO]}{[NO_2]} \tag{40}$$

Work is continuing on the NO_2-propionaldehyde system. The products of the reaction are being analyzed by mass spectroscopy, and the results of this work will be reported in the near future. At that time, rate constants will be evaluated.

Thermal Reactions of NO_2 with Acetaldehyde. The reactions of NO_2 with CH_3CHO were studied at room temperature, and it was found that the reaction was first-order in NO_2 and first-order in CH_3CHO. This result is in agreement with the results of Browning and of McDowell and Thomas as reported by Gray and Yoffe *(8)*. It also agrees qualitatively with the work of Pedler and Pollard *(23)*. Measurement of the rate at temperatures between $25°$ and $100°C$ yielded the Arrhenius curve shown in Fig. 20. From this, one obtains

$$k \text{ (liters mole}^{-1} \text{ sec}^{-1}) = 10^{2.2} e^{-6900/RT} \tag{41}$$

Although the rate expression reported by Gray and Yoffe *(8)* differs,

$$k \text{ (liters mole}^{-1} \text{ sec}^{-1}) = 10^7 e^{-13500/RT} \tag{42}$$

the rate constants at $25°C$ are very close to each other. They are 1.5×10^{-3} liter mole^{-1} sec^{-1} and 1.4×10^{-3} liter mole^{-1} sec^{-1}, respectively.

The low value of A in equation 41 may be attributed to a negative entropy of activation if the activated complex formed during the reaction is highly ordered

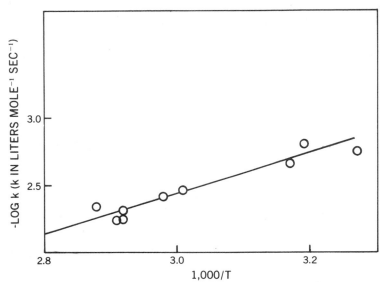

Fig. 20. Arrhenius relationship for the reaction of NO_2 with CH_3CHO.

or symmetrical. The mechanism for this reaction is expected to agree with that of Vrbaski and Cvetanovic *(12)* except that the initiation of the thermal reaction would be

$$CH_3CHO + NO_2 \longrightarrow CH_3CO + HONO \qquad (43)$$

and would include the formation of H_2O via

$$2HONO \longrightarrow H_2O + NO + NO_2 \qquad (44)$$

Thermal Reactions of NO_2 with Acetone. The acetone work is analogous to that for acetaldehyde and yielded a similar result. However, the results are more scattered, probably owing to the solubility of acetone in Kel-F grease. Fig. 21 is the Arrhenius curve from which one obtains

$$k \text{ (liters mole}^{-1} \text{ sec}^{-1}) = 3.8 \times 10^2 \, e^{-7130/RT} \qquad (45)$$

The value of k at $25°C$ is therefore 2.4×10^{-3} liter mole^{-1} sec^{-1}. This value is of the same magnitude as that of olefin and acetaldehyde reactions with NO_2.

Thermal Reactions of NO_2 and Ethylene Oxide. Figure 22 is a summary of a series of reactions in which the concentrations of NO_2 and

C_2H_4O were varied at 25°C. The best fit to a straight line was obtained with the equation

$$-\left(\frac{d[NO_2]}{dt}\right)_{t=0} = k[NO_2]_0^2[C_2H_4O]_0 \qquad (46)$$

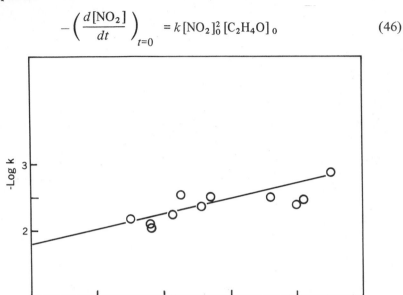

Fig. 21. Arrhenius relationship for the reaction of NO_2 with CH_3COCH_3.

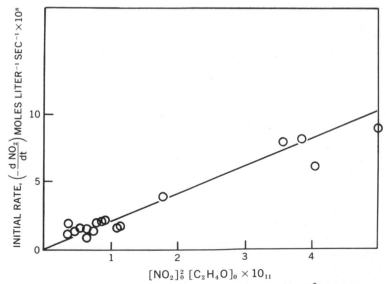

Fig. 22. Dependence of the rate of NO_2 loss on the product $[NO_2]_0^2[C_2H_4O]_0$.

The reaction was studied at temperatures varying from 25° to 100°C, and an Arrhenius curve was derived (Fig. 23). The slope of the curve yields an activation energy of about 3.7 kcal mole^{-1} and an intercept of about 1.3×10^6, yielding the relation

$$k \text{ (liters}^2 \text{ mole}^{-2} \text{ sec}^{-1}) = 1.3 \times 10^6 \ e^{-3700/RT} \tag{47}$$

The validity of these expressions will be checked in further experiments in which the products of the reactions will be determined as a function of concentrations of reactants and time. Following this, photochemical reactions will be performed at 3660 Å. The mechanism of this process is quite speculative at this time, but some insight should be gained as a result of this study.

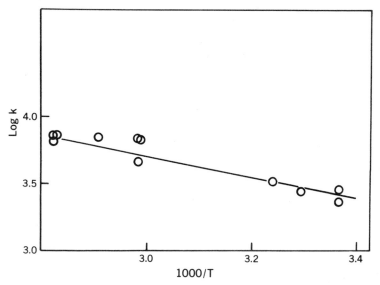

Fig. 23. Arrhenius relationship for the reaction of NO_2 with C_2H_4O.

Acknowledgments

The support of the Division of Air Pollution, U. S. Public Health Service, under Research Grant AP00462 is gratefully acknowledged. In addition, I wish to thank Mr. Sidney Chao, Mrs. Diane Hollandsworth, Mr. Hiroyuki Enomoto, and Mr. Manfred Buechler for their assistance in making some of the measurements.

References

1. T.L. Cottrell and T.E. Graham, *J. Chem. Soc.,* 556 (1953).
2. T.L. Cottrell and T.E. Graham, *J. Chem. Soc.,* 3644 (1954).
3. P.A. Leighton, "Photochemistry of Air Pollution," Academic Press, New York, 1961.
4. H.W. Ford and H. Endow, *J. Chem. Phys.,* 27, 1156, 1277 (1957).
5. N. Levy and J.D. Rose, *Quart. Rev. (London),* 1, 358 (1947).
6. N. Levy and C.W. Scaife, *J. Chem. Soc.,* 1093 (1946).
7. J.F. Brown, Jr., *J. Am. Chem. Soc.,* 79, 2480 (1947).
8. P. Gray and A.D. Yoffe, *Chem. Rev.,* 55, 1069 (1955).
9. B.H.J. Bielski and J.M. Gebicki, *J. Phys. Chem.,* 73, 1402 (1969).
10. L. Phillips and R. Shaw, in "Tenth Symposium (International) on Combustion", The Combustion Institute (1965), p. 453.
11. W.B. De More, *Intern. J. Chem. Kinetics,* 1, 209 (1969).
12. T. Vrbaski and R.J. Cvetanovic, *Can. J. Chem.,* 38, 1053 (1960).
13. J. Collin and F.P. Lossing, *J. Am. Chem. Soc.,* 81, 2064 (1959).
14. H. Niki, E.E. Daby, and B. Weinstock, Preprint of paper presented at 12th Combustion Symposium, France, 1968.
15. J.T. Herron and R.D. Penzhorn, *J. Phys. Chem.,* 73, 191 (1969).
16. A.P. Altshuller and J.J. Bufalini, *Photochem. Photobiol.,* 4, 97 (1965).
17. R.J. Cvetanovic, *Advan. Photochem.,* 1, 115-182 (1963).
18. J.J. Bufalini and A.P. Altshuller, *Can. J. Chem.,* 43, 2243 (1965).
19. S. Jaffe and J. Keith, *J. Chem. Phys.,* 48, 2805 (1968).
20. S. Jaffe and R.C.S. Grant, *J. Chem. Phys.,* 50, 3477 (1969).
21. C.S. Tuesday, in "Chemical Reactions in the Lower and Upper Atmosphere" (R.D. Cadle, ed.), Interscience, New York, 1961, pp. 1-49.
22. H.E. Avery and R.J. Cvetanovic, *J. Chem. Phys.,* 43, 3727 (1965).
23. A.E. Pedler and F.H. Pollard, *Trans. Faraday Soc.,* 53, 44 (1957).

Discussion

G.S. HAMMOND: I should like to make a mechanistic suggestion. What do you think of the possibility of going back to your original mechanism? The biradical rearranges to give acetaldehyde-enol, and this could react very rapidly with NO_2. This provides a plausible explanation for the curious bimolecular kinetics of the aldehyde and acetone reactions with NO_2. In fact, the mechanism of this reaction may be the equilibration of the ketone-enol forms of the biradicals, perhaps on the wall. The low activation energy is, in fact, the sum of the heat of isomerization, the heat of enolization, and a very, very small activation energy for extremely fast reactions between enols and NO_2.

S. JAFFE: Since I really don't know what the intermediate is, your suggested mechanism may be worth pursuing further.

I.C. HISATSUNE: You indicated that methyl alcohol was a product of the ethylene-NO_2-O_2 reaction. Am I correct in saying that methyl alcohol and NO_2 coexisted in the same system?

S. JAFFE: Yes, but methanol was only a minor product. I have not measured the thermal reaction of methanol and NO_2. Are you aware that that is a very rapid reaction, more rapid than the reaction with the aldehyde?

I.C. HISATSUNE: I don't know how fast it is, but many years ago when I tried to get the Raman spectrum of N_2O_3, using methanol as the solvent, we found that reaction with the solvent was rapid even at low temperatures.

S. JAFFE: Evidently, then, we should consider measuring this reaction before we suggest that methanol is indeed that product. But, at least at present, I have no reason to believe that it is not methanol.

J.G. CALVERT: Is there any indication from the reported spin spectrum of the NO_2-olefin complex as to the nature of the complex? Was there any structure?

S. JAFFE: Yes. I have two different references to this. One is a personal communication — the Landgraf work. The other is the Bielski and Gebicki work, in which they show what they call a π complex — the approach of an NO_2 (nitrogen first) to the olefin, polarizing the olefin, and then giving sort of a polar interaction.

J.G. CALVERT: You put the electron on nitrogen. I was wondering if you had a split spectrum that indicates nitrogen nuclei?

S. JAFFE: No. The only thing I can say about that is that Landgraf is looking at part of his spectrum in the hopes of showing this.

J.G. CALVERT: Does he have some hyperfine structure to work with?

S. JAFFE: Yes. He has several peaks in his spectrum which are not yet explained. For example, in his system he would like to think of polymers in which olefin - NO_2 - olefin - NO_2 chains are formed. I have no feeling for whether that would be probable, or whether it is related to our work. But this is not based on his complete spectrum. He has, as I said, unexplained absorptions.

SESSION III

The Methyl Radical-Sulfur Dioxide Reaction

Jack G. Calvert, David H. Slater, and James W. Gall
Chemistry Department
Ohio State University
Columbus, Ohio

Abstract

The rate of removal of SO_2 in the atmosphere appears to be much faster than can be accounted for by the photooxidation of SO_2 or by other known gas phase reactions. Catalyzed heterogeneous reactions in droplets or on particles have been proposed, but it has not been established that this is the predominant mechanism. We suggest that gas phase reactions between SO_2 and various alkyl, alkoxyl, and alkylperoxyl radicals should be considered as potential SO_2 removal paths. Accordingly, the simplest of these systems, the methyl radical addition to SO_2, was studied. Although the mechanism is more complex than heretofore believed, methyl radicals do add readily to SO_2, and CH_3SO_2 radicals add readily to the double bond in azomethane. It is possible that such reactions may initiate aerosol formation in polluted atmospheres.

Introduction

There is a need for rate data which will allow a meaningful evaluation of the importance of the possible sulfur dioxide removal mechanisms operative in the polluted atmosphere. The rate of removal of sulfur dioxide in the polluted atmosphere is commonly very much faster than the rate of its photooxidation *(1)*. It has been proposed that heterogeneous catalytic paths of oxidation may be important for conditions comparable to those found in the real atmosphere. It seems to us that there are a number of homogeneous gas phase reactions which also should be considered seriously as potential sulfur dioxide removal paths. Among the attractive possible reactions for which little or no reaction rate data now exist are the alkyl, alkoxyl, and alkylperoxyl radical addition reactions to sulfur dioxide (reaction A) and the aklylperoxyl oxygen atom transfer reaction to sulfur dioxide (reaction B). When sulfur dioxide is present with the ingredients of "photochemical smog," reactions such as A and B possibly could play important roles.

References, p. 154

$$R(RO, RO_2) + SO_2 \longrightarrow RSO_2(ROSO_2, RO_2SO_2) \qquad (A)$$

$$RO_2 + SO_2 \longrightarrow RO + SO_3 \qquad (B)$$

In this work we have attempted to study the simplest of these reactions — that of methyl radical addition to sulfur dioxide. As will be seen, this reaction is far from simple and is not cleanly measured by any of the systems which might normally be employed as methyl radical sources. We have generated methyl radicals in the presence of sulfur dioxide through the photolysis of azomethane and acetone in sulfur dioxide-containing mixtures. During the course of this work, Good and Thynne reported a similar study using azomethane-sulfur dioxide mixture photolysis *(2)*. Several of the results of our work are significantly different from those of Good and Thynne, although, overall, their data seem to be less scattered than our own, and both sets of data are amenable to the same processing to give similar results. It appears, however, that the mechanism is much more complicated than the previous workers have assumed. Hence rate constants derived in this work must be re-evaluated.

Experimental Section

Equipment. The first series of experiments with azomethane-sulfur dioxide mixtures was carried out in the large cell (55 liters) which enclosed the mirror support beam of the long-path attachment of the Perkin-Elmer Model 21 infrared spectrophotometer described previously *(3,4)*. Glass filters placed over the ultraviolet irradiation ports in the side of the cell limited the emission from the three 500-watt medium-pressure mercury lamps to wavelengths absorbed only by azomethane. The infrared analyzing beam passed through two BaF_2 windows, and the multiple reflection system was adjusted to a path length of 20 meters. The course of the photochemically initiated reaction could be followed through the changes in the infrared absorption spectrum of the sample.

In the second series of experiments with azomethane-sulfur dioxide mixtures the reaction vessel was a small Pyrex cell (90 cc). This was placed in a cylindrical aluminum block oven which was controlled in temperature by a regulator. The rates of removal of azomethane and sulfur dioxide were determined by infrared spectrophotometry; the product nitrogen was analyzed by gas chromatography on a 6-foot molecular sieve (5A, 90-100 mesh) column at 80°C.

In a third series of runs the photolysis of acetone-sulfur dioxide mixtures was carried out. In this case all analyses were made by gas chromatography. Those products not condensed at liquid nitrogen temperature were analyzed on a 10-foot Porapak-Q column at $-78^\circ C$. The condensables were analyzed on a similar column which was temperature-programmed from 85° to $180^\circ C$.

Chemicals. Azomethane was prepared by a method based on that of Renaud and Leitch *(5)*. Center cuts of vacuum-distilled Matheson sulfur dioxide and Baker analyzed reagent acetone were used in all runs. Phillips research-grade methane and ethane and Matheson C.P. grade carbon monoxide were used as standards without purification.

Experimental Results

Azomethane-Sulfur Dioxide Mixture Photolyses in the Large Infrared Cell.
A pressure of about 500 μ of axomethane was photolyzed in mixtures with sulfur dioxide in the range 0 to 1.2 mm. During the course of the reaction the consumption of both azomethane and sulfur dioxide was followed through infrared absorption at 7.8 and 8.6 μ, respectively. A large, unexpected pressure drop accompanied the photochemical reaction. In azomethane photolysis in the absence of sulfur dioxide, a very small pressure increase occurred during a similar experiment. There was no detectable dark reaction between sulfur dioxide and azomethane for these conditions. If the Good and Thynne mechanism were operative here ($CH_3SO_2CH_3$ presumed to be the major product), then the largest pressure drop expected is that corresponding to the reaction $CH_3N_2CH_3 + SO_2 \longrightarrow CH_3SO_2CH_3 + N_2$. If we assume complete condensation of the relatively nonvolatile dimethylsulfone, then for each mole of azomethane photolyzed, one mole of gas should disappear. This is not the case for our conditions. The pressure drop was closer to two or three times the azomethane photolyzed. The rate of loss of azomethane followed a pseudo-first-order relation in runs at constant sulfur dioxide pressure; however, the apparent first-order constant increased with increasing sulfur dioxide pressure. (See Fig. 1.) The rate of loss of azomethane in mixtures with 1.2 mm of sulfur dioxide was about twice that for pure azomethane photolyses. Although both a reactant decrease and a pressure change were observed, no products could be detected through infrared absorption. Since analysis for nitrogen was impossible in the infrared cell and a knowledge of the extent of azomethane photodecomposition was necessary for an understanding of the system, runs were initiated in a small Pyrex cell (90-cc volume) from which nitrogen analysis could be made by gas chromatography. The first run yielded answers to several questions raised by the experiments in the large tank. A most striking result was apparent after about 10 seconds of illumination of the sulfur dioxide-azomethane mixture. The cell was filled with a dense white fog which continued to form and settle to the bottom of the cell throughout the experiment. The transmitted light intensity dropped to about 10% of that at the start of the photolysis. Again there was no dark reaction and no

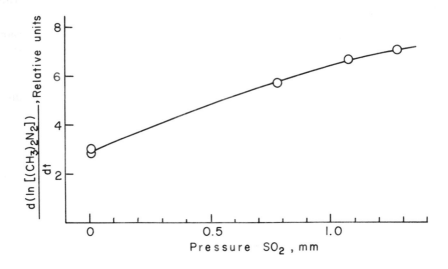

Fig. 1. The variation of the apparent first-order rate constant for azomethane disappearance as a function of sulfur dioxide pressure; photolyses at 3660 Å, 25°C; pressure of azomethane, ~500 μ.

mist formation when just azomethane or sulfur dioxide was irradiated in the cell. Nitrogen was formed, but its rate was far less than that of azomethane loss.

The formation of the condensed products explains both the substantial pressure drop and the lack of detectable products in the large-cell experiments, as only the gaseous products could be detected in this system. On opening the large cell we found the condensed product deposited over the entire cell system including the mirrors and windows. It was apparent that further use of this long-path system to study the azomethane-sulfur dioxide system was not practical. Experiments were then carried out in the small Pyrex cell which could be washed out readily after each experiment. These results are summarized in Table I.

Some clues as to the nature of the nonvolatile products were obtained from the attempts which were made to identify them. The approximate mass balance suggests the formation of a compound of the structure $CH_3SO_2(CH_3)NN(CH_3)SO_2CH_3$. The material was very soluble in water and other polar liquids. The compound(s) was of very low volatility. The form of the compound(s) was very sensitive to the presence of air; it changed quickly from an almost white crystalline appearance to a yellow oil in the presence of air. The infrared and mass spectra were inconsistent with those of dimethylsulfone. They suggested, however, the presence of SO_2 and

Table I

Kinetic Data from Azomethane-Sulfur Dioxide Photolyses at 3660 Å and 25°C

Concentration (moles/cc) $\times 10^6$		Product Rates (moles/cc-sec) $\times 10^{10}$			
$[(CH_3)_2N_2]$	$[SO_2]$	R_{N_2}	$-R_{(CH_3)_2N_2}$	$-R_{SO_2}$	$2R_{N_2}$
2.13	1.14	1.3	2.9	3.5	2.6
2.13	2.29	1.6	2.9	3.4	3.2
2.19	6.88	1.7	3.2	4.0	3.4
2.24	8.43	2.0	3.9	5.4	4.0
2.09	11.7	1.4	3.0	5.0	2.8
2.03	14.7	1.3	3.3	6.0	2.6
3.96	7.87	2.4	3.7	5.9	4.8
7.33	5.20	4.1	9.4	7.5	8.2
9.49	5.27	4.7	7.0	8.2	9.4

CH_3SO_2 groups in the compound. The intense 64 mass peak was consistent with the spectra of other compounds containing SO_2-N bonds; sulfones do not split out molecular SO_2 easily *(6)*.

The photolysis of acetone-sulfur dioxide mixtures produced no fog formation, and again no dark reaction was observed with these mixtures. However, in this photochemical system for conditions where light absorption was largely by acetone, partial quenching of acetone decomposition was effected through increased sulfur dioxide addition. (See the data of Table II.) The lamp and filter system employed in this series of experiments gave a series of mercury lines, within the absorption region of the reactants, of the following relative intensities: 3341 Å, 33%; 3126 to 3132 Å, 41%; 3022 to 3028 Å, 19%; 2967 Å, 7%.

A large number of experiments were made over a wider range of concentration of sulfur dioxide at several temperatures. (These data are summarized in Table III.)

Discussion

Azomethane Photolysis in Mixtures with Sulfur Dioxide.   Good and Thynne interpreted their experiments in terms of the importance of the following reactions *(2)*:

Table II

Rate Data for the Quenching of Triplet Acetone with Sulfur Dioxide

Concentration (moles/cc)		Rates $\times 10^{11}$ (moles/cc-sec)[a]			$\dfrac{R_{CO}}{R_{C_2H_6} + R_{CH_4}/2}$	10^{-11} $(R_{CO} - R_{CO}^{\infty})$[b]	$\dfrac{R_{CH_4}}{[Me_2CO]R_{C_2H_6}^{1/2}}$
$[Me_2CO]$ $\times 10^6$	$[SO_2]$ $\times 10^{10}$	R_{CO}	R_{CH_4}	$R_{C_2H_6}$			
Temperature, 86°C							
4.18	0.00	2.75	0.35	2.34	1.09	0.61	0.18
4.14	0.72	2.53	0.30	2.22	1.07	0.70	0.15
4.12	3.50	1.85	0.31	2.01	0.86	1.33	0.17
4.04	8.85	1.41	0.22	1.26	1.03	3.23	0.15
4.16	11.8	1.34	0.26	1.30	0.94	4.17	0.17
4.12	15.7	1.25	0.27	1.09	1.02	6.67	(0.20)
							Average 0.16
Temperature, 103°C							
4.11	0.00	2.24	0.38	2.19	0.94	1.69	(0.20)
4.18	2.94	1.94	0.47	1.77	0.97	3.45	0.27
4.18	2.94	1.94	0.37	1.04	1.58	3.45	0.27
4.18	5.88	1.90	0.52	1.69	0.97	4.00	0.30
4.08	5.89	1.91	0.39	2.11	0.83	3.85	(0.21)
4.13	8.79	1.90	0.57	1.75	0.94	4.00	0.33
4.08	11.8	1.77	0.51	1.50	1.01	8.33	0.32
							Average 0.30

			Temperature, 116°C				
4.11	0.00	2.70	0.78	2.78	0.85	0.89	0.40
4.06	2.95	2.32	0.83	1.85	1.02	1.35	0.47
4.12	5.91	2.37	0.76	1.78	1.09	1.27	0.44
4.14	8.82	1.61	0.52	1.41	0.96	–	(0.34)
4.15	11.8	1.63	0.62	1.40	0.95	–	0.40
4.10	15.7	1.85	0.62	1.26	1.18	3.70	0.42
							Average 0.43

[a] Rate data represent an average of those from near identical runs in some cases.

[b] R_{CO}^∞ used here were derived from the intercepts of the R_{CO} versus $1/[SO_2]$ plots: 1.10×10^{-11} at 86°C; 1.65×10^{-11} at 103°C; 1.58×10^{-11} cc-sec/mole at 116°C.

Table III

The Rate Data from the Photolysis of Acetone-Sulfur Dioxide Mixtures

Concentration (moles/cc) × 10^6		Rates (moles/cc-sec) × 10^12					$\frac{R_{CH_4} - R_{CH_4}(15)}{-R_{SO_2}}$	$\frac{R_{C_2H_6}[SO_2]}{-R_{SO_2}} \times 10^8$
[Me$_2$CO]	[SO$_2$]	R_{CO}	$R_{C_2H_6}$	R_{CH_4}	$-R_{SO_2}^{\,a}$	$R_{CH_4}(15)$		
					Temperature, 86°C			
4.16	0.014	8.6	9.6	2.0	2.6	2.1	-0.04	5.18
4.16	0.037	9.6	7.0	2.0	5.1	1.8	0.04	5.08
4.12	0.039	7.6	6.8	1.4	5.6	1.7	-0.05	4.73
4.14	0.067	21.8	4.2	3.5	9.2	1.3	0.24	3.06
4.12	0.067	7.0	4.8	1.4	7.9	1.4	0.00	4.07
4.18	0.067	7.2	4.9	1.7	9.7	1.5	0.02	3.39
4.20	0.067	6.5	4.0	1.4	9.7	1.3	0.01	2.76
4.21	0.068	16.4	4.2	2.5	8.5	1.4	0.13	3.36
4.11	0.131	—	1.7	2.2	11.2	0.85	0.12	1.99
4.16	0.131	7.1	2.2	1.4	13.2	1.0	0.03	2.18
4.15	0.132	6.0	2.9	0.90	13.5	1.1	-0.01	2.84
4.15	0.137	9.1	3.5	1.9	13.8	1.2	-0.05	3.48
4.16	0.137	8.5	3.6	1.3	14.6	1.3	0.00	3.38
4.10	0.264	5.0	0.87	0.65	9.9	0.61	0.00	2.32
4.20	0.267	5.2	0.75	0.67	17.6	0.58	0.00	1.14
4.05	0.269	21.3	0.84	1.2	16.5	0.60	0.04	1.37
4.14	0.270	4.5	0.82	—	19.3	0.60	—	1.15
4.16	0.276	16.5	1.10	1.4	20.3	0.70	0.03	1.50
4.21	0.279	11.9	0.86	1.3	18.2	0.63	0.04	1.32
4.23	0.281	5.8	0.58	0.58	20.0	0.51	0.00	0.82
4.13	0.283	13.6	0.51	1.5	21.5	0.61	0.04	0.67
4.20	0.350	3.6	0.37	0.59	12.7	0.88	-0.02	1.02
4.05	0.353	13.8	0.22	0.65	13.7	0.30	0.03	0.57

4.27	0.359	—	0.41	0.94	16.0	0.44	0.03	0.92
4.18	0.362	3.5	0.44	0.38	15.1	0.44	0.00	1.06
4.14	0.366	6.0	0.56	0.46	16.7	0.50	0.00	1.23
4.07	0.523	12.0	0.02	0.59	7.1	0.091	0.07	0.15
4.21	0.525	7.2	0.74	0.70	24.5	0.57	0.01	1.58
4.11	0.531	3.3	0.27	0.34	19.2	0.34	0.00	0.75
Temperature, 103°C								
4.09	0.066	7.9	3.5	1.9	1.1(1.8)	2.3	−0.22	10.1
4.04	0.142	6.0	3.4	1.1	−(1.5)	2.2	−0.73	23.6
4.11	0.142	6.2	3.4	1.7	2.5(1.8)	2.3	−0.33	21.8
4.05	0.283	5.2	2.3	1.2	2.1(1.9)	1.8	−0.32	29.6
4.18	0.283	6.2	2.2	2.3	−(1.7)	1.9	0.24	21.9
4.14	0.377	5.5	1.5	1.7	−(2.3)	1.5	0.09	18.0
4.03	0.379	3.9	0.81	1.4	0.93(1.3)	1.1	0.23	12.8
3.99	0.381	4.8	1.3	1.5	3.8(2.9)	1.4	0.03	15.1
Temperature, 116°C								
4.09	0.066	8.2	5.3	3.8	1.1(1.05)	4.0	−0.19	33.4
4.11	0.066	7.9	5.5	3.0	1.8(1.35)	4.2	−0.88	30.3
4.15	0.140	7.2	4.2	3.2	2.7(2.05)	3.7	−0.24	31.9
4.15	0.142	7.0	2.6	3.0	2.5(2.7)	2.9	0.04	13.8
4.20	0.285	7.1	2.0	3.1	−(3.55)	2.5	0.17	16.0
4.09	0.427	5.1	1.6	1.9	1.7(2.12)	2.2	−0.14	33.5
4.06	0.428	4.6	0.88	1.8	1.3(2.06)	1.6	0.10	21.2
4.15	0.568	4.1	1.1	1.9	−(2.05)	1.9	0.00	30.5
4.08	0.569	12.3	1.0	3.5	9.2(9.38)	1.8	0.18	7.0

a Measured rates of sulfur dioxide loss; in parentheses for runs at 103°C and 116°C are the average of the measured rates and the rates calculated from the assumed mass balance $(-R_{SO_2} = R_{CO} - R_{C_2H_6} - R_{CH_4})$; the latter values were used to calculate the rate function of Good and Thynne, $k_4/(k_3 + k_4)$.

$$(CH_3)_2N_2 + h\nu \quad \rightarrow \quad 2CH_3 + N_2 \tag{I}$$

$$\rightarrow \quad C_2H_6 + N_2 \tag{II}$$

$$CH_3 + SO_2 \quad \rightarrow \quad CH_3SO_2 \tag{1}$$

$$CH_3SO_2 \quad \rightarrow \quad CH_3 + SO_2 \tag{2}$$

$$CH_3 + CH_3SO_2 \quad \rightarrow \quad CH_3SO_2CH_3 \tag{3}$$

$$\rightarrow \quad CH_4 + CH_2SO_2 \tag{4}$$

$$CH_3 + (CH_3)_2N_2 \quad \rightarrow \quad CH_4 + CH_2N_2CH_3 \tag{5}$$

$$2CH_3 \quad \rightarrow \quad C_2H_6 \tag{6}$$

They have assumed a mass balance in terms of this mechanism to derive rates of sulfur dioxide removal and rate constant estimates for reactions 1 and 2. The present results require that additional reactions be considered in this system, particularly in those experiments with relatively high concentrations of sulfur dioxide. Note that the Good and Thynne mechanism predicts that the rate of azomethane loss will be equal to the rate of nitrogen formation. Our experiments in the long-path cell show that this is not the case; the rate of azomethane removal is a function of the sulfur dioxide concentration. (See Fig. 1.) At near equal concentrations of sulfur dioxide and azomethane the rate of azomethane loss is about twice that for pure azomethane photolysis. (Note also the data of Table I.) For the concentration conditions employed it can be seen that azomethane disappears at a rate which is about twice that of nitrogen formation. The loss of sulfur dioxide is roughly equal to twice the rate of azomethane loss or twice the rate of nitrogen formation for near equal azomethane and sulfur dioxide concentrations. Also, R_{SO_2} becomes even greater at larger $[SO_2]$, as much as four times the rate of nitrogen formation. All our data suggest that additional reaction steps beyond those considered important by Good and Thynne must be operative in azomethane photolysis in the presence of near equal amounts of sulfur dioxide. The following additional steps involving chemical interaction of CH_3SO_2 radicals with azomethane and sulfur dioxide seem in accord with the data presented:

$$CH_3SO_2 + CH_3N_2CH_3 \rightarrow CH_3SO_2(CH_3)N_2CH_3 \tag{7}$$

$$CH_3SO_2(CH_3)N_2CH_3 \rightarrow CH_3SO_2 + CH_3N_2CH_3 \tag{8}$$

$$CH_3SO_2(CH_3)N_2CH_3 + CH_3SO_2 \rightarrow CH_3SO_2(CH_3)N_2(CH_3)SO_2CH_3 \qquad (9)$$

$$CH_3SO_2 + SO_2 \rightarrow CH_3(SO_2)_2 \qquad (1a)$$

$$CH_3(SO_2)_2 + CH_3N_2CH_3 \rightarrow CH_3(SO_2)_2(CH_3)N_2CH_3 \qquad (7a)$$

$$CH_3(SO_2)_2 + CH_3SO_2(CH_3)N_2CH_3 \rightarrow CH_3(SO_2)_2(CH_3)N_2(CH_3)SO_2CH_3 \quad (9a)$$

For the conditions employed in the experiments of Table I, practically all methyl radicals formed in reaction I appear to combine with SO_2. Very little methane or ethane (other than that small amount from reaction II) is formed, and the rate of methyl addition to azomethane is insignificant for these conditions. Probably radical decompositions in reactions 2 and 8 are unimportant for this temperature. Thus reactions I, 1, 7, 9, 1a, and 9a may dominate here. If one makes this assumption and further assumes that CH_3SO_2 and $CH_3(SO_2)_2$ react with similar rates ($k_7 \cong k_{7a}$), then the following rate expression should hold:

$$\frac{-R_{SO_2} - 2R_{N_2}}{R_{N_2}} \cong \frac{k_{1a}[SO_2]}{k_7[(CH_3)_2N_2]} \qquad (C)$$

A test of this functional form is made with the data of Table I in Fig. 2. Within the error of the experimental data, relation C appears to hold. The slope of the plot suggests that $k_{1a}/k_7 \cong 0.36$. This work presents the first evidence of which the authors are aware that radicals containing more than one sulfur dioxide molecule can be important.

Apparently the addition reaction 7 is very fast, as it competes successfully with radical-radical combinations for these conditions. However, it was not observed by Good and Thynne. One must accept their work at the lower temperatures ($21°$ to $39°C$) with some caution, since the complications of reaction 7 would be most favored for these conditions. The original data for this series of experiments used to derive an estimate of k_1 were not presented in their paper, so we cannot evaluate this possibility at this time. However, it is instructive to test their published data for the higher temperatures in terms of this possible complication. If only reactions I, II, and 1-6 occur, as Good and Thynne assume, then relation D is expected to hold:

$$\frac{R_{C_2H_6(6)}[SO_2]}{-R_{SO_2}} = \frac{k_2 k_6}{k_1(k_3 + k_4)} + \frac{k_6^{1/2}R_{C_2H_6}^{1/2}}{k_1} \qquad (D)$$

($R_{C_2H_6(6)}$ represents the rate of ethane formation from reaction 6 alone.) Good and Thynne have in essence assumed that the first term of relation D dominates for their conditions ($k_2 \gg [CH_3](k_3 + k_4)$) and have averaged the individual estimates of the rate function D at each temperature to derive $k_2 k_6 / k_1 (k_3 + k_4)$. The individual estimates are rather scattered; they vary from 1.9×10^{-9} to 0.5×10^{-9} at 50°C, 1.3×10^{-8} to 0.19×10^{-8} at 65°C, 3.8×10^{-8} to 0.53×10^{-8} at 75°C, and 3.2×10^{-8} to 0.68×10^{-8} at 85°C. We found, however, that the apparently large random scatter of the data was practically eliminated if we applied the more complete functional form of our relation D to their data; that is, $R_{C_2H_6(6)}[SO_2]/ -R_{SO_2}$ was assumed to be proportional to $R_{C_2H_6(6)}^{1/2}$. The data of Good and Thynne are plotted in this fashion in Fig. 3. Obviously there is a real trend in accord with function D; this was apparently missed by Good and Thynne. That the more complete form of the relation D should be used rather than the first term is also suggested by the rate data derived by Good and Thynne. They give $k_1 \cong 10^{10.82} e^{-1.5/RT}$, $k_2/k_1 \cong 10^{2.16} e^{-20.9/RT}$, $k_3 + k_4 \cong 10^{10.48}$ (units cc, mole, sec). Using these data at 50°C, the first term of D is 9.3×10^{-10}, and the second term varies

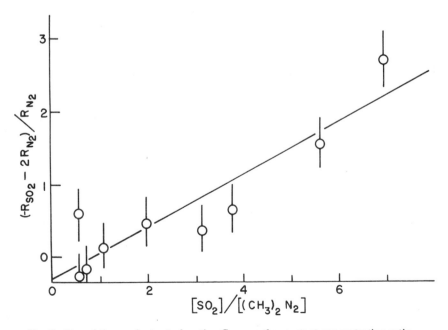

Fig. 2. Plot of the product rate function C versus the reactant concentration ratio, $[SO_2]/[(CH_3)_2N_2]$; calculated from the product rate data of Table I derived from azomethane-sulfur dioxide photolyses at 3660 Å and 25°C; the slope is presumably equal to k_{1a}/k_7.

from 2.2 to 7.8 $\times$ 10^{-10} mole/cc for their conditions and rates of ethane formation. Even if the Good and Thynne mechanism were correct, an accurate description of the results could be expected only through the use of the complete function D. Although the fit to form D is gratifying, the data from the higher temperatures give a theoretically impossible negative intercept which suggests some unresolved problem. Furthermore, the slopes of the plots at all the temperatures, presumably equal to $k_6^{1/2}/k_1$, give a surprising result; the values are 1.75 $\times$ 10^{-3} at 50°C, 7.32 $\times$ 10^{-3} at 65°C, 19.4 $\times$ 10^{-3} at 75°C, and 34.6 $\times$ 10^{-3} (sec-mole/cc)$^{1/2}$ at 85°C. Assuming the simple Good and Thynne mechanism to be operative and taking k_6 = 2.2 $\times$ 10^{13} cc/mole-sec *(7)*, one derives the following estimates of k_1: 2.7 $\times$ 10^9 at 50°C, 0.64 $\times$ 10^9 at 65°C, 0.24 $\times$ 10^9 at 75°C, and 0.14 $\times$ 10^9 cc/mole-sec at 85°C. Thus the data suggest an unexpected large negative temperature dependence ($E_{apparent}$ = −20 kcal/mole). Since the R_{SO_2} data of Good and Thynne are based on an assumed mass balance relation, one

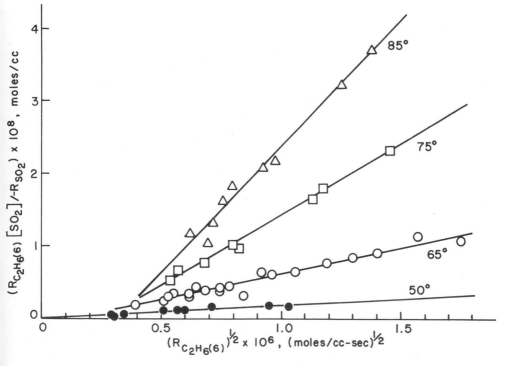

Fig. 3. Plot of the rate function D versus $R_{C_2H_6(6)}^{1/2}$ as derived from the rate data of Good and Thynne *(2)* from azomethane-sulfur dioxide mixture photolyses; the R_{SO_2} was calculated from the mass balance equation of Good and Thynne.

may legitimately question the validity of these data. The use of the alternative rate function E, which is also indirectly dependent on a mass balance, gives very similar results, although the data are more scattered. The data for

$$\frac{R_{C_2H_6(6)}[SO_2]}{R_{CH_4(4)}} = \frac{k_6 k_2}{k_1 k_4} + \frac{k_6^{1/2}(k_3 + k_4) R_{C_2H_6(6)}^{1/2}}{k_1 k_4} \tag{E}$$

the lower temperatures are the most accurate, since the difference between the two terms involved in the calculation of $R_{CH_4(4)}$ ($R_{CH_4(4)} = R_{CH_4} - R_{CH_4(5)}$) is more significant for these conditions. The recalculated data coupled with the rate ratios derived from Good and Thynne data, $k_4/(k_3 + k_4)$ = 0.025 (50°C), 0.033 (65°C), and 0.034 (75°C), give estimates of k_1 = 2.7 × 10^9 (50°C), 0.30 × 10^9 (65°C), and 0.66 × 10^9 cc/mole-sec (75°C). These estimates check reasonably well with those derived from the alternative method of calculation.

The anomalous result of the theoretically impossible negative intercepts found in the treatment of the Good and Thynne data by function D (Fig. 3) appears to be a fortuitous consequence of the nature of the mass balance relation chosen by Good and Thynne. If the mass balance relation $-R'_{SO_2}$ = $R_{N_2} - R_{C_2H_6} - R_{CH_4}$ is used rather than the one employed by Good and Thynne, $-R_{SO_2} = R_{N_2} - R_{C_2H_6} - R_{CH_4(5)}/2 - R_{CH_4(4)}$, then the plots of data from all temperatures have a near-zero intercept. (See the data of Fig. 4.) Since the fate of the $CH_2N_2CH_3$ radical formed in reaction 5 probably involves the removal of a second CH_3 radical at some point in its reaction scheme, this balance may be more reasonable than that used by Good and Thynne. The slopes of the lines for the data from runs at the different temperatures (Fig. 4) yield the following estimates of k_1: 2.8 × 10^9 at 50°C; 0.97 × 10^9 at 65°C; 0.66 × 10^9 at 75°C; and 0.32 × 10^9 liters/mole-sec at 85°C. The apparent activation energy for these data is about −14 kcal/mole.

The anomalous, large negative activation energy for k_1, to which application of the simple Good and Thynne mechanism leads, suggests that the mechanism is incomplete in some sense. Among the many alternatives which we have considered to rationalize these data is the inclusion of reactions 7 and 8 which we proposed to explain our data from the experiments under quite different conditions. For Good and Thynne's conditions of relatively high temperature and low [SO$_2$], the radical $CH_3SO_2(CH_3)N_2CH_3$ formed in reaction 7 would probably either decompose by reaction 8 or react with another radical; the dominant radical for their conditions is CH_3. Thus reaction 10 should be added also to the Good and Thynne mechanism. Then,

$$CH_3 + CH_3SO_2(CH_3)N_2CH_3 \rightarrow CH_3SO_2(CH_3)N_2(CH_3)_2 \tag{10}$$

assuming the mechanism I, II, 1-6, 7, 8, and 10, and taking the rates of reactions 7 and 8 as fast compared to reaction 10, the rate function $R_{C_2H_6(6)}[SO_2]/-R_{SO_2}$, formerly described by D, now becomes F:

$$\frac{R_{C_2H_6(6)}[SO_2]}{-R_{SO_2}} = \frac{k_6 k_2 k_8}{k_1 k_7 [Az]} + \frac{(k_3 + k_4) k_8 k_6^{1/2} R_{C_2H_6(6)}^{1/2}}{k_1 k_7 [Az]} \qquad (F)$$

Since the concentration of azomethane was held constant in the work of Good and Thynne, one cannot test well this mechanism from the data at hand. However, the apparent activation energy from the plots such as those of Fig. 3 for this case correspond to:

$$E_{\text{apparent}} = \frac{k_3 E_3 + k_4 E_4}{k_3 + k_4} + E_8 + \frac{E_6}{2} - E_1 - E_7$$

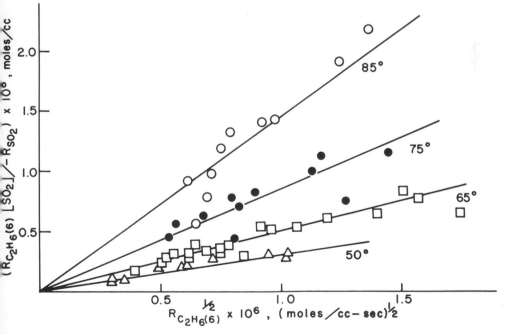

Fig. 4. Plot of the rate function D versus $R_{C_2H_6(6)}^{1/2}$ as derived from the data of Good and Thynne from azomethane-sulfur dioxide mixture photolyses; the R'_{SO_2} was calculated from the mass balance equation, $-R'_{SO_2} = R_{N_2} - R_{C_2H_6} - R_{CH_4}$.

Probably E_3, E_4, and E_6 are near zero, so that if the mechanism considered here were operative, then $E_{apparent} \cong E_8 - E_1 - E_7 \cong -14 \pm 6$ kcal/mole. Presumably any small activation energy which reaction 1 may have will be buried in the larger difference corresponding to the $E_8 - E_7 \cong \Delta H_7$. It has been estimated that the reaction of addition of alkyl sulfonyl radicals to olefins is near to thermal neutrality *(8)*. If the equilibrium mechanism involving CH_3SO_2 and azomethane is correct, the ΔH_7 must be significantly negative.

The results with azomethane-sulfur dioxide mixtures seem to be so complicated that a firm interpretation of these results alone seemed impossible. Thus we chose to try further studies of the CH_3-SO_2 reaction system using an alternative source of methyl radicals.

Acetone Photolysis in Sulfur Dioxide-Containing Mixtures. The use of acetone as an alternative methyl radical source to azomethane was chosen. However, acetone-sulfur dioxide mixture photolysis has serious complications to its use in the determination of the CH_3-SO_2 rate data. First, the absorption regions overlap for acetone and sulfur dioxide, and sulfur dioxide is the stronger absorber of light. Thus, mixtures at very low sulfur dioxide concentrations must be used if the complicating reactions of photoexcited sulfur dioxide are to be avoided. In addition, temperatures near 100°C are necessary if rather complete decomposition of the CH_3CO radical product of acetone photolysis is to be achieved and complications from acetyl radical reactions are to be avoided. Lastly, the triplet energies of acetone $(E_T = 80.5 \pm 1.5$ kcal/mole) *(9)* and sulfur dioxide $(E_T = 73.7$ kcal/mole) *(10)* theoretically would allow a rapid triplet energy transfer from excited acetone to sulfur dioxide. A series of runs were made to determine the seriousness of the latter complication. (See Table II.) Indeed, very small concentrations of SO_2 quench detectably the acetone photolysis in runs at 86° to 116°C. The following simple mechanism may be used to rationalize the data. Acetyl radical decomposition is probably near complete for all the conditions used here, so the excited molecule decomposition reactions 11 and 13 are written in this simplified form.

$$CH_3COCH_3 + h\nu \rightarrow {}^1CH_3COCH_3 \qquad (III)$$

$$^1CH_3COCH_3 \rightarrow CO + 2CH_3 \qquad (11)$$

$$\rightarrow {}^3CH_3COCH_3 \qquad (12)$$

$$^3CH_3COCH_3 \rightarrow CO + 2CH_3 \qquad (13)$$

$$^3CH_3COCH_3 + SO_2 \rightarrow CH_3COCH_3 + {}^3SO_2 \qquad (14)$$

$$CH_3 + CH_3COCH_3 \rightarrow CH_4 + CH_2COCH_3 \tag{15}$$

$$CH_3 + CH_3 \rightarrow C_2H_6 \tag{6}$$

At the very low $[SO_2]$ employed in the experiments of Table II, no detectable reaction leading to the loss of sulfur dioxide occurred. Note the mass balance $R_{CO}/(R_{C_2H_6} + R_{CH_4}/2)$ shown in Table II; there is no significant trend with increased $[SO_2]$ for the range covered. This conclusion is further substantiated by rates of methane and ethane in these runs. The rate function, $R_{CH_4}/R_{C_2H_6}^{1/2} [CH_3COCH_3]$, theoretically equal to $k_{15}/k_6^{1/2}$, is shown in Table II to be essentially constant at a given temperature. The average values of the function, 0.16 (86°C), 0.30 (103°C), and 0.43 (116°C), give the estimate $k_{15}/k_6^{1/2} \cong 6.3 \times 10^4 e^{-9.2/RT}$ (cc/mole-sec$^{1/2}$). Taking $k_6 = 2.2 \times 10^{13}$ cc/mole-sec, one derives $k_{15} \cong 3.0 \times 10^{11} e^{-9.2/RT}$ cc/mole-sec. This result checks well with previous estimates of this constant *(11)*. Thus there appears to be no excess methane from reaction 4 for these conditions.

Assuming the above mechanism for the sulfur dioxide quenching of the carbon monoxide formation, one obtains the following expected rate function relation, which should describe the data:

$$\frac{1}{R_{CO} - I_a\phi_{III}k_{11}/(k_{11} + k_{12})} = \frac{(k_{11} + k_{12})(k_{13} + [SO_2]k_{14})}{k_{12}k_{13}I_a\phi_{III}} \tag{G}$$

The data of Table II have been treated by assuming the applicability of function G. The term $I_a\phi_{III}k_{11}/(k_{11} + k_{12})$ represents the rate of carbon monoxide formation from excited singlet acetone decomposition and was estimated from the set of data for each temperature (for which the incident light intensity was essentially constant) from the intercept of the R_{CO} versus $1/[SO_2]$ plots. Although the function G shows considerable scatter, the ratio of slopes to intercepts, as determined by least-squares fit for the plots of G versus $[SO_2]$, gives the following estimates of k_{14}/k_{13} : 6.0 × 10^9 at 86°C; 2.8 × 10^9 at 103°C; and 2.0 × 10^9 at 116°C. The Arrhenius plot of these data gives $k_{14}/k_{13} \cong 3.2 \times 10^3 e^{+10.3/RT}$ cc/mole. Taking $k_{14} \leqslant 1.2 \times 10^{14}$ cc/mole-sec (collision number), one obtains $k_{13} \leqslant 4 \times 10^{10} e^{-10.3/RT}$ sec^{-1}. Previous estimates of this rate constant are $2 \times 10^{12} e^{-9.5/RT}$ sec^{-1} obtained by Larson and O'Neal *(12)* and 2.5 × $10^{10} e^{-6.4/RT}$ sec^{-1} reported by Cundall and Davies *(13)*.

Thus the transfer of triplet excitation from acetone to sulfur dioxide appears to occur efficiently; if acetone is to be used effectively as a methyl radical source at reasonable pressures of sulfur dioxide, then relatively high temperatures must be employed. This condition ensures that the triplet lifetime is shortened and the triplet decomposition reaction *13* can compete successfully with the rapid quenching reaction 14. This finding is a particularly unfortunate feature of acetone for the study of the SO_2-CH_3 reaction, since the stability of the radical CH_3SO_2 probably falls off fast at higher temperatures.

The photolysis of acetone-sulfur dioxide mixtures was made in a series of runs in an attempt to measure the rate of methyl reaction with sulfur dioxide. These should provide a test of the equilibrium hypothesis given above involving CH_3SO_2 and azomethane. The data from runs at 86°C were used to calculate the rate function D and are plotted in Fig. 5. In this case no assumption based on mass balance was necessary, as the measured rates of sulfur dioxide removal were used. The slope in this case leads to an apparent rate constant $k_1 = 2.6 \times 10^8$ cc/mole-sec. Runs were also made at 103°C and 116°C. Under these conditions the rate of sulfur dioxide removal was much slower than at 86°C, and there was much more scatter to the data. An average of the measured rates of SO_2 removal and those calculated

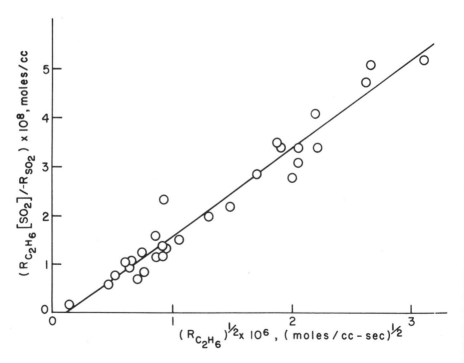

Fig. 5. Plot of the rate function D versus $R_{C_2H_6}^{1/2}$ as derived in this work from the rate data from acetone-sulfur dioxide mixture photolyses at 86°C.

from the mass balance were used; a least-squares treatment of the data gave estimates of the apparent rate constant k_1 = 0.90 × 10^8 at 103°C and 0.30 × 10^8 cc/mole-sec at 116°C. An Arrhenius plot of our rate constant data and those derived from a recalculation of the data of Good and Thynne is given in Fig. 6. The surprising feature of the combined data is that both azomethane and acetone data follow the same functional forms and show approximately the same negative temperature dependence for the apparent rate constant of reaction 1. Furthermore the acetone rate constant data obtained at $[CH_3COCH_3] \cong 4.2 × 10^{-6}$ mole/cc are very close to a factor of 2 in displacement from those derived from the Good and Thynne data for azomethane obtained at $[CH_3N_2CH_3] \cong 2.1 × 10^{-6}$ mole/cc.

The data appear to rule out the importance of the possible equilibrium mechanism involving reaction with the N–N double bond, since the carbonyl bond in acetone is quite dissimilar to the azo bond, and a similar ΔH for the addition reactions is not a reasonable expectation.

An alternative hypothesis is that reaction 1 is in transition between the third-order and second-order regions for these conditions. Assuming this description of reactions 1 and 2 and taking the rates of 1' and 2' as fast compared to 16 for our conditions, then the rate function H should apply:

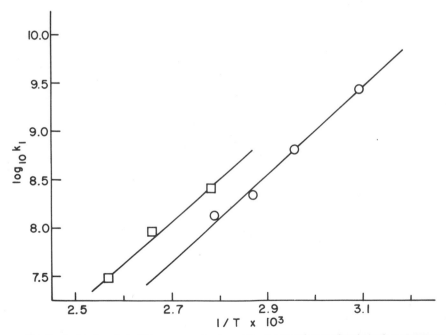

Fig. 6. Arrhenius plot of the apparent values of k_1 (assumed second-order); the squares are from the acetone ($\sim 4.2 × 10^{-6}$ mole/cc)-sulfur dioxide mixture photolyses; circles are from recalculated data of Good and Thynne *(2)* from azomethane ($\sim 2.1 × 10^{-6}$ mole/cc)-sulfur dioxide mixture photolyses.

$$CH_3 + SO_2 \underset{(2')}{\overset{(1')}{\rightleftharpoons}} CH_3SO_2*$$

$$CH_3SO_2* + M \underset{(17)}{\overset{(16)}{\rightleftharpoons}} CH_3SO_2 + M$$

$$\frac{R_{C_2H_6}[SO_2]}{-R_{SO_2}} = \frac{k_{17}k_2'k_6}{k_1'k_{16}(k_3 + k_4)} + \frac{R_{C_2H_6}^{1/2}k_2'k_6^{1/2}}{k_1'k_{16}[M]} \tag{H}$$

Presumably the apparent rate constant k_1 derived above is equal to $k_1'k_{16}[M]/k_2'$.

This mechanism appears to fit many of the observations on the CH_3-SO_2 system. The apparent discontinuity in the Arrhenius plot of the apparent rate constant, k_1, is eliminated when the factor of 2 difference in [M] is taken into account. However, the large negative activation energy is certainly higher than one expects for the temperature coefficient of the rate constant ratio, $k_1'/k_2'k_{16}$. The absolute magnitude of the apparent activation energy has a large uncertainty at present ($E_{apparent} = 14 \pm 6$ kcal/mole) because of the accumulation of errors which may arise from the mass balance assumption and the complex nature of the system studied. Presumably $\Delta H_1 \cong E_2 - E_1 = 25$ kcal/mole at 25°C *(8)*; of course CH_3SO_2* in reaction $1'$ is not a thermally equilibrated radical but a very abnormal, energy-rich species.

Unfortunately all the work reported by Gall *(14)* and Good and Thynne *(2)* was done at near constant concentration, although the concentration differed between the two studies by a factor of 2. We are now carrying out further experiments in which a more significant test of the order of reaction 1 is being made. In this attempt we have returned to the use of azomethane photolysis as the source of methyl radicals, but experiments are being made at very high light intensities and low sulfur dioxide concentrations. In view of the present rate data, it appears that for these conditions reactions of addition of CH_3SO_2 to azomethane should be minimized and reactions 1, 2, 3, 4, and 6 should dominate the reaction scheme.

There is a further, rather fascinating possible mechanism which may account for the apparent negative activation energy of k_1. Norrish and Oldershaw have suggested that sulfur dioxide may exist in two isomeric forms which differ in thermal stability *(15)*. They found that sulfur dioxide which became heated in a near adiabatic flash photolysis experiment lost the absorption bands characteristic of the room-temperature form. Recently Hayes and Pfeiffer *(16)*, using LCAO-SCF-MO methods, suggest that there is evidence of a double minimum in the potential energy surface of the SO_2

molecule. If these interpretations are correct, and one attributes a greater reactivity with CH_3 to an SO_2 isomer which predominates at lower temperatures, then conceivably the apparent decrease of the rate constant k_1 with temperature increase results largely from a shift in the thermal equilibrium between the isomeric forms. We are determining the temperature dependence of the apparent extinction coefficient of SO_2 to test this hypothesis. Definite conclusions concerning the order and the detailed nature of reaction 1 must await the results of further studies.

The Ratio of the Rates of the Disproportionation and Combination Reactions of the CH_3SO_2 and CH_3 Radicals. A check on the relative importance of reactions 3 and 4 derived by Good and Thynne can be had from our acetone-sulfur dioxide data. Note in Table III, column 8, the ratio of the excess rate of methane formation, beyond that of reaction 15, to that of sulfur dioxide removal. Presumably this ratio is equal to $k_4/(k_3 + k_4)$. The most accurate acetone-sulfur dioxide data are from the 86°C runs; these give an average ratio of $k_4/(k_3 + k_4) = 0.029$. Good and Thynne estimated $k_4/(k_3 + k_4)$ values which varied from 0.025 for 60°C to 0.046 at 85°C. Our data from the rate ratios at the higher temperatures are very scattered and do not allow a meaningful estimate in these cases. However, the present data confirm the occurrence of an additional source of methane, besides that of hydrogen atom abstraction by methyl from the reactant molecule, and the magnitude of this reaction, attributed to reaction 4, is in qualitative accord with the Good and Thynne data.

Conclusion

It has been shown that methyl radicals add readily to sulfur dioxide. The apparent second-order rate constant shows an anomalous temperature dependence for which a firm explanation is not now possible. The apparent second-order rate constant as extrapolated to 25°C is $\sim 7.6 \times 10^{10}$ cc/mole-sec. If, as appears likely, the reaction is third-order for the conditions employed, the rate constant is $\sim 3.6 \times 10^{16}$ cc^2/mole^2-sec at 25°C. This rate constant is only slightly smaller than that estimated for the analogous third-order reaction, $CH_3 + O_2 + M \rightarrow CH_3O_2 + M$, for which $k \cong 3.8 \times 10^{16}$ cc^2/mole^2-sec at 25°C *(17)*.

It has been shown that CH_3SO_2 radicals add very readily to the double bond in azomethane. In view of these results, it is a reasonable possibility that the demonstrated enhancement of aerosol formation by the presence of sulfur dioxide in photochemical smog-producing atmospheres *(18)* is initiated by radical addition to sulfur dioxide, reaction A, and subsequent addition of the RSO_2, $ROSO_2$, or RO_2SO_2 radicals to olefin molecules in the polluted atmosphere. Experiments to test this hypothesis are now in progress.

Acknowledgment

We acknowledge gratefully the support of this work through a research grant from the National Air Pollution Control Administration, Department of Health, Education, and Welfare, Public Health Service, Consumer Protection and Environmental Health Service, Research Triangle Park, North Carolina.

References

1. For a recent review of the literature on the reactions of sulfur dioxide in air, see P. Urone and W.H. Schroeder, *Environ. Sci. Technol.,* **3**, 436 (1969).
2. A. Good and J.C.J. Thynne, *Trans. Faraday Soc.,* **63**, 2708 (1967).
3. G.R. McMillan, J.G. Calvert, and S.S. Thomas, *J. Phys. Chem.,* **68**, 116 (1964).
4. G.R. McMillan, J.G. Calvert, and J.N. Pitts, Jr., *J. Am. Chem. Soc.,* **86**, 3602 (1964).
5. R. Renaud and L. C. Leitch, *Can. J. Chem.,* **32**, 545 (1954).
6. M.F. Grostic, R.J. Wnuk, and F.A. MacKellar, *J. Am. Chem. Soc.,* **88**, 4664 (1966).
7. A. Shepp, *J. Chem. Phys.,* **24**, 939 (1956).
8. W.K. Busfield, K.J. Ivin, H. Mackle, and P.A.G. O'Hare, *Trans. Faraday Soc.,* **57**, 1064 (1961).
9. R.F. Borkman and D.R. Kearns, *J. Chem. Phys.,* **44**, 945 (1966).
10. G. Herzberg, "Molecular Spectra and Molecular Structure. III. Electronic Spectra and Electronic Structure of Polyatomic Molecules," Van Nostrand, Princeton, New Jersey, 1966, p. 605.
11. A.F. Trotman-Dickenson and G.S. Milne, "Tables of Bimolecular Gas Reactions," National Standard Reference Data Series, National Bureau of Standards 9, U.S. Printing Office, Washington, D.C., 1967.
12. C.W. Larson and H.E. O'Neal, *J. Phys. Chem.,* **70**, 2475 (1966).
13. R.B. Cundall and A.S. Davies, *Proc. Roy. Soc.,* **A290**, 563 (1966).
14. J.W. Gall, Ph.D. Dissertation, Chemistry Department, The Ohio State University, Columbus, Ohio, 1969.
15. R.G.W. Norrish and G.A. Oldershaw, *Proc. Roy. Soc.,* **A249**, 498 (1959).
16. E.F. Hayes and G.V. Pfeiffer, *J. Am. Chem. Soc.,* **90**, 4773 (1968).
17. G.R. McMillan and J.G. Calvert, "Oxidation and Combustion Reviews," Vol. 1 (C.F.H. Tipper, ed.), Elsevier, New York, 1965, p. 84.
18. E.A. Schuck and G.J. Doyle, Air Pollution Foundation (Los Angeles), Report 29, October, 1959; see also reference *1* for further later work.

Discussion

G.S. HAMMOND: First, I should like to make a comment. Although I don't think the absolute reactivity data are the same, the behavior of SO_2 in vinyl polymerization is entirely consistent with everything that has been said. It does copolymerize with vinyl monomers. Apparently, RSO_2 radicals react very rapidly and readily in addition reactions. Second, did you observe sensitized phosphorescence of SO_2 in the experiments with acetone?

J.G. CALVERT: We have not done that experiment, although we hope to. We have identified a phosphorescence from SO_2 by energy transfer, but in a system apart from any chemical measurements. There is indeed an energy transfer that can be demonstrated both by the phosphorescence emission of SO_2 and by the chemistry. Let me mention one other thing. One can excite directly the triplet state of SO_2 with 3829 Å radiation which happens to be a Raman-shifted, double ruby line. We have done this, and observed for the first time pure triplet SO_2. It does not have to go through the singlet on its way to triplet. We have, I think, the first realistic measurements of the lifetime of the triplet. Caton and Duncan[*] also have a value for a lifetime, but their rate constant for quenching with SO_2 is very unusual — it is almost zero. The slope of their plot of reciprocal lifetime versus SO_2 is flat. I think they are looking at something beside triplet SO_2 which they excited in the electric discharge. Our data, both from flash photolysis systems — where we populate the triplet by intersystem crossing, quench the singlet, and measure the triplet decay lifetime — as well as from the directly excited triplet, give exactly the same rate constant, which is about 3.8×10^8 liters/mole-sec. Furthermore, this particular source of triplets is ideal to study the reaction rate constant with oxygen. We have a published value on oxygen plus triplet SO_2 quenching, which was measured very indirectly. Now we can measure it directly, and are doing so. So rate constants for triplet SO_2 should be readily accessible with this laser technique we are using.

P.A. LEIGHTON: Have you been able to estimate the rate of formation of triplet SO_2 by solar radiation in air?

J.G. CALVERT: I tried that, but your solar energy distribution function is in $100 - $Å intervals, and I should really like to have a continuous function. Let me ask you a question. Is it all right if I put a continuous function through your block chart?

P.A. LEIGHTON: Well, that would be one way to do it. However, in the region around 4000 Å there is a very strong Fraunhofer line in the solar spectrum.

J.G. CALVERT: It might just match the absorption peak of SO_2 in that region. But, knowing the perversity of nature, I suspect not. However, that would be a very interesting thing to check.

G.R. McMILLAN: With reference to the apparent negative activation energy for k_1, the evidence for an isomer of SO_2 from Norrish and Oldershaw's flash work is something like this. You flash SO_2, and a certain amount of the SO_2 disappears and then returns after a time which is too

*R.B. Caton and A.B.F. Duncan, *J. Am. Chem. Soc.*, **90**, 1945 (1968).

long to be representative of the excited state. Norrish has made similar observations in other systems, with other molecules. Methyl nitrite is one that comes to mind. So this behavior of isomeric forms may be something very general, or there may be something peculiar about his flash photolysis experiment.

J.G. CALVERT: That is indeed possible. In the case of methyl nitrite, though, one does have the possibility of photodissociation being rather complete, whereas with SO_2 we did not have that possibility, because the wavelength band is such that you could not get photodissociation.

G.R. McMILLAN: But the rate of return is the important parameter. The buildup of methyl nitrite is of the order of milliseconds, and that is too long for any recombination process.

J.G. CALVERT: This may be just an anomaly. I really don't know if this is the explanation for the apparent negative activation energy of k_1 or not. I bring it out because I'm hard pressed for an explanation.

J. HEICKLEN: There is evidence to support this. Myerson *et al.** studied the explosion of carbon disulfide. They also found that the SO_2 was preceded by some other absorber. They claim it is SOO. As with the Norrish and Oldershaw work, they can follow its disappearance and the appearance of SO_2 with a delay. And it is not a flash experiment. It is not clear that it is SOO, but it is clear that there is some other absorber present.

S. BENSON: Jack, in your recent publication on SO_2 chemistry† you looked at the reaction of triplet sulfur dioxide with O_2. You postulate some sort of a complex between SO_2 and O_2. Would you care to discuss that?

J.G. CALVERT: Dr. Katz is here, and he is probably the greatest proponent of SO_4 in the world. Let him talk about that.

M. KATZ: I wish to ask a question first. In your experiments on the photosensitized oxidation of SO_2, did you notice whether this reaction went to completion?

J.G. CALVERT: The conversions were always rather small.

M. KATZ: We have been working on the problem of SO_2 oxidation for a number of years. The SO_2-photosensitized reaction does not go to completion. One of the reasons people in this field have been misled is because they worked at small conversions. Some never went beyond 5% conversion of the SO_2. If you carry the reaction further, you will find that it is a first-order equilibrium reaction. The most you can expect is about 50% conversion, no matter how long you irradiate. We also noticed something else. If you put an unsaturated hydrocarbon into the system, the SO_2 starts to disappear, but it is not oxidized. It forms some sort of addition complex. If you continue irradiation, the complex breaks down, the SO_2

---

*A.L. Myerson, F.R. Taylor, and P.L. Hanst, *J. Chem. Phys.,* **26**, 1309 (1957).
†T.N. Rao, S.S. Collier, and J.G. Calvert, *J. Am. Chem. Soc.,* **91**, 1616 (1969).

reappears, and then proceeds to oxidize according to the first order equilibrium reaction.

J.G. CALVERT: It will be interesting to see that work, Dr. Katz.

M. KATZ: Going back to Professor Leighton's mechanism,* I think there is an SO_4 kinetically involved in this equilibrium.

S. BENSON: Is the implication, then, that SO_4 reacts with another SO_2 to form two SO_3?

M. KATZ: This looks like a possible path, but I prefer SO_4 to $SO_2 \text{-} O_2$.

J.G. CALVERT: SO_4, transferring an oxygen atom to an oxygen molecule to make ozone plus SO_3, is another interesting possibility. We have never looked for ozone in these systems, and furthermore, the analytical methods for ozone have problems. You can get responses on a Mast ozone meter from many things.

M. KATZ: I agree with you. We have looked for ozone, but we have not found it. However, we think that ozone does exist in these systems in a very transient state. It may be formed, but it disappears very rapidly. If you have a hydrocarbon in the system, you can detect that ozone must have been there because you can isolate a peroxide by gas chromatography.

P.A. LEIGHTON: Do you find that this SO_4 or SO_2 complex has an appreciable life?

M. KATZ: I think so. Yes.

G.S. HAMMOND: The more I hear about this, the more it sounds as if the interaction of triplet SO_2 with O_2 is energy transfer to give singlet oxygen which then reacts with SO_2 among other species.

J.G. CALVERT: This is, of course, a good possibility. If this indeed is what is happening, it must have a very abnormal rate constant. The rate constant for triplet quenching by oxygen is almost exactly the same as it is by SO_2, and that is a little bit abnormal for energy transfer processes.

W.S. ZIMMT: It might be some comfort to you in your work with the azo compounds that it has recently been found that, if you take benzaldehyde and decompose it with azo bis-isobutyryl nitrile, the phenylcarbonyl radical adds to the nitrogen double bond.

J.G. CALVERT: Yes. This is indeed to be expected. Mandelcorn and Steacie† found that you could add methyl radicals to olefins, and later work, which we did with Alistair Kerr‡, showed that you could add methyl radicals to the nitrogen double bond in azomethane. The barrier for an alkyl radical addition is about 7 kcal, which is a bit on the high side for what one needs to explain methyl-SO_2 addition. For the conditions we used, I had assumed that rates of addition would be about the

---

*P.A. Leighton, "Photochemistry of Air Pollution," Academic Press, New York, 1961, p. 236.
†L. Mandelcorn and E.W.R. Steacie, *Can. J. Chem.*, 32, 474 (1954).
‡J.A. Kerr and J.G. Calvert, *J. Phys. Chem.*, 69, 1022 (1965).

same for the radicals involved. However, that is not the case. Thank you for the confirming information.

S. BENSON: Is your negative activation energy for methyl plus SO_2 really anomalous? It is in line essentially with the data on the copolymerization reactions of sulfur dioxide and olefins. Have you looked at those energetics?

J.G. CALVERT: Yes. The way these data have been treated, it should sort out the dissociation reaction. That equilibrium should be reflected in the intercept. For the temperature range we have looked at, the intercepts are very near zero. This means that the term involving dissociation is not very important at these temperatures. At low temperatures things seem to be under control, but as one goes to higher temperatures, I do not think the temperature coefficient is very meaningful. It may have inherent mechanistic difficulties associated with it. It is obvious that at high temperatures there is an apparent loss of SO_2 which is a great deal slower than one would anticipate.

Reactions of Sulfur Dioxide of Possible Atmospheric Significance

Richard B. Timmons, Henry F. LeFevre, and Gerald A. Hollinden
Department of Chemistry
The Catholic University of America
Washington, D.C.

Abstract

In this work the reactions of electronically excited SO_2 molecules with hydrocarbons and CO have been investigated. In general the quantum yields for SO_2 consumption are very low, ranging from $<10^{-2}$ for methane to 0.080 for n-butane. The quantum yield for the oxidation of CO to CO_2 by excited SO_2 was also very low, being 0.005 under conditions of equal pressures of SO_2 and CO. From the observed quantum yields and their pressure dependence a general mechanism is proposed whereby the reactions of SO_2 are believed to arise from the $^3SO_2$ excited state.

The susceptibility of SO_2 toward attack by CF_3 radicals and O atoms has also been investigated. The CF_3 radicals were generated by the photolysis of hexafluoroacetone. Addition of SO_2 resulted in a net scavenging of CF_3 radicals at temperatures below $65°C$. From the observed temperature dependence of the SO_2 scavenging, a value of 15 ± 5 kcal mole^{-1} was found for the C–S bond energy in the CF_3SO_2 radical.

The reaction of O atoms with SO_2 was investigated by using ESR atom detection. Under our reaction conditions the reaction $O + SO_2$ is shown to be a termolecular process. The value of the specific rate constant for the reaction

$$O + SO_2 + M \rightarrow SO_3 + M$$

was found to be 4.1×10^{16} cm^6 mole^{-1} sec^{-1} when M is SO_2. The reaction rate was found to be slower by a factor of 40 when helium or argon was the inert gas. From the observed temperature dependence of this reaction an activation energy of 3.43 kcal mole^{-1} was obtained.

Introduction

The research reported in this paper was undertaken in an attempt to obtain more information concerning the reactivity of SO_2. It is hoped that this information will be helpful in establishing the role SO_2 plays in problems of air pollution. It is to be noted that the exact mechanism whereby SO_2 enters into chemical reactions in the atmosphere is still a very open question. This is particularly true in view of the recent report by Altshuller *et*

References, pp. 188-189

al. (1), who observed that the rate of oxidant formation from the photo-oxidation of 2 ppm of propylene plus 0.5 ppm of nitrogen oxide was independent of SO_2 concentration over the range 0 to 1.2 ppm. A detailed review of the current state of knowledge with respect to photochemical changes in reaction systems containing SO_2 has recently been presented by Urone and Schroeder *(2)*.

Under atmospheric conditions, the high S-O bond dissociation energy of SO_2 precludes its direct photochemical decomposition. Hence if SO_2 is to enter into reactions of atmospheric importance it must do so via (1) reactions of electronically excited SO_2 molecules or (2) reactions of free radicals with SO_2. We have undertaken research to investigate the chemical activity of SO_2 with respect to each of these categories.

The first investigation of reactions of electronically excited SO_2 molecules appears to be the studies of Dainton and Ivin *(3,4)*. In irradiations of mixtures of SO_2 + hydrocarbons at wavelengths >2300 Å, they reported the formation of sulfinic acids (RSO·OH). Subsequent investigations by other workers have confirmed the existence of reactions of electronically excited SO_2 molecules under a variety of conditions *(5-8)*.

Appreciable absorption by SO_2 commences around 3300 Å with an absorption band extending to 2300 Å. It appears that this band corresponds to a $^1B_1 \leftarrow {}^1A_1$ transition *(9)*, although a definitive assignment has yet to be made. The lifetime of the $^1B_1$ state with respect to fluorescence is unusually long, with values of 4×10^{-5} sec *(10)* and 2×10^{-4} sec *(11)* having been reported. This lifetime is long compared to collision frequencies at normal pressures and thus confirms the possible importance of reactions of electronically excited SO_2 molecules. The recent studies by Rao *et al. (11,12)* represent an impressively detailed investigation of SO_2 photochemistry in this absorption band. Among the significant results they report is the efficient quenching of $^1SO_2$ by SO_2 with 92% of the collisions resulting in relaxation of the $^1SO_2$ to the ground state and/or chemical change not involving excited SO_2 and the remaining 8% of the collisions producing spin inversion ($^3SO_2$). The collisional quenching of $^1SO_2$ by ground-state SO_2 was found to be within an order of magnitude of the collision frequency. They also report that collisional quenching of $^1SO_2$ by CO_2 is approximately as efficient as that by SO_2, whereas quenching by O_2 is only one-third as efficient as that by SO_2. On the other hand, collisional deactivation of $^3SO_2$ by SO_2, CO_2, and O_2 are all much slower processes, occurring more slowly than deactivation of $^1SO_2$ by a factor of approximately a thousand, and thus of the order of 10^{-4} of the collisional frequency. This is a most important observation, and the low value for O_2 quenching is particularly significant.

Although the SO_2-hydrocarbon reactions were investigated by Dainton and Ivin, it is important to repeat some of their measurements with newer analytical methods, particularly gas chromatography, unavailable at the time of their investigations. In addition, we felt it would be desirable to extend the SO_2 + hydrocarbon reaction system to include the presence of added oxygen. It was soon discovered that irradiation of these SO_2-containing mixtures represents an extremely complex system for kinetic studies. Nevertheless, it was possible to obtain overall quantum yields for the disappearance of SO_2 in these reactions. In an attempt to obtain a cleaner system for kinetic studies and, at the same time, get a better estimate of the chemical reactivity of excited SO_2 molecules, the study was extended to the photolysis of SO_2 + CO mixtures. The reactivity of SO_2 in this system was followed by measuring the quantum yield for CO_2 production. The reaction between excited SO_2 and CO to produce CO_2 was found to be a very inefficient process under all the reaction conditions employed.

In general, low quantum yields for SO_2 consumption were observed in these investigations, with the quantum yields obtained in the runs with added hydrocarbon being significantly lower than previously reported values *(3,4)*. From the rates of product formation and pressure dependence of these reactions, a possible reaction sequence is proposed; however, the complexity of these systems rules out detailed mechanistic interpretations at this time.

In the second phase of this work, the reactivity of SO_2 toward attack by atoms and free radicals was investigated. Although a wealth of information exists on the addition of alkyl radicals to various low-molecular-weight inorganic molecules (for example, O_2 and NO) few studies have been devoted to the kinetics of the interaction of alkyl radicals with SO_2. This is particularly unfortunate in view of the possible importance of such reactions in the chemistry of air pollution.

If one considers the reactions

$$R + SO_2 \rightleftharpoons RSO_2$$

where R is an alkyl radical, it can be shown, from known thermochemical data, that the equilibrium should lie to the right at room temperature, with k decreasing with increasing temperature. Despite a favorable equilibrium, the initial investigations of alkyl radical + SO_2 reactions failed to reveal any net addition of the free radical to SO_2 *(13,14)*. However, in more recent work, Good and Thynne *(15,16)* have reported on the kinetics of CH_3 and C_2H_5 reactions with SO_2. They found that CH_3 and C_2H_5 radicals are efficiently removed from the normal reaction sequence by the addition of small amounts of added SO_2. At higher tempertaures, the scavenging of the alkyl radicals by SO_2 becomes much less complete, disappearing entirely at temperatures above 164°C for CH_3 radicals and at a somewhat lower temperature for C_2H_5 radicals.

In this paper we wish to report on our studies of CF_3 radical reactions with SO_2. The interaction of CF_3 radicals with SO_2 does not appear to have been studied prior to our investigation.

Finally, we also wish to report on our studies of the reaction of O atoms with SO_2. This latter work was investigated by using quantitative gas phase ESR to monitor the O atom concentration. The application of ESR to study elementary gas phase reactions has been reviewed by Westenberg [17]. The apparatus and experimental approach employed in the current study is similar to that developed by Westenberg and de Haas [18].

Experimental Section

Reactions were carried out in a conventional high-vacuum apparatus, with the reaction section maintained mercury-free. The studies of reactions of electronically excited SO_2 molecules were investigated by using both a static reaction system and a flow (circulation) apparatus. The deposition of an oily substance on the window of the reaction vessel resulted in a rapid decrease in reaction rate with time in the static investigations. In an attempt to avert or, at least, minimize this problem, an all-glass gas circulation system was constructed. The circulation pump was similar in design to that described by Watson [19]. With this arrangement it was possible to pump the reaction mixture at rates from 1.0 to 5.0 liters min^{-1} in the pressure range employed in these studies. The cold trap on the exit side of the reaction cell was maintained at −20°C. With this arrangement it was hoped that condensable reaction products from the reaction mixture would be removed before they had a chance to undergo further photolysis or reaction. It was found that this circulation method reduced but did not eliminate the deposition of reaction products on the cell window. The oily deposit on the reaction window absorbed UV light strongly and, whereas the initial deposit was colorless, continued irradiation quickly resulted in the production of a dark brown film on the reaction window. In view of this problem, we were forced to make our quantum yield measurements under conditions of relatively short irradiation times and thus small conversions.

The same reaction cell was used in both the static and flow systems. It was cylindrical in shape with a total volume of 110 cm^3. Photolysis was carried out with a General Electric UA-2 medium pressure lamp. The effective wavelengths were limited to the 3130-Å region by the use of a preirradiated $NiSO_4$-K_2CrO_4-potassium biphthalate filter plus the insertion of a Corning glass filter 7-54 [20]. Actinometry measurements were made with a highly purified sample of acetone. The decomposition quantum yield of acetone as measured by CO production was assumed to be unity at a temperature of 150°C and acetone pressure of 20 mm Hg. The extinction coefficient for acetone absorption under our wavelength conditions was determined to be 2.65 liters mole^{-1} cm^{-1}, in good agreement with reported values *(21)*. In attempting to determine the incident photon intensity in the SO_2-hydrocarbon reactions, it was necessary to take two separate photometer readings. First, a reading was made with a clean, evacuated cell. Then a second reading was taken after the cell had been reevacuated but with the oily deposit present on the window. To compensate for this window deposition during photolysis, a simple average of the first and second readings was taken to be the incident light intensity during the kinetic run. From the acetone actinometry this could then be converted to photons per second. The vast majority of our experiments were done under conditions of complete photon absorption by SO_2, as the cell path length was 9.8 cm. In making this correction we have assumed, of course, that the rate of oil deposition increases linearly with time. This procedure almost certainly introduces some error, as it would seem most unlikely that this deposit would increase indefinitely with time. However, since we limited the quantum yield measurements to relatively small percent conversion of the SO_2 and the oil deposit resulted in about 40% decrease in light transmission, it is hoped that the error in the quantum yields introduced by this averaging procedure is not more than 10 to 20%.

The photolysis of SO_2-CO mixtures provides a much cleaner system for kinetic investigation. In these experiments we monitored the rate of CO_2 production as a function of the various reaction variables. Thus the quantum yield measurements in this system are given with respect to CO_2 formation. This could be done with considerably more precision than in the hydrocarbon work. After removal of the noncondensable CO by pumping at 77°K, aliquots of the remaining mixture of SO_2-CO_2 were analyzed by mass spectrometry. Although the SO_2 was present in large excess, the only contribution to the *m/e* peak at mass 44 comes from the CO_2, with an appropriate correction made for background CO_2. From this mass spectrometer reading, the ratio of CO_2 to SO_2 could be accurately determined. From this ratio plus a knowledge of the total moles of $SO_2 + CO_2$, the absolute rate of CO_2 production was calculated.

The photolysis of SO_2-hydrocarbon mixtures was accompanied by a pressure drop which was followed as a function of time. Pressure measurements were made with a Bourdon gauge, and it was possible to measure pressure changes as small as 0.02 mm. Quantum yields were then calculated on the basis of the pressure change and absorbed photon intensity. In a number of runs an attempt was made to determine the relative consumption of SO_2

and the hydrocarbon employed. To obtain this latter result, an aliquot of the SO_2-hydrocarbon reaction mixture was taken at the end of a run, and the total moles of SO_2 + RH determined in a gas buret. The sample was then transferred to a bulb and condensed at $77°K$. The SO_2 was removed by admitting an excess of iodine solution, after which the hydrocarbon was reclaimed in the gas buret by distillation through a trap at $-80°C$ to remove water vapor. This procedure was also carried out on an aliquot of the reaction mixture prior to photolysis. Thus the ratio SO_2 : RH could be accurately determined before and after the reaction. However, in order to observe significant changes in this ratio — that is, outside the experimental error — photolysis had to be carried out for longer times (10 hours instead of 1 hour) than were employed in the quantum yield measurements. In Tables I and II, the relative consumption of the reactants has been converted to a 1-hour basis; however, it must be borne in mind that these numbers actually refer to a time-averaged 10-hour result.

We had hoped to correlate the pressure drop with rates of production of various sulfur-containing products. To this end extensive work was carried out on the chromatographic analysis of reaction products. Analyses were carried out using a dual column-dual detector (flame ionization and thermal conductivity) temperature-programmed chromatograph. The more volatile products plus gaseous reactants were analyzed on various columns including a Chromosorb W column coated with squalane, an alumina column, and a silica gel column. Although a number of reaction products could be detected, these products were all present in relatively small amounts and were detectable only with the flame ionization detector. Most of the chromatographic studies were carried out on products from SO_2-isobutane or SO_2-n-butane irradiations. It was readily apparent that negligible amounts of cracking of the hydrocarbon occurred during photolysis, as no chromatographic trace of methane, ethane, or propane was obtained above the small impurities initially present. In the isobutane experiments, trace 2,2-dimethylbutane and isobutene were detected. In the n-butane experiments, retention times corresponding to a number of C_8-saturated compounds could be detected, all present in small amounts. In general, reactions carried out at higher temperatures tended to produce somewhat larger amounts of these C_8 hydrocarbons.

The liquid phase products were analyzed by gas phase chromatography at temperatures of $100°C$ to $150°C$ on various columns including firebrick coated with tricresyl phosphate, Teflon coated with Carbowax, and a Porapak Q column. Of specific interest was the possible formation of oxidation products such as alcohols, aldehydes, or ketones. Surprisingly, only trace amounts of such compounds could be observed under any of the reaction conditions employed. The products from the isobutane reaction showed four reasonably large peaks, whereas the *n*-butane system yielded at least seven different products. It thus appears that the SO_2*-hydrocarbon reaction does not proceed only to sulfinic acid formation as reported *(3,4)*, but rather a number of important products are produced.

Qualitative chemical tests of the oils produced in these reactions gave results in essential agreement with those of Johnston and Dev Jain *(5)*. These products are strong organic acids, and they appeared to be highly oxidized. It is interesting to note that elemental analysis of the oils gives averaged empirical formulas for C, H, S, and O which depend on extent of reaction, with the degree of oxidation increasing slowly with increasing time. These latter studies were done under conditions of much longer reaction times than the quantum yield measurements in order to obtain sufficient material for analysis. In experiments with *n*-butane and 5% conversion of the SO_2, an empirical formula of $C_3H_7SO_3$ was obtained, whereas for 20% conversion of the SO_2 a formula of $C_3H_6SO_4$ was observed. These results fall between the formulas of $C_4H_{10}SO_2$ observed by Dainton and Ivin *(3,4)* and $C_2H_5SO_5$ observed by Johnston and Dev Jain *(5)*. Presumably this simply reflects the different extents of conversion of the SO_2 in these various studies.

In this connection it is important to note that we observe a stoichiometric ratio of one SO_2 removed per molecule of hydrocarbon reacted only under experimental conditions of $[SO_2] < [RH]$. For reaction mixtures with $[SO_2] > [RH]$, the ratio $[SO_2]/[RH]$ consumed always exceeded unity. Both this result and the previously mentioned empirical formula studies suggest that initially formed reaction products are being further oxidized during the course of the reaction.

Although Dainton and Ivin *(3,4)* have interpreted their results in terms of the formation of one type of sulfoxidation product, namely sulfinic acids, it would appear that even in their experiments other products were obtained. It is only within recent years that pure low-molecular-weight aliphatic sulfinic acids have been isolated and characterized. The recent reports show that the three acids prepared to date — namely, *n*-butane- and *n*-octanesulfinic acids *(22)* and methanesulfinic acid *(23)* — are all solids. In addition, these compounds are thermally unstable; for example, methanesulfinic acid decomposed at 25°C even when stored under nitrogen *(23)*. Since the products of the studies of Dainton and Ivin were viscous liquids and since the majority of their work was done at elevated temperatures, it would appear that the reaction of electronically excited SO_2 with RH does not lead uniquely to sulfinic acid formation. The gas chromatographic analyses in the current investigation plus those of Johnston and Dev Jain *(5)* substantiate the fact that a variety of sulfur-containing products are produced. Although a determined effort was made in this study to identify some of these reaction products by matching chromatographic retention times of known samples containing C, S, O, and H, no definitive conclusions could be made. One fact observed by all workers on these reactions is that these products are strong organic acids having pK_a values of approximately 2, thus implying the presence of an $-S-O-H$ linkage in at least some of the molecules.

In many experiments the rate of SO_3 formation was followed by converting the SO_3 to SO_4^{-2} and then quantitatively determining the sulfate, usually by the barium chloranilate method. In general, it was found for a given ratio of alkane to SO_2 that the rate of SO_3 increased linearly with time of photolysis. It was also observed that increasing the ratio of alkane to SO_2 resulted in a decrease in the rate of SO_3 production. However, in experiments where the ratio alkane : $SO_2 \gg 1$, a large experimental uncertainty was associated with the SO_3 determination, as the amounts of SO_3 formed were very small. In the isobutane experiments using equal partial pressures of SO_2 and isobutane, the rate of SO_2 consumption was six times the rate of SO_3 formation.

All reactant materials employed in these studies were of the best research grade commercially available. The hydrocarbons were obtained from Phillips Petroleum and the SO_2 and CO from Matheson Scientific Company. The reactants were analyzed by gas chromatography prior to use and, in the cases deemed necessary, were further purified by fractional distillation. This was necessary to remove trace impurities, particularly olefins. The anhydrous-grade SO_2 was passed through a concentrated sulfuric acid trap before use in order to remove traces of SO_3.

The photolysis of hexafluoroacetone (HFA) was used as the source of CF_3 radicals in the $CF_3 + SO_2$ investigations. Photolysis was again carried out with a General Electric UA2 lamp. From the known emission output of the lamp plus the absorbance of the reactants, the effective wavelengths were limited to $\lambda > 2000$ Å and the most prominent intensities were those at 2537 Å and 3130 Å. In some experiments the 2537-Å radiation was eliminated by the insertion of a Corning 0-53 glass filter into the optical train. This was done to determine if any anomalous wavelength effects were involved in these experiments. No such wavelength effects were noted.

After photolysis the products noncondensable at 77°K were collected in a Toepler pump and transferred to a gas buret. Mass spectrometric analysis revealed this fraction to consist solely of CO. The traps were then warmed to -160°C, and a second fraction was collected. Mass spectrometric and gas chromatographic analysis showed this fraction to contain only C_2F_6.

The use of HFA photolysis as the CF_3 radical source in the presence of SO_2 poses an experimental problem in view of the fact that absorption by SO_2 can also take place. As noted in the previous section this would lead to the production of electronically excited SO_2 molecules. However, in the current study no complications from excited SO_2 reactions will result provided they do not increase C_2F_6 production. Since the various kinetic parameters obtained in this study are independent of the ratio of initial reactants, we conclude that no complications arise from the reactions of electronically excited SO_2 molecules.

The photolysis of HFA + SO_2 is a good deal simpler, in principle, than previous work done with CH_3 and C_2H_5 radicals. This arises from the fact that abstraction from the parent HFA by CF_3 radicals does not occur. In addition, it is now established that the photolysis of HFA does not produce CF_3CO radicals in the initial step, but, rather, the initial photolytic fission leads directly to $2CF_3$ + CO at temperatures above 25°C. Although evidence for CF_3CO formation was originally claimed to have been observed *(24)*, it now appears that complications arising from reactions of electronically excited HFA were present in these systems *(25,26)*. Thus, in these reactions, the production of CO can be used as an internal actinometer of the rate of CF_3 production, and the addition of CF_3 to SO_2 can be followed by measuring the ratio $CO:C_2F_6$ as a function of added SO_2.

The reaction of O atoms with SO_2 was studied by using a fast-flow apparatus equipped with ESR atom detection (Varian Model 4503 Spectrometer.) The apparatus employed was similar to that developed by Westenberg and de Haas and has been described previously *(27)*. The only significant change made for the current study was the replacement of the high-temperature furnace with an aluminum-lined Styrofoam box in which the flow tube was suspended. In runs carried out below room temperature, the flow tube was immersed in a bath at the appropriate temperature. In this way we were able to study the O + SO_2 reaction over a temperature range of 205° to 298°K.

Oxygen atoms were generated by electrodeless discharge of O_2 in the presence of a large excess of inert carrier gas. The percent of O_2 entering the discharge was kept to 1% or less. In this way we were able to achieve decomposition of a large fraction of the O_2 and, at the same time, minimize possible complications from reactions of electronically excited oxygen molecules. Wall loss of oxygen atoms was corrected for in the usual manner by taking "on" and "off" readings of the O atom ESR signal — that is, in the presence and absence of added SO_2. In general, linear atom decay plots were obtained for a plot of the O atom ESR signal versus the time of reaction. Both helium and argon were employed as the inert carrier gases.

Results and Discussion

Reactions of Electronically Excited SO_2. The results obtained in the photolysis of SO_2-isobutane mixtures at various temperatures and for various reactant ratios are shown in Table I. The quantum yields given in this table were calculated from the total pressure drop observed in these runs. This was done so that these results would be directly comparable to those of Dainton and Ivin. Also shown in Table I are the relative amounts of SO_2 and isobutane consumed. Thus the quantum yields with respect to each reactant can easily be calculated.

A number of important observations can be made. First, the overall quantum yields observed in this work are somewhat lower than those previously reported for this reaction. For example, at equal pressures of SO_2 and hydrocarbon and 25°C we obtain $\Phi = 0.070$, as opposed to the results of Dainton and Ivin who obtained 0.18.

The effect of increasing isobutane pressure on the overall reaction rate is shown in Fig. 1. Whereas there is a definite pressure effect at low pressure, the rate of reaction eventually becomes independent of pressure when isobutane $\gg SO_2$. This is shown to be true for the data obtained at 25°C and 100°C, with the pressure dependence being very comparable at each of these temperatures. In Fig. 2, a plot of the log_{10} rate versus reciprocal

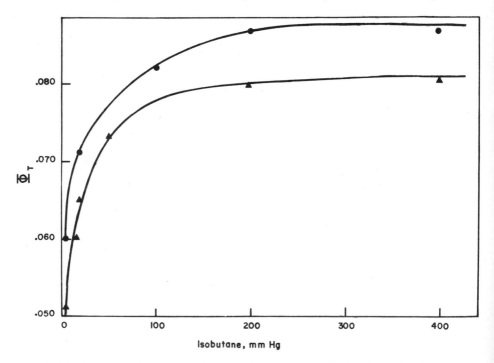

Fig. 1. Pressure dependence of the overall quantum yield in the photolysis of SO_2-isobutane.mixtures. $P_{SO_2} = 20$ torr in the runs at 25°C (●); $P_{SO_2} = 25$ torr in the runs at 100°C (▲).

Table I

Rate of Pressure Fall in the Photolysis of SO_2 + Isobutane Mixtures

Temperature (°C)	Initial Partial Pressures (mm Hg)		Pressure Fall (mm Hg hr^{-1})	Pressures Consumed* (mm Hg hr^{-1})		Φ_T†
	SO_2	Isobutane		SO_2	Isobutane	
25	20	5.1	0.30	0.22	0.08	0.060
	20	20.2	0.35	0.21	0.14	0.071
	20	103	0.40	0.20	0.20	0.082
	20	198	0.44	0.22	0.22	0.086
	20	395	0.43	0.21	0.22	0.086
100	25	5.2	0.32	0.21	0.11	0.051
	25	15.7	0.38	0.22	0.16	0.060
	25	22.8	0.41	0.22	0.19	0.065
	25	52.1	0.41	0.20	0.21	0.073
	25	198	0.50	0.24	0.26	0.079
	25	399	0.51	0.25	0.26	0.081
	40	43	0.43	0.21	0.22	0.068
	100	103	0.40	0.21	0.19	0.064
65	23	22.5	0.37	0.21	0.16	0.065
150	28	27.0	0.42	0.22	0.25	0.058

*Calculated by assuming that the total pressure fall is attributed to SO_2 and isobutane consumption.
†Φ_T represents the total quantum yield calculated from the overall pressure drops.

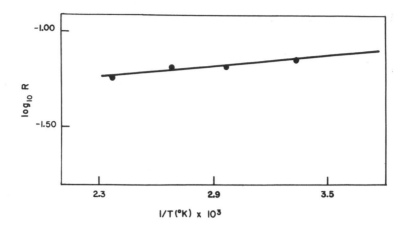

Fig. 2. Effect of temperature on the quantum yield of the photochemically induced re-action of SO_2 with isobutane. The partial pressure of SO_2 and that of isobutane were equal at each data point, and the total concentrations were constant over the temperature range investigated.

temperature shows a slight decrease in reaction rate with increasing temperature. The apparent negative activation energy calculated from this plot is 950 cal mole^{-1}.

It is of interest to note that, as shown in Table I, the relative consumption of isobutane to SO_2 is strongly dependent on the ratio of reactants. When [isobutane]/[SO_2] $\gg$ 1, equal amounts, within experimental error, of hydrocarbon and SO_2 are removed. However, under conditions where this ratio is $\leqslant$ 1, the SO_2 consumed always exceeds the isobutane reacted. This observation was also found to hold in experiments with propane and *n*-butane.

The effect of added oxygen on the rate of the isobutane-SO_2 reaction was studied at 25°C; the results are shown in Table II. It is apparent that the added oxygen has a decelerating effect on the rate of pressure decrease. It is especially important to note that the rate of isobutane consumption decreases with increasing oxygen pressure, eventually reaching the point where negligible amounts react.

In Table III the relative rates of reaction of various hydrocarbons with SO_2 are shown. Although our measured quantum yields are consistently lower than those of Dainton and Ivin, we observe essentially the same ordering of reactivity of pentane $\approx$ *n*-butane $\approx$ isobutane > ethane > methane. For all these hydrocarbons, nonvolatile deposits were obtained on the walls of the reaction cell, although the amount obtained in the methane experiments was very small.

In the experiments with added CO, the quantum yield is computed with respect to CO_2 production. In the SO_2-CO photolysis only a small pressure drop was observed even after prolonged photolysis. As shown in Table IV, the quantum yield for CO_2 production was always small, increasing slowly with increasing pressures of added CO, but decreasing with increasing temperature. It was impossible to determine experimentally the relative amounts of CO and SO_2 consumed in these reactions.

Table II

Effect of Added Oxygen on the Rate of Isobutane Consumption in the Photolysis of SO_2 + Isobutane + O_2 Mixtures at 25°C

Initial Partial Pressures (mm Hg)			Pressure Fall (mm Hg hr^{-1})	Pressures Consumed* (mm Hg hr^{-1})	
SO_2	Isobutane	O_2		SO_2	Isobutane
20	22.0	2	0.30	0.20	0.10
20	19.8	9	0.21	0.16	0.05
20	19.6	41	0.18	0.14	0.04
20	23.2	198	0.18	0.15	0.03
20	20.2	–	0.35	0.21	0.14

*Calculated by assuming that the total pressure fall can be attributed to SO_2 and isobutane consumption. Although the absolute values are probably too high, the relative amounts of reactants consumed are correct.

Table III

Comparison of the Relative Rates of Reaction of Various Alkanes with SO_2*: Equal Partial Pressures of Alkane and SO_2; Total Pressure 40 mm Hg and Reaction Temperature of 25°C

Alkane	Pressure Fall (mm Hg hr^{-1})	Φ_T
Methane	<0.03	<10^{-2}
Ethane	0.13	0.026
Propane	0.22	0.045
Isobutane	0.35	0.071
n-Butane	0.40	0.080
n-Pentane	0.42	0.084

Table IV

Rates of Production of CO_2 in the Photolysis of SO_2-CO Mixtures

Temperature	Initial Partial Pressures (mm Hg)		Φ_{CO_2}
(°C)	SO_2	CO	
25	25	25	0.0052
	25	110	0.0061
	25	420	0.0074
100	28	25	0.0049
	28	150	0.0056

It is apparent that, in order to discuss the mechanism and kinetics of the reactions of electronically excited SO_2, one must do so within the framework of the detailed findings of Rao and co-workers *(11,12)*. Their basic reaction sequence for the photolysis of pure SO_2 is as follows:

$$SO_2 + h\nu \;\rightarrow\; {}^1SO_2 \tag{I}$$

$$^1SO_2 + SO_2 \;\rightarrow\; (2SO_2) \tag{1}$$

$$\rightarrow\; {}^3SO_2 + SO_2 \tag{2}$$

$$^1SO_2 \;\rightarrow\; SO_2 + h\nu_f \tag{3}$$

$$\rightarrow\; SO_2 \tag{4}$$

$$\rightarrow\; {}^3SO_2 \tag{5}$$

$$^3SO_2 \;\rightarrow\; SO_2 + h\nu_p \tag{6}$$

$$\rightarrow\; SO_2 \tag{7}$$

$$^3SO_2 + SO_2 \;\rightarrow\; (2SO_2) \tag{8}$$

In the presence of added hydrocarbon one must also, in principle, consider the following additional reactions:

$$^1SO_2 + RH \;\rightarrow\; (RH\text{-}SO_2) \tag{9}$$

$$\rightarrow \quad ^3SO_2 + RH \qquad\qquad (10)$$

$$^3SO_2 + RH \quad \rightarrow \quad (RH-SO_2) \qquad\qquad (11)$$

where reactions 9 and 11 represent removal of electronically excited SO_2 by quenching to the ground state and/or chemical reaction. That is, we must consider

$$^1SO_2 + RH \rightarrow \quad \text{reaction products} \qquad\qquad (9a)$$

$$\rightarrow \quad SO_2 + RH' \qquad\qquad (9b)$$

$$^3SO_2 + RH \rightarrow \quad \text{reaction products} \qquad\qquad (11a)$$

$$\rightarrow \quad SO_2 + RH' \qquad\qquad (11b)$$

where RH' is used simply to denote the energy transfer from excited SO_2.

With respect to the relative importance of these various reactions and the nature of reactions 9a and 11a, a number of interesting conclusions can be drawn from the experimental observations. First, under experimental conditions of $\lambda > 3000$ Å, noncondensable products at 77°K were never obtained. The suggestion (7) that the interaction between excited SO_2 and RH proceeds via the initial step:

$$SO_2{}^* + RH \quad \rightarrow \quad SO_2 + H + R \qquad\qquad (A)$$

is thus not in agreement with these results. If reaction A is important, then the formation of H_2 should have been observed, particularly under reaction conditions where [isobutane] $\gg$ [SO_2]. In addition, Ogata *et al.* (7) have suggested that the initially formed alkyl radicals then initiate a chain reaction involving SO_2 and leading to sulfinated products. In view of the low quantum yields observed in the current work, plus the lack of hydrogen formation or disproportionation/recombination products expected from alkyl radicals, it is felt that the gas phase reaction between SO_2 and RH does not proceed via reaction A as the initiating step of a chain reaction. Whereas it has been shown that SO_2 is an efficient alkyl radical scavenger at lower temperatures, no net scavenging of the alkyl radicals takes place at temperatures above 150°C (15,16). Therefore, it is felt that, if $SO_2{}^*$ did cause the sensitized decomposition of RH, we should have observed the free radical products from these decompositions. In addition, the suggestion that the subsequent reaction of alkyl radicals with SO_2 proceeds via a chain mechanism seems unlikely in view of the relatively low quantum yields observed.

Since no evidence for a free radical mechanism was obtained in the current study, it is felt that the formation of the sulfoxidation products proceeds by a direct molecular reaction. In terms of the proposed reaction mechanism these sulfur-containing products can arise by either reactions 9a or 11a (or both). In an effort to determine the relative importance of these two reactions, several runs were carried out with equal amounts of isobutane and SO_2 but with varying amounts of added CH_4. The rationale behind these experiments was that, in view of the very low quantum yield observed in the SO_2-CH_4 photolysis, only insignificant amounts of $^1SO_2$ would be removed chemically. On the other hand, collisional deactivation of $^1SO_2$ by CH_4 is expected to be a very fast reaction, since $^1SO_2$ molecules behave like highly vibrationally excited ground-state molecules *(11)*, and, from the results obtained to date, it is known that SO_2, O_2, and CO_2 *(11,12)* are all efficient deactivators of $^1SO_2$. Experimentally it was observed that with a CH_4-to-isobutane ratio of $2:1$, the quantum yield changed from 0.070 to 0.058. In view of this result it seems quite definite that the chemically active intermediate in these systems is not $^1SO_2$, as we would have observed a much larger decrease in the quantum yield on the addition of CH_4 diluent.

In view of the above results we are led to the conclusion that the chemically reactive intermediate in these photolytic systems is $^3SO_2$ formed by intersystem crossing from $^1SO_2$ (reactions 2, 5, and 10). The suggestion that the reactive intermediate is probably $^3SO_2$ appears to have been first made by Johnston and Dev Jain *(5)* on the basis of the low quantum yields observed in the photolysis of mixtures containing SO_2. The photophysical process studies of Rao *et al.* *(11,12)* and the results in this current study support this view. It has been found that, whereas deactivation of $^1SO_2$ by SO_2 is an efficient process, 8% of the collisions result in the production of $^3SO_2$ *(11)*. Although the efficiency of the intersystem crossing via collisional deactivation of $^1SO_2$ by O_2 or CO_2 was not observed directly, it appeared that approximately the same fraction of the collisions in the case of O_2 or CO_2 deactivation results in $^3SO_2$ production *(12)*.

If we assume that roughly the same percentage of $^3SO_2$ is formed in collisions between $^1SO_2$ and RH as in the above work with O_2, SO_2, and CO_2, then the quantum yields observed in the present study are consistent with the notion of $^3SO_2$ as being the active intermediate. In view of the pressure dependence of the quantum yields, it is apparent that the hydrocarbon must compete with ground-state SO_2 for reaction with the $^3SO_2$. The limiting high-pressure quantum yield is then interpreted in terms of essentially all $^3SO_2$ being removed by hydrocarbon molecules. In terms of this interpretation it is interesting to note that, if a substantial difference existed in the efficiency of the intersystem quenching collisions by SO_2 and RH, then one would anticipate an inflection in the plot of the quantum yield versus RH pressure. For example, if RH + $^1SO_2$ never produces $^3SO_2$, then one would observe $\Phi \rightarrow O$ as RH $\rightarrow \infty$. On the other hand, if RH + $^1SO_2$ produced significantly larger amounts of $^3SO_2$, then the pressure dependence of the quantum yields should have been much greater than those actually observed. Therefore it is felt that rates of reactions 2 and 10 must be of comparable magnitude.

The effect of temperature on these reactions is interesting in that one notes a slight decrease in rate with increasing temperature. Again, if $^3SO_2$ is the reactive intermediate, then increasing the temperature may decrease the lifetime of the $^3SO_2$ with respect to phosphorescence, thus leading to a slower rate of reaction with RH. However, in view of the complex mechanism involved, there are a number of other reaction steps which could show a temperature dependence — for example, reactions 2 and 10 — and as such there is no point in further speculation. Unfortunately the fluorescent and phosphorescent lifetimes of $^1SO_2$ and $^3SO_2$ as functions of temperature have not been determined.

The analysis of the experimental results in terms of $^3SO_2$ leading to sulfoxidation products but via a non-free radical path involves somewhat of a paradox. In terms of spin conservation the reaction of $^3SO_2$ + ^1RH is expected to proceed via the formation of free radicals. In this connection, however, Ring and Rabinovitch *(28)* have demonstrated the importance of insertion reactions of $^3CH_2$ in alkane systems. Thus the reaction $^3SO_2$ + RH could conceivably proceed via a diradical intermediate of the type

$$
\begin{array}{c}
O\cdot \\
| \\
R-S-H \\
| \\
O\cdot
\end{array}
$$

followed by subsequent isomerization. In view of the very low quantum yield observed in the CH_4 reaction, it seems possible that this insertion reaction may proceed via a cyclic reaction intermediate by analogy to that suggested by Gunning and Strausz in ^3Hg photosensitized reactions *(29)*. Obviously these reactions proceed by interesting chemical routes, and a good deal more work will be required before any definitive reaction mechanisms can be provided.

The reactions of excited SO_2 with CO are interesting from the standpoint of providing a measure of the reactivity of SO_2 as an oxidizing agent leading to O atom transfer. For example, nitrogen dioxide oxidizes CO to CO_2 via the reaction

$$NO_2 + CO \rightarrow CO_2 + NO$$

with activation energies of 31.6 and 27.8 kcal mole^{-1} *(30,31)* having been reported. Although the S–O bond in SO_2 is much stronger than the N–O bond in NO_2, it is to be noted that the electronically excited SO_2 molecules contain ~ 85 kcal mole^{-1} of excess energy and thus could conceivably undergo the reaction

$$SO_2{}^* + CO \rightarrow CO_2 + SO \tag{II}$$

In view of the very low quantum yields obtained for CO_2 production, it is apparent that oxygen transfer from $SO_2{}^*$ is not a rapid process. Actually this confirms the work done with the alkanes where only trace quantities of aldehydes, ketones, or alcohols are observed. It is again felt, for the same reasons as given above, that the reactive intermediate in this reaction is $^3SO_2$. The relative slowness of reaction II is interesting from the standpoint that, with SO_2 as the reactant, the overall process would be spin-allowed, as the ground state of the SO radical is a triplet state. Apparently the S–O bond dissociation energy must remain large even in the excited state. The alternative suggestion that reaction II proceeds with a large activation energy seems unlikely in view of the slight negative temperature effect observed on the reaction rate.

The relatively small effect of oxygen on the rate of the reactions with added alkanes is contrary to the normally large effects caused by the addition of small amounts of O_2 to organic photochemical systems involving triplet intermediates *(32)* and would seem to dictate against the involvement of $^3SO_2$ in these reaction systems. However, the studies of Rao *et al. (12)* have shown O_2 to be a remarkably inefficient scavenger or deactivator of $^3SO_2$. They have suggested that this lack of energy transfer arises from the relative unimportance of charge-transfer states in the $^3SO_2 + O_2$ collision complex.

From the reaction mechanism proposed, an attempt was made to correlate the observed pressure drops and quantum yield measurements to the relative partial pressures of the reactants via the application of the steady-state treatment assumption to the reactive intermediates $^1SO_2$ and $^3SO_2$. However, it was found that to obtain workable equations an unreasonably large number of assumptions had to be made concerning the relative importance of many of the proposed reaction steps. From the equations obtained it was obvious that, to determine absolute rate constants for the reaction steps leading to product formation, one must monitor the fluorescent and phosphorescent quantum yields as well as the rate of product formation. It is hoped that future work in this area will be devoted to obtaining such data. From the observations on the rates of SO_3 production and the pressure dependence of the quantum yields, it is apparent that a competition exists between SO_2 and added reactant for reaction with electronically excited SO_2 molecules. Whereas our current study indicates that sulfoxidation products arise from $^3SO_2$ reactions, it remains to be determined if the SO_3 production also arises by this route.

Reaction of $CF_3 + SO_2$. Since the available experimental data indicate that the primary step in the photolysis of HFA does not involve the formation of trifluoroacetyl radicals, the reaction mechanism anticipated in these reactions is reasonably simple:

$$HFA + h\nu \rightarrow 2CF_3 + CO \tag{12}$$

$$2CF_3 \rightarrow C_2F_6 \tag{13}$$

$$CF_3 + SO_2 \rightarrow CF_3SO_2 \tag{14}$$

$$CF_3SO_2 \rightarrow CF_3 + SO_2 \tag{15}$$

$$CF_3SO_2 + CF_3 \rightarrow CF_3SO_2CF_3 \tag{16}$$

$$CF_3SO_2 + HFA \rightarrow \text{addition product} \tag{17}$$

If scavenging of CF_3 radicals does take place with added SO_2, the ratio C_2F_6/CO should decrease with added SO_2. If the steady-state assumption is applied to the reaction intermediates CF_3 and CF_3SO_2, the above mechanism gives:

$$\frac{d[CF_3]}{dt} = 0 = 2\Phi I_A - 2k_{13}[CF_3]^2 - k_{14}[CF_3][SO_2] + \tag{III}$$
$$k_{15}[CF_3SO_2] - k_{16}[CF_3SO_2][CF_3]$$

$$\frac{d[CF_3SO_2]}{dt} = 0 = k_{14}[CF_3][SO_2] - k_{15}[CF_3SO_2] - \tag{IV}$$
$$k_{16}[CF_3SO_2][CF_3] - k_{17}[CF_3SO_2][HFA]$$

and $\quad [CF_3SO_2] = \dfrac{k_{14}[CF_3][SO_2]}{k_{15} + k_{16}[CF_3] + k_{17}[HFA]}$

where Φ is the quantum yield for HFA decomposition.

We can simplify this expression by assuming $k_{15} \gg k_{16}[CF_3] + k_{17}[HFA]$. This assumption will be true under conditions of relatively high SO_2 pressures. Substituting the resulting expression for CF_3SO_2 into equation III and solving for CF_3, we obtain the expression

$$(CF_3)^2 = \frac{2\Phi I_A}{2k_{13} + \dfrac{k_{14}k_{16}}{k_{15}}\,[SO_2]}$$

since the rate of CO production is simply ΦI_A, we can write

$$\frac{R_{CO}}{R_{C_2F_6}} = 1 + \frac{k_{14}k_{16}}{k_{13}k_{15}}\;\frac{[SO_2]}{2} \tag{V}$$

Thus, the mechanism predicts that at a fixed temperature an increase in SO_2 concentration should result in an increase in $R_{CO}/R_{C_2F_6}$. As shown in Table V, the latter ratio is essentially independent of SO_2 concentration at temperatures above 65°C. At lower temperatures, there appears to be some net addition to SO_2; however, the data show a good deal of scatter. Treatment of the data shown in Fig. 3 by the method of least squares at reaction temperatures of 30°C, 45°C, and 55°C gave lines of slopes 4.0 ± 1.0, 2.0 ± 0.9, and $0.65 \pm 0.60 \times 10^{-7}$ mole^{-1}. From equation V, it is apparent that a plot of log[slope] versus T^{-1} (°K) should give a straight line whose slope is given by $-(E_{14} + E_{16} - E_{13} - E_{15})/2.303R$. Since the activation energies of reactions 16 and 13 are essentially zero, this calculation gives the value of $E_{14} - E_{15}$. Using the method of least squares, we obtain a value for $E_{14} - E_{15}$ of 15 ± 5 kcal mole^{-1}. Unfortunately, the relatively small temperature range accessible in this work and the large uncertainty in the results at temperatures above 45°C result in a relatively large uncertainty in the value of $E_{14} - E_{15}$. However, within experimental error, it is safe to conclude that the value of $D(CF_3 - SO_2)$ is significantly less than that of $D(CH_3 - SO_2)$ [15].

Thus the C–S bond dissociation energy in CF_3SO_2 appears to be of the order of 4 kcal mole^{-1} less than in CH_3SO_2. Apparently a similar difference must also exist in comparing the C–C bond energy in CH_3CO and CF_3CO, as the CF_3CO radical has been shown to be considerably less stable than CH_3CO. Thus the effect of fluorine substitution for hydrogen results in a decrease in the adjacent C–C or C–S bond energy.

O Atom + SO_2 Reaction. If the reaction between O atom and SO_2 is treated as a bimolecular process — that is:

Table V

**Product Yields in the Photolysis of Hexafluoroacetone
in the Presence of Added Sulfur Dioxide**

10^6 [HFA] (moles/cc)	10^7 [SO$_2$] (moles/cc)	$10^{12}R_{CO}$ (moles/cc sec)	$10^{12}R_{C_2F_6}$ (moles/cc sec)	$R_{CO}/R_{C_2F_6}$
		30°C		
1.75	0.120	4.28	3.04	1.41
1.78	0.112	4.63	4.03	1.15
1.69	0.203	4.30	2.61	1.65
1.60	0.526	4.10	1.97	2.08
1.81	0.410	4.05	2.18	1.86
1.78	0.292	4.43	2.88	1.54
		45°C		
1.74	0.062	4.52	4.34	1.04
1.70	0.216	4.13	3.11	1.33
1.79	0.367	4.08	3.16	1.29
1.69	0.485	4.21	3.12	1.35
1.78	0.372	4.02	2.54	1.58
1.75	0.530	4.19	2.62	1.60
		55°C		
1.76	0.104	4.73	4.50	1.05
1.73	0.213	4.52	4.18	1.08
1.65	0.384	4.03	3.84	1.05
1.64	0.305	3.98	3.55	1.12
1.69	0.254	4.25	3.94	1.08
1.78	0.528	3.96	3.30	1.20
		65°C		
1.74	0.143	4.55	4.46	1.02
1.80	0.258	4.01	3.89	1.03
1.71	0.519	4.08	3.96	1.03
		85°C		
1.76	0.080	4.42	4.33	1.02
1.69	0.206	4.35	4.44	0.98
1.65	0.492	4.16	4.04	1.03

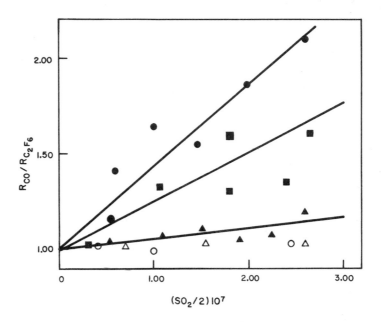

Fig. 3. The effect of added SO_2 on the product ratio $R_{CO}/R_{C_2F_6}$, obtained in the photolysis of HFA + SO_2 mixtures. • 30°C; ■ 45°C; ▲ 55°C; △ 65°C; ○ 85°C.

$$O + SO_2 \rightarrow SO_3 \tag{B}$$

then we can write

$$\frac{-d[O]}{dt} = k_B [O] [SO_2] + k_w [O]$$

where k_B is the specific rate constant for reaction B and k_w represents the rate of wall removal of O atoms. Using the same procedure as described by Westenberg and de Haas *(18)*, we can easily show that

$$\ln \left[[O]_{c,SO=0}/[O]_c \right] = k_B [SO] \frac{d}{v} + K \tag{VI}$$

where $[O]_{c,SO_2=0}$ represents the O atom ESR signal (peak height) when $SO_2 = O$, and $[O]_c$ is the signal intensity when SO_2 is flowing through the injector; d is the distance of the injector from an arbitrary zero position; and v is the linear flow velocity expressed in centimeters per second. The assumptions involved in the derivation of equation VI have been discussed elsewhere *(18,27)*.

As predicted by equation VI, a plot of the log of the ratio of ESR signals obtained with and without added SO_2 versus the position of the injector, d, should yield a straight line whose slope is $k_B [SO_2]/v$. As shown in Fig. 4 such linear atom-decay plots were obtained experimentally. If the reaction is indeed a bimolecular process as shown in reaction B, then the value of k_B obtained for varying amounts of SO_2 should be independent of the SO_2 concentration. That this is not the case is shown in Table VI. It is obvious that the rate constant is increasing with increasing pressures of SO_2. This, of course, must be interpreted as showing that reaction B is not a true bimolecular process.

If we treat the data in terms of termolecular removal of O atoms:

$$O + SO_2 + SO_2 \rightarrow SO_3 + SO_2 \tag{18}$$

$$O + SO_2 + M \rightarrow SO_3 + M \tag{19}$$

where M is any third body other than SO_2, then we can write

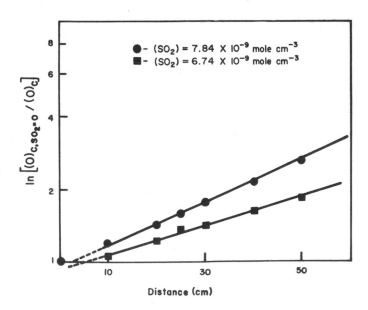

Fig. 4. Atom-decay plots obtained in the reaction of O atoms with SO_2.

$$\frac{-d[O]}{dt} = k_{18}[O][SO_2]^2 + k_{19}[O][SO_2][M] + k_w[O]$$

Integration of this expression leads to the result

$$\ell n\, [\,[O]_{c,SO_2=0}/[O]_c\,] = [\,k_{18}[SO_2] + k_{19}[M]\,]\,[SO_2]\frac{d}{v} + K$$

If we let

$$\frac{\ell n\, [\,[O]_{c,SO_2=0}/[O]_c\,]}{d} = \text{slope of the atom decay plot}$$

then we can write

$$v \times \text{slope}/[SO_2] = k_{18}[SO_2] + k_{19}[M] \qquad\qquad (VII)$$

Thus a plot of the left-hand side versus $[SO_2]$ should result in a straight line whose slope is k_{18} and intercept is $k_{19}[M]$. As shown in Fig. 5, such linear plots were obtained. Thus we feel that these results show that the reaction of O atoms with SO_2 is a termolecular process.

Under our experimental conditions of discharging very small amounts of O_2 in the presence of large amounts of added inert carrier gas, the

Table VI

Value of k_B Calculated from Equation VI

$[SO_2]10^9$ (moles cm^{-3})	$k_B(10^{-9})$ (cm^3 mole^{-1} sec^{-1})
298°K	
4.98	0.51
7.31	0.72
9.58	0.91
11.33	1.04
222°K	
6.62	0.17
8.62	0.18
11.16	0.20
13.11	0.23
14.70	0.25

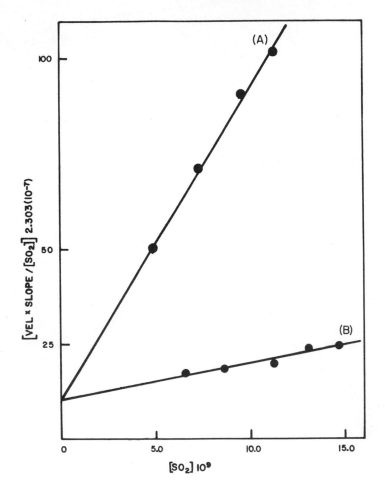

Fig. 5. Plot illustrating that the reaction of O atoms with SO_2 is a termolecular process as predicted by equation VII (see text). Curve A − 298°K; curve B − 222°K.

third body written in equation 19 refers essentially to the inert carrier gas. Thus from the intercepts of the plots shown in Fig. 5, we can calculate the value of k_{19} for the two inert gases employed, namely argon and helium. The results obtained in our work are compared with those from several other investigations in Table VII. The value for k_{18} obtained by us, 4.1×10^{16} cm^6 mole^{-2} sec^{-1}, is higher than that obtained by Mulcahy and co-workers *(33)*. Although they also used an ESR detector, their experimental apparatus was very different from ours. It is not entirely obvious how they compensated for wall loss of O atoms in their work. The value we obtain for k_{19} where M = Ar is significantly lower than those

Table VII

Comparison of Rate Constants Obtained in the Reactions $O + SO_2 + M$ in Units of cm^6 $mole^{-2}$ sec^{-1} (10^{-16}) at 25°C.

M	Halstead and Thrush *(34)*	Allen and Cadle *(35)*	Kaufman *(36)*	Mulcahy and co-workers *(33)*	This work
SO_2				1.0	4.10
He					0.08
Ar	0.47			0.24	0.10
O_2		0.45	3	0.27	

reported by Halstead and Thrush *(34)* or Allen and Cadle *(35)*. However, it is not clear to what extent their values include contributions from k_{18}. Since we observe that $k_{18} > k_{19}$, any contribution from k_{18} under their reaction conditions would tend to make their reported value for k_{19} larger than that reported in this work.

It was also possible to investigate the effect of temperature on the rate of the O atom reaction with SO_2. The results are plotted in Fig. 6. As

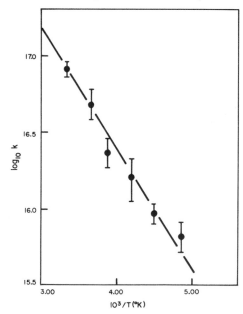

Fig. 6. Arrhenius plot of the rate constant of the reaction $O + SO_2 + SO_2 \rightarrow SO_3 + SO_2$.

shown in Table VIII, data were obtained over the temperature range of $205°$ to $298°K$. The addition complex lives for only a few vibrations. To obtain a value of 10^{19}, as observed in this work, we must assume that the initial complex formed between O and SO_2 lives for an appreciable time — for example, of the order of 1000 vibrations *(37)*. That is, the lifetime of the SO_3* intermediate would be of the order of 10^{-9} to 10^{-10} sec. However, at the low pressures employed in this work, this lifetime is still small compared to collision frequencies, and thus we observe that the O + SO_2 reaction is termolecular in nature.

It is of interest to note that of the various reports of the reaction of O + SO_2 only the paper by Jaffe and Klein *(38)* treats the reaction as a bimolecular process. However, their work was done at considerably higher pressures than those employed in fast-flow systems. Thus their SO_2 pressures ranged from 21 to 210 torr. In view of the preexponential factor observed in our studies and the high efficiency of SO_2 as a third body, it seems reasonable to expect that at higher SO_2 pressures essentially all the SO_3* molecules would be deactivated. Under these conditions the overall kinetics would then become bimolecular as observed by Jaffe and Klein *(38)*.

Summary

It is felt that a number of important points concerning the chemical reactivity of SO_2 become apparent from the work reported in this paper.

1. The rather low quantum yields observed in the photolysis of mixtures of SO_2 + hydrocarbon or SO_2 + CO leads one to the conclusion that reactions of electronically excited SO_2 molecules are probably of minor importance in urban atmospheres. The low absorption coefficient of SO_2 couples with the apparent efficient physical deactivation of excited $^1SO_2$ molecules will result in relatively small SO_2 removal from the urban atmospheres by way of photon absorption. In view of the fact that the quantum yield of the reaction of excited SO_2 with O_2 is of the same order of magnitude as the reaction of excited SO_2 with hydrocarbons, we can conclude that the $*SO_2$-hydrocarbon reaction is not a significant process under atmospheric conditions where the concentration of O_2 is so much greater than RH.

2. On the other hand, the reactions of CF_3 radicals and O atoms with SO_2 are relatively fast processes. These results coupled with studies of CH_3 and C_2H_5 radical reactions with SO_2 strongly point to the fact that SO_2 reacts readily with free radicals. As such, it would indicate that an important atmospheric removal mechanism of SO_2 most probably involves reactions with free radicals.

Table VIII

Experimental Conditions Used to Obtain the Rate of the Reaction of O Atoms with SO_2. Inert Carrier Gas was Helium

Temperature ($^\circ$K)	Pressure (torr)	Velocity (cm/sec)	$[SO_2]$ (moles cm^{-3})	$[He]$ (moles cm^{-3})	$[SO_2]/[O_2]$	k (cm^6 mole^{-2} sec^{-1})
298	4.25	388	7.84×10^{-9}	2.20×10^{-7}	10.91	
	4.20	383	4.76×10^{-9}	2.21×10^{-7}	6.53	
	4.21	396	6.74×10^{-9}	2.19×10^{-7}	9.54	$(8.03 \pm 0.97) \times 10^{16}$
298	4.23	395	9.58×10^{-9}	2.17×10^{-7}	13.54	
	4.25	395	7.31×10^{-9}	2.21×10^{-7}	10.20	
	4.21	390	4.98×10^{-9}	2.21×10^{-7}	6.95	
	4.25	389	11.33×10^{-9}	2.17×10^{-7}	15.79	$(8.32 \pm 0.30) \times 10^{16}$
273	3.78	402	8.85×10^{-9}	2.13×10^{-7}	12.30	
	3.90	405	11.60×10^{-9}	2.17×10^{-7}	16.20	
	3.80	408	9.96×10^{-9}	2.13×10^{-7}	14.00	
	3.80	402	7.91×10^{-9}	2.15×10^{-7}	11.00	
	3.86	416	5.66×10^{-9}	2.20×10^{-7}	8.12	$(4.78 \pm 1.05) \times 10^{16}$
252	4.04	343	8.08×10^{-9}	2.48×10^{-7}	11.43	
	4.00	354	11.67×10^{-9}	2.42×10^{-7}	17.02	
	4.00	345	5.46×10^{-9}	2.48×10^{-7}	7.76	$(2.33 \pm 0.55) \times 10^{16}$
238	4.03	318	11.96×10^{-9}	2.67×10^{-7}	15.69	
	4.11	317	15.98×10^{-9}	2.69×10^{-7}	20.90	
	4.04	319	12.91×10^{-9}	2.67×10^{-7}	16.96	
	3.98	318	8.96×10^{-9}	2.67×10^{-7}	11.76	$(1.62 \pm 0.52) \times 10^{16}$

222	3.73	343	6.62×10^{-9}	2.47×10^{-7}	7.65	
	3.75	327	11.16×10^{-9}	2.59×10^{-7}	12.30	
	3.78	329	14.70×10^{-9}	2.58×10^{-7}	16.30	
	3.76	330	13.11×10^{-9}	2.58×10^{-7}	14.57	
	3.71	328	8.62×10^{-9}	2.59×10^{-7}	9.52	$(9.37 \pm 1.38) \times 10^{15}$
205	3.46	322	7.25×10^{-9}	2.63×10^{-7}	8.06	
	3.52	322	12.31×10^{-9}	2.62×10^{-7}	13.67	
	3.60	320	18.71×10^{-9}	2.62×10^{-7}	20.66	
	3.58	319	14.83×10^{-9}	2.64×10^{-7}	16.34	
	3.68	319	22.14×10^{-9}	2.65×10^{-7}	24.36	$(6.58 \pm 1.59) \times 10^{15}$

3. In view of the above conclusions, it is felt that a good deal of future SO_2 research should be concentrated on the area of investigating the reactivity of SO_2 toward attack by other radicals. For example, alkoxyl (RO) and alkylperoxyl (RO_2) radical reactions with SO_2 should be thoroughly studied.

Acknowledgment

We acknowledge gratefully the support of this work through a research grant from the National Air Pollution Control Administration, U.S. Department of Health, Education and Welfare, Grant Number AP 00502.

References

1. A.P. Altshuller, S.L. Kopczynski, W.A. Lonneman, T.L. Becker, and D.L. Wilson, *J. Environ. Sci. Technol.,* **2**, 696 (1968).
2. P. Urone and W.H. Schroeder, *J. Environ. Sci. Technol.,* **3**, 436 (1969).
3. F.S. Dainton and K.J. Ivin, *Trans. Faraday Soc.,* **46**, 374 (1950).
4. F.S. Dainton and K.J. Ivin, *Trans. Faraday Soc.,* **46**, 382 (1950).
5. H.S. Johnston and K. Dev Jain, *Science,* **131**, 1523 (1960).
6. T.C. Hall, Jr., Photochemical Studies of NO_2 and SO_2, Ph.D. Thesis, University of California, Los Angeles, 1953.
7. Y. Ogata, Y. Izawa, and T. Tsuda, *Tetrahedron,* **21**, 1349 (1965).
8. P. Urone, H. Lutsep, C.M. Noyes and J.F. Parcher, *J. Environ. Sci. Technol.,* **2**, 611 (1968).
9. G. Herzberg, "Molecular Spectra and Molecular Structure. III. Electronic Spectra and Electronic Structure of Polyatomic Molecules," D. Van Nostrand, Princeton, New Jersey, 1966, p. 511.
10. K.F. Greenough and A.B.F. Duncan, *J. Am. Chem. Soc.,* **83**, 555 (1961).
11. T.N. Rao, S.S. Collier and J.G. Calvert, *J. Am. Chem. Soc.,* **91**, 1609 (1969).
12. T.N. Rao, S.S. Collier and J.G. Calvert, *J. Am. Chem. Soc.,* **91**, 1616 (1969).
13. W.K. Busfield, K.J. Ivin, H. Mackle and P.A.G. O'Hare, *Trans. Faraday Soc.,* **57**, 1064 (1961).
14. F.P. Lossing, quoted in reference *1.*
15. A. Good and J.C.J. Thynne, *Trans. Faraday Soc.,* **63**, 2708 (1967).
16. A. Good and J.C.J. Thynne, *Trans. Faraday Soc.,* **63**, 2720 (1967).
17. A.A. Westenberg, *Science,* **164**, 381 (1969).
18. A.A. Westenberg and N. de Haas, *J. Chem. Phys.,* **40**, 3087 (1964).
19. J.S. Watson, *Can. J. Technol.,* **34**, 373 (1956).
20. J.G. Calvert and J.N. Pitts, Jr., "Photochemistry," Wiley, New York, 1966, p. 732.
21. C.W. Larson and H.E. O'Neal, *J. Phys. Chem.,* **70**, 2475 (1966).
22. H. Reinheckel and D. Jahnke, *Chem. Ber.,* **99**, 1718 (1966).
23. F. Wudl, D.A. Lightner, and D.J. Cram, *J. Am. Chem. Soc.,* **89**, 4099 (1967).

24. B.G. Tucker and E. Whittle, *Proc. Chem. Soc.*, 93 (1963).
25. J.S.E. McIntosh and G.B. Porter, *Trans. Faraday Soc.*, **64**, 119 (1968).
26. J.D. Kale and R.B. Timmons, *J. Phys. Chem.*, **72**, 4239 (1968).
27. M.J. Kurylo and R.B. Timmons, *J. Chem. Phys.*, **50**, 5706 (1969).
28. D.F. Ring and B.S. Rabinovitch, *J. Am. Chem. Soc.*, **88**, 4285 (1966).
29. H.E. Gunning and O.P. Strausz, *Adv. Photochemistry*, **1**, 209 (1963).
30. H.S. Johnston, W.A. Bonner and D.J. Wilson, *J. Chem. Phys.*, **26**, 1002 (1957).
31. F.B. Brown and R.H. Crist, *J. Chem. Phys.*, **9**, 840 (1941).
32. C.S. Foot, S. Wexler, W. Ando, and R. Higgins, *J. Am. Chem. Soc.*, **19**, 975 (1968).
33. M.F.R. Mulcahy, J.R. Stevens and J.C. Ward, *J. Phys. Chem.*, **71**, 2124 (1967).
34. C.J. Halstead and B.A. Thrush, *Proc. Roy. Soc.*, **A295**, 363 (1966).
35. J.W. Powers and R.D. Cadle, as quoted by E.A. Allen and R.D. Cadle, *Photochem. Photobiol.*, **4**, 979 (1965).
36. F. Kaufman, *Proc. Roy. Soc.*, **A247**, 123 (1958).
37. See, for example, V.N. Kondrat'ev, "Chemical Kinetics of Gas Reactions," Addison-Wesley, 1964, p. 323.
38. S. Jaffe and F.S. Klein, *Trans. Faraday Soc.*, **62**, 2150 (1966).

Discussion

J. HEICKLEN: We have looked at SO_2 photolysis in two systems. We excite SO_2 at 3130 Å. In the first system, we react electronically excited SO_2 with C_2F_4. We get only CF_2O and cyclo-C_3F_6. The system is very clean; no polymer is formed. These are the same products that are formed in the oxygen-atom-C_2F_4 reaction. This work is now being pursued by Mr. Chet Spicer of our laboratory.

J.G. CALVERT: Where is the sulfur?

J. HEICKLEN: We have not yet determined what happens to the sulfur in the system. We do get a small amount of sulfur deposited in the system. Presumably, we get SO, and the SO probably goes to sulfur and SO_2.

In the second system, we react SO_2* with CO to get CO_2, as Dr. Timmons has just discussed. Mr. Cehelnik of our laboratory is looking at this. Figure 7 shows that the quantum yield of CO_2 increases linearly with the pressure of CO and is independent of SO_2 pressure. Dr. Timmons' quantum yields are slightly higher than ours.

We also varied the intensity by about a factor of 13 and found essentially no effect on the quantum yield. We have also added biacetyl to quench the triplet state.† When we do this, the quantum yield of CO_2 is reduced two-thirds. Presumably, about two-thirds of the CO_2 is coming from triplet SO_2, therefore, and one-third from someplace else. I must cau-

---

†T.N. Rao, S.S. Collier, and J.G. Calvert, *J. Am. Chem. Soc.*, **91**, 1616 (1969).

tion that these results are as yet only tentative, since these data were obtained only last week.

A. LEVY: We looked at the $SO_2 \cdot O$ atom reaction in hydrogen sulfide and carbonyl sulfide flames.*† Our $SO_2 \cdot O$ atom results appear to be consistent with yours, although our reactions were up around $1200°$ or $1300°K$.

In our flame studies, the SO_3 produced was about 1% or 2% of the sulfur in the system. This is explained quite well by the reaction of SO_3 with an oxygen atom to remove the SO_3. In post-flame reactions, the SO_3 concentration reaches a peak and then is depleted by back-reaction with oxygen atoms. We have seen this at several pressures. In the carbonyl sulfide flame, you first form CO and then oxidize the CO to CO_2. So we have a steady increase in oxygen atom production, and as a result the decrease of SO_3 because of the back-reaction with oxygen atoms is more pronounced.

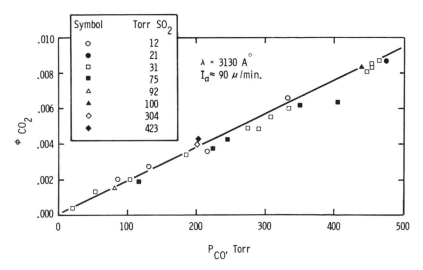

Fig. 7. The photolysis of SO_2 in the presence of CO: quantum yield of CO_2 versus pressure of CO.

*A. Levy and E.L. Merryman, *Environ. Sci. Technol.,* **3**, 63 (1969).
†A. Levy and E.L. Merryman, *Combust. Flame,* **9**, 229 (1965).

The Reactions of Unstable Intermediates in the Oxidation of CS_2

Julian Heicklen, William P. Wood,*
Kenneth J. Olszyna,* and Edwin Cehelnik*
Department of Chemistry and Center for Air Environment Studies
The Pennsylvania State University
University Park, Pennsylvania

Abstract

The photooxidation of CS_2 was studied with radiation at 3130 Å in a conventional static photochemical system at room temperature. The reactant pressures varied from 2 to 70 torr of CS_2 and from 1 to 745 torr of O_2. The absorbed light intensity, I_a, varied from 2.0 to 111 μ/min. The products of the reaction were CO, OCS, SO_2, and a polymer. CO_2 and SO_3 were not produced. In the absence of O_2, only the polymer was formed, but in smaller amounts.

The quantum yields of the gaseous products were small and typically ranged from 3×10^{-4} to 10^{-1}. In spite of significant variations in the quantum yields, the ratios of products were invariant for all the runs with $\Phi\{OCS\}/\Phi\{CO\} \sim 1.2$ and $\Phi\{SO_2\} \sim \Phi\{OCS\} + 2\Phi\{CO\}$. The latter expression indicates a carbon-sulfur mass balance among the gaseous products.

The product quantum yields depended only on $[O_2]/[CS_2]$; otherwise they were invariant to changes in $[O_2]$, $[CS_2]$, or I_a. The mechanism which best explains the results is

$$CS_2 + h\nu \rightarrow CS_2^* \qquad (1)$$

$$CS_2^* + CS_2 \rightarrow 2CS + S_2 \qquad (2a)$$

$$\rightarrow 2CS_2 \qquad (2b)$$

$$CS_2^* + O_2 \rightarrow CS_2 + O_2 \qquad (3a)$$

$$\rightarrow CS + SO_2 \qquad (3b)$$

$$\rightarrow polymer \qquad (3c)$$

$$CS + O_2 \rightarrow OCS + O \qquad (4a)$$

$$\rightarrow CO + SO \qquad (4b)$$

---

*U.S. Public Health Service Air Pollution Trainee.

References, pp. 220-221

$$SO + O_2 \rightleftharpoons OSOO \tag{5}$$

$$CS \rightarrow polymer \tag{6}$$

$$O + CS_2 \rightarrow CS + SO \tag{7}$$

$$OSOO + SO \rightarrow 2SO_2 \tag{8}$$

where $CS_2{}^*$ is electronically excited CS_2. Furthermore, our findings are consistent with the earlier work of H.E. Gunning and co-workers indicating that $k_2/k_3 = 7.6$. Our results also indicate that $k_{4a}/k_{4b} \sim 1.2$, $k_{2a}/k_2 = 0.8 \times 10^{-4}$, and $k_{3b}/k_3 = 0.062$.

To check the reactions of SO, this species was prepared in separate experiments by reacting oxygen atoms with OCS. The oxygen atoms, prepared by mercury photosensitization of N_2O, react with OCS via

$$O + OCS \rightarrow CO + SO \tag{15}$$

Thus we anticipated that $\Phi\{CO\}$ should be unity and that the fate of SO could be studied. In fact, $\Phi\{CO\}$ was always between 0.33 and 0.50, indicating that reaction 15 may have always been followed by

$$O + SO + N_2O \rightarrow SO_2 + N_2O \tag{16}$$

$$O + SO_2 + N_2O \rightarrow SO_3 + N_2O \tag{17}$$

SO_2 was found as a product of the reaction, and SO_3 was indicated at longer conversions by polymer deposition and inhibition of product formation (including N_2, which was an internal actinometer). The ratio k_{17}/k_{15} was found to be $\sim 5 \times 10^3$ ℓ mole^{-1}. Some runs were done with added O_2, in which case $\Phi\{CO\}$ exceeded 0.5, indicating that SO reacted with O_2.

The reaction of O_3 with CS_2 was found to be rapid at room temperature. Ozone disappearance was monitored by absorption spectroscopy and followed the rate law

$$-d[O_3]/dt = k'[O_3]^2/[O_3]_0$$

where $[O_3]_0$ is the initial value of $[O_3]$ in any experiment. This rate law held for at least 80% decomposition in any experiment with 4.8 to 80 torr of CS_2 and initial ozone pressures of 0.15 to 4.0 torr. The constant k' was found to be 1.83 min^{-1}.

The products of the reaction have been measured and found to be O_2, CO, CO_2, OCS, and SO_2. Compared to the O_3 decomposed, the relative amounts of these products are 0.79, 0.095, 0.040, 0.180, and 0.40, respectively. Some polymer was produced also. Experiments were done with the product gases added initially. They had no effect on the product ratios, the rate law, or the rate constant unless added in large excess of that produced in the reaction. In large excess they still had no effect on the product ratios, but could alter the rate constant and/or the rate law.

Introduction

Carbon disulfide is used as a solvent in industrial processing, notably in rubber and viscose rayon manufacture. It may also be present in small amounts in petroleum. Consequently it may be emitted into the atmosphere and undergo oxidation.

During the oxidation of CS_2, the intermediates CS and SO have been observed in the cold flame *(1,2)*, in the explosion *(3)*, and in photochemical oxidation *(4,5)*. An examination of the oxidation of these species will aid our understanding, not only of CS_2 oxidation, but also of the oxidation of other compounds which can produce these intermediates. For example, CS has been reported in the photolysis of thiophene *(6)* and should be produced in the photolysis of thioketones and thioaldeldes. We have evidence in our laboratory that SO can be produced in the photolysis of SO_2 at 3130 Å in the presence of CO or C_2F_4 (E. Cehelnik and C. Spicer, unpublished results, 1969).

We have initiated a comprehensive program for studying the oxidation of CS and SO. These species are being produced as follows:

1. *Production of CS*
   1. Photolysis of thiophene
   2. $CS_2 + hv$ (3130 Å) $\rightarrow CS_2^*$
   3. $CS_2 + hv$ (<2200 Å) $\rightarrow CS + S$

II. *Production of* SO
   1. Photolysis of SO_2 in the presence of CO or C_2F_4
   2. $O + OCS \rightarrow CO + SO$

III. *Production of both* CS *and* SO
   1. $O + CS_2 \rightarrow CS + SO$
   2. $O_3 + CS_2$

In this paper we present our results on the room-temperature studies of the photooxidation of CS_2 at 3130 Å, the reaction of oxygen atoms with OCS, and the reaction of O_3 with CS_2.

Experimental Procedure

Most of the gases used were from the Matheson Co. These included extra-dry-grade O_2 and cp-grade CO which were used without further purification. The N_2O and anhydrous SO_2 showed no impurities and were used after degassing at $-196°C$. Commercial-grade CO_2 showed one unidentified impurity ($\sim$3%) but was used without purification except degassing at $-196°C$. The introduction of CO_2 into the O_3-CS_2 reaction has no noticeable effect, so the impurity is of no consequence. The OCS contained about 3% CO_2 and much smaller amounts of H_2S. In the O_3 experiments it was used after degassing at $-196°C$, since CO_2 does not influence the reaction and the amount of H_2S is too small to be of any significance. However, for the oxygen atom – OCS reaction, the OCS was purified either by gas chromatographic separation utilizing a 12-foot Porapak Q column or by passing the OCS through concentrated sodium hydroxide solution. Both impurities were completely removed; the OCS was degassed at $-196°C$ before use.

Both Fisher Scientific Co. spectral-grade and Matheson Coleman Bell reagent-grade CS_2 were used after degassing at $-196°C$. No impurities were present.

The CF_3I and C_2F_4, both of which were used for actinometer studies, were from Peninsular ChemResearch Inc. The CF_3I was first degassed at $-160°C$ to remove CO_2. The C_2F_4 was distilled to remove the polymerization inhibitor; the fraction volatile at $-160°C$, but condensable at $-196°C$, was used.

Ozone was prepared from a Tesla coil discharge through O_2. The O_3 was collected at $-196°C$ and the residual O_2 removed.

Gas pressures were measured by Wallace-Tiernan absolute-pressure indicators, mercury manometers, or a McLeod gauge except for the ozone experiments, where an H_2SO_4 manometer was used. The O_3 pressure was checked by optical absorption at 2537 Å. The gases were introduced into the cell, and the reaction was monitored continually by ultraviolet absorption spectroscopy utilizing low intensities so that photochemical reactions were not induced by the monitoring lamp.

In the O_3-CS_2 experiments the reaction vessel was a quartz cell 5 cm long and 5 cm in diameter. The monitoring light source was a Philips 93109E low-pressure mercury resonance lamp. The radiation passed through a Corning 7-54 filter to remove radiation below 2200 Å and a cell filled with chlorine to remove radiation above 2800 Å before passing through the reaction vessel to an RCA 9-35 phototube.

In the photochemical experiments the reaction vessels were quartz cells 10 cm long by 5 cm in diameter. The monitoring source was an Osram 150-watt high-pressure xenon lamp. Its radiation was passed through a Jarrell Ash 82-410 1/4-meter Ebert monochrometer with 500-μ slits and an 1180-groove/mm grating blazed at 3000 Å. After passing through the windows of the reaction cell, the radiation was focused on an RCA 9-35 phototube.

In the photooxidation of CS_2, the photochemical source was a Hanovia

Model 30620 150-watt medium-pressure U-shaped lamp. The radiation passed through a Corning 0-54 filter to remove radiation below 3050 Å before entering the side of the reaction vessel. The effective radiation was at 3130 Å. Actinometer runs were done by measuring the CF_2O produced in the photooxidation of CF_3I using matched absorbances of the CF_3I and CS_2 at 3130 Å. In this way all geometrical corrections are eliminated. The CF_2O produced, assumed to have a quantum yield of 1.0 (7), was converted to CO_2 which was measured on a gas chromatograph.

The reaction of oxygen atoms was studied by the mercury-sensitized photodecomposition of N_2O in the presence of OCS. A Hanovia low-pressure flat-spiral mercury resonance lamp was used, and the radiation was passed through a Corning 9-54 filter to eliminate radiation below 2200 Å before entering the side of the reaction vessel. The N_2 quantum yield was the same as in the mercury-sensitized photolysis of N_2O in the presence of about 1% C_2F_4 and was taken to be 1.0 (8).

In each experiment, after the reaction was terminated, the products were collected and analyzed by gas chromatography. The products noncondensable at $-196°C$ were analyzed on a 5A molecular sieve column. Either an aliquot portion was used or, in the photooxidation of CS_2 where the amount of products was small, the total sample was collected.

In the experiments of the photooxidation of CS_2, the products noncondensable at $-196°C$ were collected with a Toepler pump and passed through a 15-foot-long 5A molecular sieve column operating at $50°C$ and a He flow rate of 150 cc/min. The condensable products were collected and analyzed on a 10-foot-long Porapak Q column at $70°C$ with a He flow rate of 250 cc/min. In the other experiments where larger amounts of products were produced, aliquot portions of the noncondensable gases were analyzed on a 8-foot-long 5A molecular sieve column at room temperature with a flow rate of 100 to 122 cc/min. The condensable gases were passed through Porapak T columns, either 8.5 feet long operated at $81°$ to $84°C$ and a He flow rate of 217 cc/min (O_3-CS_2), or 4 feet long operated at $65°C$ with a He flow rate of 200 cc/min (O + OCS). In all cases a Gow Mac Model 40-05D chromatograph with a thermistor detector was used in conjunction with a 1-mV recorder.

An attempt was also made to analyze for SO_3 by passing the products condensable at $-160°C$ through either oxalic acid or an oxalate salt immediately after the reaction. It has been reported (9) that oxalic acid quantitatively reacts with SO_3 to produce CO_2. We have verified this result for samples of SO_3 corresponding to about 50 μ or more SO_3 in our reaction vessel. In none of our experiments did we find evidence of SO_3 formation with this technique. However, SO_3 may have been produced, but in an insufficient quantity to be detected.

Photooxidation of CS$_2$

Results. Four products were found when mixtures of CS$_2$ and O$_2$ were photolyzed with 3130-Å radiation at room temperature. These were CO, OCS, SO$_2$,
and a polymer which deposited on the walls. The polymer could be removed
after the run by flaming the cell or by prolonged pumping. No other products
were found, though repeated attempts were made to find CO$_2$, SO$_3$, S$_2$O,
and O$_3$. It is certain that CO$_2$ was not produced, but the other products might
have been produced in small amounts below the detection limit of our
analytical scheme. Typically the final pressures of gaseous products were 3
to 60 μ. Our analytical scheme should have detected 60 μ of SO$_3$, but
might be inadequate to detect less than 10 μ. However, there was no
evidence to suggest SO$_3$, except possibly at the very highest [O$_2$]/[CS$_2$]
ratios. Consequently we assume it to be negligible, if produced at all.
Analyses for S$_2$O and O$_3$ were attempted by absorption spectroscopy at
2500 and 2700 Å. Both molecules absorb in this region, and the extinction coefficients for both molecules were determined. If more than 10 μ
of either gas was produced, it would have been detected. During the photolysis, absorption at both wavelengths grew, that at 2700 Å being stronger
than that at 2500 Å. The ratio of absorbance at the two wavelengths did
not correspond to that of either O$_3$ or S$_2$O, though it could have been
due to both gases being present. However, it seems unlikely that both
gases would have been produced in the same ratio under all conditions,
and we have discarded this possibility. Furthermore, the ratio of absorbance
at the two wavelengths was exactly identical to that found when CS$_2$ was
photolyzed in the absence of O$_2$, where the only product is polymer. Thus
we attribute the absorbance as due exclusively to the polymer. Nevertheless, undetectable amounts of O$_3$ and/or S$_2$O might have been produced.

If the photolysis was performed in a cell cleaned either by prolonged
evacuation ($\sim$2 weeks) or by nitric acid solution, then the reproducibility
of the results was poor and the product quantum yields were as much as
three times as great as for a cell conditioned by several previous photolyses.
Furthermore, even in conditioned cells, the product quantum yields dropped
as the exposure time was lengthened. To obtain initial quantum yields, very
low conversions were required; it was often necessary to keep the final
pressure of some of the gases to less than 5 μ.

Thus all the data reported here were obtained in conditioned cells at
very short conversions. As a result, the accuracy is poor and the data
show considerable scatter.

Experiments were done at various absorbed intensities, I_a, and reactant
pressures. The absorbed intensity was varied by a factor of 56; [CS$_2$], by
a factor of 35; [O$_2$], by a factor of 620; and [O$_2$]/[CS$_2$], by a factor of

2.2×10^4. The results are listed in Table I. For the polymer, only relative yields, $\Phi\{P\}$, were found, and they are reported in units of absorbance per micron. The product quantum yields were independent of I_a but increased about 100-fold as $[O_2]/[CS_2]$ increased by a factor of 2.2×10^4. However, for a given ratio of reactants, the yields were independent of total pressure, and even the ratios of yields were nearly independent of $[O_2]/[CS_2]$. The quantum yields of the gaseous products were small and varied between 3×10^{-4} and 0.11.

The ratio $\Phi\{CO\}/\Phi\{OCS\}$ is listed for each of the runs in Table I. It is seen to be invariant at 0.83 with a mean deviation of 0.15 with all changes in experimental variables. The variation of $\Phi\{SO_2\}/\Phi\{OCS\}$ with $[O_2]/[CS_2]$ is shown in Fig. 1. The data points are quite scattered, but the solid line representing the average value of the ordinate at each value of $[O_2]/[CS_2]$ indicates that $\Phi\{SO_2\}/\Phi\{OCS\}$ is essentially constant at about 2.4 for $[O_2]/[CS_2]$ between 0.3 and 30. If a carbon-sulfur mass balance exists among the gas phase products, then

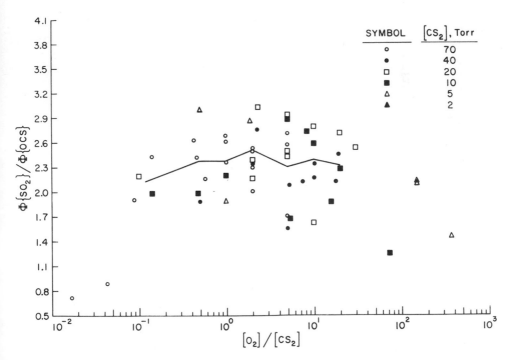

Fig. 1. Plot of $\Phi\{SO_2\}/\Phi\{OCS\}$ versus $[O_2]/[CS_2]$ in the photolysis of CS_2-O_2 mixtures at 3130 Å and room temperature.

Table I

Photolysis of CS$_2$–O$_2$ Mixtures at 3130 Å and Room Temperature

[O$_2$] (torr)	Exposure Time (min)	Φ {CO}	Φ {OCS}	Φ {SO$_2$}	10^5 Φ {P} (absorbance/μ)	$\dfrac{\Phi\{CO\}}{\Phi\{OCS\}}$
[CS$_2$] = 2.0 torr, I_a = 2.0 μ/min						
740	120.0	0.054	0.069	0.100	—	0.79
[CS$_2$] = 5.0 torr, I_a = 5.0 μ/min						
1.0	240.0	—	0.0025	0.0047	—	—
2.5	120.0	0.0060	0.0055	0.0163	—	1.09
9.2	60.0	0.0166	0.0160	0.045	—	1.04
405	120.0	0.060	0.056	—	—	1.07
740	120.0	0.053	0.046	0.098	—	1.15
745	120.0	0.048	0.044	0.093	—	1.09
[CS$_2$] = 10.0 torr, I_a = 9.7 μ/min						
1.4	240.0	0.0034	0.0034	0.0068	—	0.98
4.8	90.0	0.0060	0.0078	0.0154	0.84	0.77
10.0	45.0	0.0109	0.0125	0.028	1.54	0.87
[CS$_2$] = 10.0 torr, I_a = 20.5 μ/min						
50	10.0	0.029	0.039	0.112	2.5	0.74
54	10.0	—	0.029	0.049	2.3	—
82	10.0	0.023	0.034	0.093	2.7	0.68
100	10.0	—	0.039	0.100	5.3	—
159	10.0	0.024	0.042	0.078	—	0.59
200	10.0	—	0.037	0.083	—	—
740	10.0	—	0.0195	0.024	—	—
[CS$_2$] = 20.0 torr, I_a = 2.05 μ/min						
42	90.0	—	0.021	0.029	1.45	—
100	110.0	0.033	0.035	0.086	5.3	0.94
200	90.0	0.021	0.036	0.058	1.47	0.60
[CS$_2$] = 20 torr, I_a = 38 μ/min						
2.0*	120.0	0.00119	0.00113	0.0025	—	1.05
10	10.0	—	—	—	1.21	—
40	10.0	0.0081	0.0135	0.029	—	0.60
46	10.0	0.0081	0.0170	0.051	1.41	0.48
100	10.0	0.0184	0.032	0.096	2.9	0.57
100	10.0	—	0.028	0.068	—	—

200	10.0	0.021	0.032	0.088	2.2	0.66
400	10.0	0.025	0.026	0.071	3.2	0.95
600	10.0	0.0137	0.022	0.055	6.8	0.63
$[CS_2] = 40$ torr, $I_a = 6.0$ μ/min						
90	60.0	0.024	0.024	0.065	2.7	1.00
200	45.0	0.026	0.033	0.052	3.3	0.78
300	60.0	0.0153	0.024	0.050	2.9	0.65
400	45.0	0.021	0.033	0.072	1.92	0.62
720	60.0	0.0153	0.024	0.050	2.9	0.65
$[CS_2] = 40$ torr, $I_a = 70$ μ/min						
20	10.0	—	0.0057	0.0107	1.26	—
80	10.0	0.0192	0.0143	0.033	1.52	—
209	10.0	—	0.021	0.043	2.2	0.92
410	10.0	—	0.021	0.049	3.8	—
770	10.0	0.0179	0.0192	0.047	2.8	0.93
$[CS_2] = 70$ torr, $I_a = 11$ μ/min						
30	520.0	0.0039	0.0043	0.0113	0.25	0.92
40	60.0	0.0030	0.0043	0.0093	0.68	0.70
70	100.0	0.0059	0.0057	0.0152	—	1.05
140	60.0	0.0086	0.0121	0.031	1.06	0.71
140	100.0	0.0080	0.0099	0.024	0.94	0.81
350	60.0	0.0100	0.0192	0.033	1.44	0.52
350	100.0	0.0144	0.0167	0.045	1.85	0.87
700	60.0	—	0.0161	0.046	2.1	—
$[CS_2] = 70$ torr, $I_a = 111$ μ/min						
1.2	213.0	0.00034	0.00040	0.00030	0.022	0.84
3.0	150.0	0.00042	0.00054	0.00048	0.044	0.78
6.0	60.0	0.00083	0.00075	0.0014	0.072	1.10
10.0	25.0	0.0022	0.0022	0.0052	0.187	1.00
20	30.0	0.0032	0.0033	0.0066	0.22	0.96
33	15.0	0.0048	0.0057	0.0138	0.44	0.84
70	10.0	—	0.0075	0.0197	—	—
70	25.0	0.0070	0.0076	0.0178	0.85	0.93
141	10.0	0.0112	0.0136	0.0314	2.1	0.82
350	10.0	0.0162	0.0195	0.050	2.6	0.83

* $I_a = 28$ μ/min.

$$\Phi\{SO_2\} = \Phi\{OCS\} + 2\Phi\{CO\} \tag{I}$$

Since $\Phi\{CO\}/\Phi\{OCS\} = 0.83$, then $\Phi\{SO_2\} = 2.66\ \Phi\{OCS\}$. Within the experimental uncertainty, this relationship is obeyed; the polymer C-S ratio must be similar to that of CS_2 itself.

Discussion

The initial steps in the photolysis of CS_2 have been shown to be *(10,11)*

$$CS_2 + h\nu \rightarrow CS_2{}^* \tag{1}$$

$$CS_2{}^* + CS_2 \rightarrow 2CS + S_2 \tag{2a}$$

$$\rightarrow 2CS_2 \tag{2b}$$

where the asterisk denotes electronic excitation. The excited electronic state is quenched by oxygen *(11)*. If nonchemical quenching were the only step, then the oxidation would ultimately diminish as O_2 completely quenched $CS_2{}^*$, contrary to our results. Furthermore, polymer production is also enhanced, and the polymer has the same C-S ratio as CS_2. Thus we add the steps

$$CS_2{}^* + O_2 \rightarrow CS_2 + O_2 \tag{3a}$$

$$\rightarrow CS + SO_2 \tag{3b}$$

$$\rightarrow \text{polymer} \tag{3c}$$

The precursor to SO_2 formation may be the unstable species SOO as proposed by de Sorgo *et al. (11)*. Myerson *et al. (3)* believed that this species was responsible for the transient absorption they observed prior to SO_2 formation in the explosive oxidation of CS_2.

The invariance of the ratio $\Phi\{CO\}/\Phi\{OCS\}$ with all our experimental parameters suggests that CO and OCS are produced in parallel processes. We suggest the oxidation of CS:

$$CS + O_2 \rightarrow OCS + O \tag{4a}$$

$$\rightarrow CO + SO \tag{4b}$$

That CS can be oxidized under our conditions conflicts with at least three earlier studies *(4,5,11,12)*; this discrepancy will be discussed later.

The steps necessary to complete the mechanism are

$$SO + O_2 \rightleftharpoons OSOO \tag{5}$$

$$CS \overset{wall}{\rightarrow} polymer \tag{6}$$

$$O + CS_2 \rightarrow CS + SO \tag{7}$$

$$OSOO + SO \rightarrow 2SO_2 \tag{8}$$

Reaction step 5 has been discussed by Myerson *et al. (3)*, who even suggested SOOO as a possibility. In our system it must be followed by reaction 8 or a comparable step if SO_3 is not a product. In our system there is no evidence for reaction 6, as will be shown. However, since others *(5)* have included it, and since it must occur at sufficiently low $[O_2]$, we have included it for generality. Reaction 7 has now been firmly established *(13)*, and alternate product possibilities need not be considered. Another step which could be included without changing the mechanistic conclusions is

$$SO + O_2 \rightarrow SO_2 + O$$

This reaction proceeds with an activation energy and has been measured at higher temperatures *(14,15)*. However, there is no compelling evidence from our results to include this step, so it has been omitted for simplicity.

The above mechanism predicts that

$$\Phi\{CO\}/\Phi\{OCS\} = k_{4b}/k_{4a} \tag{II}$$

The results show that $\Phi\{CO\}/\Phi\{OCS\}$ is invariant to all changes in experimental parameters, and k_{4b}/k_{4a} is found to be 0.83 ± 0.15 based on 44 experiments. Another prediction is that at low $[O_2]/[CS_2]$, where CS is produced primarily by reaction 2a,

$$\Phi\{SO_2\} = \Phi\{OCS\} + \Phi\{CO\} = 1.83\Phi\{OCS\} \tag{III}$$

On the other hand, at high $[O_2]/[CS_2]$, where CS is produced primarily by reaction 3b, equation I should hold. The results in Fig. 1 indicate that reaction 3b is the primary source of CS for $[O_2]/[CS_2] \geqslant 0.3$. There is no clear indication that equation III ever applies.

Another prediction of the mechanism is

$$\Phi\{OCS\} = \frac{k_{4a}[O_2]}{(k_{4b}[O_2] + k_6)} \frac{(2k_{2a}[CS_2] + k_{3b}[O_2])}{(k_2[CS_2] + k_3[O_2])} \tag{IV}$$

where $k_2 \equiv k_{2a} + k_{2b}$ and $k_3 \equiv k_{3a} + k_{3b} + k_{3c}$. In Fig. 2, $\Phi\{OCS\}$ is plotted against $[O_2]/[CS_2]$. The log-log plot initially rises, reaches unit slope, and then levels off at $\Phi\{OCS\} = 0.050$ at high $[O_2]/[CS_2]$. The surprising feature is the invariance of $\Phi\{OCS\}$ to $[CS_2]$ for a given $[O_2]/[CS_2]$. This result can be consistent with equation IV only if reaction 6 is negligible under all conditions. Furthermore, if reaction 6 is omitted, then equation IV requires the $\Phi\{OCS\}$ to reach some lower limit equal to $2k_{2a}k_{4a}/k_2k_{4b}$. This value is just being approached at our lowest values of $[O_2]/[CS_2]$ and is about 2×10^{-4}. The linear portion of the curve

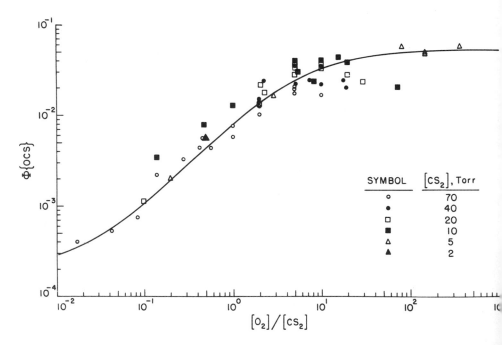

Fig. 2. Plot of $\Phi\{OCS\}$ versus $[O_2]/[CS_2]$ in the photolysis of CS$_2$-O$_2$ mixtures at 3130 Å and room temperature.

gives $k_{3b}k_{4a}/k_2k_{4b}$ = 0.90 × 10^{-2}, whereas the upper limit gives $k_{3b}k_{4a}/k_3k_{4b}$ = 0.050. The theoretical curve based on these values is shown by the solid line in Fig. 2. The appropriate rate constant ratios are listed in Table II. Our value of 0.18 for k_3/k_2 agrees reasonably well with the value of 0.13 obtained by de Sorgo *et al. (11)*.

Table II

Summary of Rate Constant Data

Rate Constant	Value	Units	Source
k_{4b}/k_{4a}	0.83 ± 0.15	None	Equation II
k_{2a}/k_2	0.8 × 10^{-4}	None	Equation IV, Fig. 2
k_{3b}/k_3	0.042	None	Equation IV, Fig. 2
k_{3b}/k_3	0.062	None	Equation IV, Fig. 2 + reaction 10
k_3/k_2	0.18	None	Equation IV, Fig. 2
k_3/k_2	0.17	None	Equation V, Fig. 3
k_3/k_2	0.12	None	Equation IV, Fig. 2 + reaction 10
k_3/k_2	0.13	None	de Sorgo *et al. (11)*
k_{3c}/k_3	~0.027	None	See text
k_5^2/k_{11}	3.9 × 10^{-4}	$1\,mole^{-1}\,sec^{-1}$	Fig. 1
k_5^2/k_{11}	~0.5	$1\,mole^{-1}\,sec^{-1}$	O + OCS [‡]
k_{17}/k_{15}	~5 × 10^3	$1\,mole^{-1}$	Equation XIII [*]
k_{17}/k_{15}	1.7 × 10^3	$1\,mole^{-1}$	Cohen and Heicklen *(13)* [†]
k_{11}	<10^3	$1\,mole^{-1}\,sec^{-1}$	O + OCS [¶]
k_{11}	<4 × 10^6	$1\,mole^{-1}\,sec^{-1}$	Halstead and Thrush *(16)*
k_{11}	~2.3 × 10^6	$1\,mole^{-1}\,sec^{-1}$	k_5 plus k_5^2/k_{11} [¶]
k_5	~30	$1\,mole^{-1}\,sec^{-1}$	O + OCS + O_2 [¶]
k'	1.83	Min^{-1}	Fig. 5
$(k_{24b} + k_{24c})$	0.180	None	O_3 + CS_2
k_{24d}/k_{24e}	0.095/0.040		

*N_2O as a chaperone.
†SO_2 as a chaperone.
‡Second mechanism.
¶First mechanism.

With reaction 6 omitted, and S_2 absorption assumed negligible, the quantum yield of polymer formation $\Phi\{P\}$ is given by

$$\Phi\{P\} = k_{3c}[O_2]/(k_3[CS_2] + k_3[O_2]) \qquad (V)$$

Figure 3 is a plot of $\Phi\{P\}$ versus $[O_2]/[CS_2]$. At low values of $[O_2]/[CS_2]$ the log-log plot has unit slope, giving a relative value of $k_{3c}/k_2 = 1.0 \times 10^{-5}$. If we take the upper limit of $\Phi\{P\} = 6.0 \times 10^{-5}$, then this value corresponds to the relative ratio for k_{3c}/k_3. The resulting value for k_3/k_2 becomes 0.17, in good agreement with the result deduced from equation IV and Fig. 2. The theoretical curve based on the above relative rate constants is shown in Fig. 3, and it adequately represents the data points. A run was done with 80 torr of CS_2 at an intensity of about 120 μ/min in the absence of O_2. Polymer absorption corresponding to $\Phi\{P\} = 0.035 \times 10^{-5}$ was observed after 17 hours of exposure. This value is slightly higher than that found at our lowest ratios of $[O_2]/[CS_2]$, and corresponds to CS and S_2 deposition rather than polymer formation via reaction 3c. If the extinction coefficients of the polymers formed by the two processes

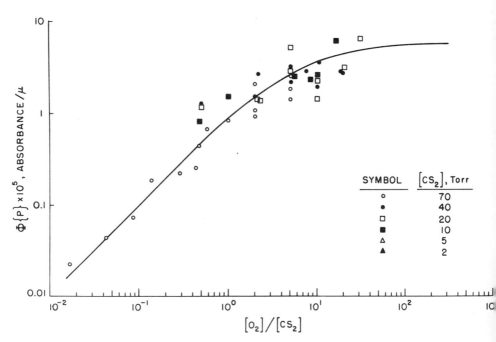

Fig. 3. Plot of relative quantum yield of polymer formation versus $[O_2]/[CS_2]$ in the photolysis of CS_2-O_2 mixtures at 3130 Å and room temperature.

are the same, then the absolute value k_{3c}/k_3 = 0.027. Furthermore, since $\Phi\{P\}$ is lower at $[O_2]/[CS_2]$ = 0.017 than in the absence of O_2, at least some of the CS must have been scavenged by O_2.

A final piece of evidence in support of the mechanism comes from the work of de Sorgo *et al. (11)* on the flash photolysis of CS_2. In the absence of O_2, the spectrum of S_2 was observed, but it was completely suppressed in the presence of O_2.

A reexamination of Fig. 1 suggests that other reactions might play some role at very high or very low $[O_2]/[CS_2]$. For example, at very high $[O_2]/[CS_2]$, the ratio $\Phi\{SO_2\}/\Phi\{OCS\}$ may be reduced. This would be expected if the SO were removed sufficiently rapidly by O_2 so that it could not react with OSOO, which would then rearrange to SO_3:

$$OSOO \rightarrow SO_3 \tag{9}$$

Under the conditions at which our experiments were performed, the SO_3 would have been too small for us to detect. The ratio $\Phi\{SO_2\}/\Phi\{OCS\}$ should drop, which is compatible with our findings.

Furthermore, at very high $[O_2]/[CS_2]$ the ozone-producing reaction could be important:

$$O + 2O_2 \rightarrow O_3 + O_2 \tag{10}$$

The rate constant k_{10} = 2.5 $\times$ 10^8 ℓ^2 mole^{-2} sec^{-1} *(17)*, whereas that for reaction 7 is 2.5 $\times$ 10^9 ℓ mole^{-1} sec^{-1} *(18-20)*. Thus at our highest value of $[O_2]/[CS_2]$, reaction 10 consumes 58% of the oxygen atoms. Of course, if the O_3 produced reacts with CS_2 to produce CS and SO, there is no net difference in the two reactions. However, if the O_3 does not further react, then reaction 10 would reduce $\Phi\{OCS\}$ by one-third; the value of k_3/k_2 would drop to 0.12, in even better agreement with de Sorgo *et al. (11)*, while k_{3b}/k_3 would become 0.062.

At the lowest values of $[O_2]/[CS_2]$, $\Phi\{SO_2\}/\Phi\{OCS\}$ is markedly reduced, which indicates that not all the SO species are oxidized. The indicated competing overall reaction is *(21)*

$$3SO \rightarrow SO_2 + S_2O$$

The S_2O produced would have been below our detection limits. The reaction is a composite reaction which presumably proceeds via the second-order step

$$2SO \rightarrow products \tag{11}$$

The details of this reaction have not been ascertained, but SO_2 and S_2O are produced *(13,21)*, presumably in equal amounts; the ratio $\Phi\{SO_2\}/\Phi\{OCS\}$ would drop to one-third its value at higher O_2 pressures, in conformance with the results indicated in Fig. 1. These results suggest that reactions 5 and 11 are of equal importance when $I_a = 111$ μ/min, $[O_2] \sim 5.6$ torr, and $[CS_2] = 70$ torr. The ratio k_5^2/k_{11} is estimated to be 3.9×10^{-4} ℓ mole^{-1} sec^{-1}. Reaction 11 could also be the route to SO_2 production if the initially formed SO dimer reacted with O_2. Thus reactions 5 and 8 might not be needed.

The above mechanism explains all our observations. Nevertheless, all investigations from other laboratories have concluded that CS does not react with O_2, even at elevated temperatures *(13)*. Thus we must consider other possible mechanisms. Apparently, the only other mechanism which produces a constant ratio of OCS and CO without oxidizing CS includes the additional steps

$$CS_2{}^* + O_2 \rightarrow OCS + SO \tag{3d}$$

$$SO + CS \rightarrow CO + S_2 \tag{12}$$

This mechanism will give a constant value for $\Phi\{OCS\}/\Phi\{CO\}$ under all conditions if the SO undergoes no other reactions. Thus the mechanism would consist of reactions 1, 2a, 2b, 3a-3d, 6, and 12. This mechanism predicts that

$$\Phi\{OCS\}/\Phi\{CO\} = 1.0 \tag{VI}$$

and

$$\Phi\{SO_2\}/\Phi\{OCS\} = k_{3b}/k_{3d} > 1.0 \tag{VII}$$

Equation VI might be consistent with our results. For most of our conditions, equation VII is obeyed, but it fails to explain the low values obtained for $\Phi\{SO_2\}/\Phi\{OCS\}$ at low $[O_2]/[CS_2]$. However, this mechanism also predicts that the steady-state pressures of both CS and S_2 should be markedly greater in the presence of O_2 than in its absence. Both predictions are contrary to the findings of de Sorgo *et al.* *(11)*, who observed not much change in [CS] and complete quenching of $[S_2]$ when O_2 was present.

Therefore we discard this mechanism.

The question still remains concerning CS oxidation. Two earlier studies of the low-intensity photooxidation of CS_2 with energy above 2300 Å (where no photodissociation occurs) were reported by Thompson and Kearton *(22)* and de Sorgo *et al. (11)*. In neither study was OCS found, but this can be attributed to insufficient analytical sensitivity for the low quantum yields produced. However, de Sorgo *et al. (11)* monitored [CS] in the flash photolysis and found that it was only slightly different in the absence or presence of O_2, even at large O_2 pressures (90 torr of O_2, 22 torr of CS_2, and 280 torr of N_2). From this they concluded that CS does not react with O_2. Nevertheless, this result can be consistent with our mechanism. In the absence of O_2, the steady-state pressure of CS is given by

$$[CS] = 2k_{2a} I_a/k_2 k_6 \qquad \text{(VIII)}$$

while under their conditions with O_2 present, our rate constant ratios give

$$[CS] \sim \frac{k_{3b}}{k_{4b}} \frac{I_a}{(k_2 [CS_2] + k_{13}[N_2])} \qquad \text{(IX)}$$

where reaction 13 is

$$CS_2{}^* + N_2 \rightarrow CS_2 + N_2 \qquad \text{(13)}$$

Consequently [CS] is nearly independent of $[O_2]$ and would be similar in the absence and presence of O_2 if $2k_{2a}/k_2 k_6 \sim k_{3b}/k_{4b}(k_2 [CS_2] + k_{13}[N_2])$.

The flash photolysis of CS_2 was examined by Wright *(5)* both in the absence of O_2 and in the presence of 0.2 and 5 torr of O_2. He also monitored [CS] and found that [CS] decreased as $[O_2]$ increased, but that the rate of CS disappearance was independent of O_2. The latter result led him to conclude also that CS did not react with O_2. In fact, his observation can also be consistent with our mechanism for appropriate CS_2 pressures. Unfortunately, he did not list the pressure of either CS_2 or the diluent gas. However, reasonable values of these parameters do exist such that our mechanism predicts [CS] varying inversely with $[O_2]$, in which case $d[CS]/dt$ is independent of $[O_2]$, if CS is removed only by reaction 4.

Kondrat'ev and his co-workers *(4,12)* also report that CS does not react with O_2 at temperatures below 100°C. This conclusion is particularly surprising from the results of Kondrat'ev and Yakovleva *(4)*, who photolyzed CS_2 with effective radiation essentially at 2000Å where the primary process is

$$CS_2 + h\nu \,(< 2300 \text{ Å}) \rightarrow CS + S(^1D) \tag{14}$$

They found OCS as a principal product of the photooxidation. Furthermore, they monitored the CS absorption bands and found that they were completely suppressed in the presence of O_2.

Finally, Wiebe and Heicklen *(6)* found both OCS and CO in the photooxidation of thiophene, where the only reasonable precursor could have been CS, though it might have been excited.

Reaction of O(^{3}P) with OCS

In order to further examine the reactions of SO, it was generated from the reaction

$$O(^3P) + OCS \;\rightarrow\; CO + SO \tag{15}$$

The oxygen atoms were prepared from the mercury-sensitized photodecomposition of N_2O in the presence of OCS. The ratio $[N_2O]/[OCS]$ was kept above 6.6 and usually above 34 so that essentially all the Hg $6(^3P_1)$ atoms were scavenged by N_2O which is 0.64 as efficient as OCS *(23)*. Thus, for all but one run, less than 5% of the Hg $6(^3P_1)$ was quenched by OCS, and this step can be neglected.

Both CO and N_2 were measured; the results are tabulated in Table III. The OCS pressure was varied from 1.18 to 52 torr, the N_2O pressure from 100 to 481 torr, the absorbed intensity by a factor of 156, and the extent of conversion by a factor of 12.9. In addition to the gaseous products, a solid was deposited on the windows. However, all runs reported in Table III were sufficiently short so that the absorbed intensity dropped by less than 10% as verified by actinometer runs before and after. Furthermore the rate of N_2 production, $R\{N_2\}$, was the same for the OCS-N_2O mixtures as for the N_2O-C_2F_4 actinometer runs. Consequently, the N_2 produced in the OCS-N_2O runs serves as an internal actinometer. SO_2 was also a product of the reaction, but O_2 was not.

For all the runs but the last one, the $[CO]/[N_2]$ ratio was about 0.39; most of the oxygen atoms do not react with CO. The indicated mechanism is reaction 15 followed by

$$O + SO + N_2O \rightarrow SO_2 + N_2O \tag{16}$$

$$O + SO_2 + N_2O \rightarrow SO_3 + N_2O \tag{17}$$

$$SO_3 + Hg \rightarrow \text{solid} \tag{18}$$

Table III

Mercury-Sensitized Photolysis of N_2O in the Presence of OCS
at Room Temperature

[OCS] (torr)	[N$_2$O] (torr)	R {N$_2$} (μ/min)	Total N$_2$ Produced (μ)	[CO] / [N$_2$]	k_{17}/k_{15} (ℓ mole^{-1})
1.18	100	62	154	0.39	7.2×10^3
1.48	122	70	174	0.39	7.0×10^3
2.17	330	33	410	0.42	0.8×10^3
3.35	439	0.63	132	0.40	5.0×10^3
3.70	344	0.90	237	0.36	10.2×10^3
3.74	257	0.79	71	0.40	15.1×10^3
5.30	324	92	915	0.39	1.70×10^3
5.40	444	5.2	311	0.39	3.6×10^3
5.75	481	4.5	270	0.39*	4.2×10^3
10.3	343	86	215	0.39	13.0×10^3
52	342	62	156	0.55	–

*$[SO_2]/[N_2]$ = 0.195; O_2 not produced.

The mechanism predicts that after the termination of exposure, when [SO] is negligible, then

$$[SO_2]/[N_2] = 3[CO]/[N_2] - 1 \qquad (X)$$

For the one run in which the SO_2 yield was measured, the value predicted for $[SO_2]/[N_2]$ from equation X is ~ 0.17, in good agreement with the measured value of 0.195.

If SO reaches a steady state, then

$$[SO]/[OCS] = k_{15}/k_{16}[N_2O] \qquad (XI)$$

The mean value reported *(13)* for k_{15} is 7×10^6 ℓ mole^{-1} sec^{-1}. Halstead and Thrush *(16)* found $k_{16} = 3.2 \times 10^{11}$ ℓ^2 mole^{-2} sec^{-1}, presumably with SO_2 as the chaperone; a similar value should apply with N_2O as a chaperone. Thus the steady-state value of [SO] is less than 3 μ in all but the last experiment in Table III. This is very much less than the N_2 produced, so the steady-state assumption on SO is valid.

Utilizing the steady-state approximation on SO leads to the result

$$\frac{d[SO_2]}{dt} = \frac{(k_{15}[OCS] - k_{17}[SO_2][N_2O])R\ \{N_2\}}{2k_{15}[OCS] + k_{17}[SO_2][N_2O]} \tag{XII}$$

Integrating this expression, incorporation equation X, and rearranging leads to

$$\frac{k_{17}}{k_{15}} = \frac{[OCS]}{[N_2O](3[CO] - [N_2])}\left(1 - \exp\left\{\frac{-k_{17}[CO][N_2O]}{k_{15}[OCS]}\right\}\right) \tag{XIII}$$

This transcendental equation can be solved for k_{17}/k_{15}; the results are listed in Table III. The values range from $(0.8-15.1) \times 10^3$ ℓ mole^{-1}, which is almost a 20-fold variation. However, this large discrepancy is within the experimental uncertainty of the product yields measurement, because the results are extremely sensitive to small changes in $[CO]/[N_2]$. For example, the experiment which yielded 0.8×10^3 would have given 1.9×10^3 if $[CO]/[N_2]$ were 0.38 instead of 0.42, and the experiment which yielded 15.1×10^3 would have given 6.0×10^3 if $[CO]/[N_2]$ were 0.44 instead of 0.40. Thus our determination of k_{17}/k_{15} is quite crude but gives a value of $\sim 5 \times 10^3$ ℓ mole^{-1}. Values for k_{17} have been reported by others *(13)* with different chaperone gases. With SO$_2$, the only triatomic chaperone gas used, the average value for k_{17} is 1.2×10^3 ℓ^2 mole^{-2} sec^{-1}, which gives $k_{17}/k_{15} = 1.7 \times 10^3$ ℓ mole^{-1}. Our results suggest a slightly higher value for N$_2$O as a chaperone.

Our results indicate that reaction 11 is unimportant compared to reaction 16, if the above mechanism is correct. Thus we can compute an upper limit for $k_{11} < 10^3$ ℓ mole^{-1} sec^{-1}, which is considerably less than the previous upper limit of 4×10^6 ℓ mole^{-1} sec^{-1} reported by Halstead and Thrush *(16)*.

In order to study the reaction of SO with O$_2$, some experiments were done with O$_2$ present. The results are given in Table IV. The addition of 0.5 to 1 torr of O$_2$ noticeably raised both the CO and SO$_2$ yields, but further increases in the O$_2$ pressure then reduced the yields. The indicated reactions in addition to 15 through 18 are reactions 5, 8, and 10. With 0.5 to 1 torr of O$_2$, 470 torr of N$_2$O, and 5 torr of OCS, reaction 10 is only 10 to 20% as effective as OCS in consuming oxygen atoms and can be neglected. Then, since $[CO]/[N_2O]$ is approximately doubled from that in the absence of O$_2$, reaction 5 is about as efficient as reaction 16 in removing SO, and k_5 can be estimated to be ~ 30 ℓ mole^{-1} sec^{-1}.

With the value of k_5 estimated above and $k_5{}^2/k_{11} \sim 3.9 \times 10^{-4}$ ℓ mole^{-1} sec^{-1} estimated from Fig. 1, k_{11} becomes $\sim 2.3 \times 10^6$ ℓ mole^{-1} sec^{-1}, which is more than three orders of magnitude larger than the upper limit

Table IV

Mercury-Sensitized Photolysis of N_2O in Presence of OCS and O_2 at Room Temperature[a]

$[O_2]$ (torr)	[OCS] (torr)	$R \{N_2\}$ (μ/min)	Total N_2 Produced (μ)	$\dfrac{[CO]}{[N_2]}$	$\dfrac{[SO_2]}{[N_2]}$
0.510	6.04	4.38	263	0.60[b]	0.36
0.625	6.9	0.67	480	0.64	0.38
0.974	4.78	2.89	173	0.60	0.37
2.70	4.83	6.53	196	0.49	0.33
4.65	6.02	1.30	215	0.48	0.29

[a] $[N_2O] \sim 470 \pm 20$ torr.
[b] CO_2 not produced.

of 10^3 ℓ mole^{-1} sec^{-1}. Perhaps this discrepancy can be attributed to wall removal of SO in the photooxidation of CS_2. With $[CS_2] = 70$ torr and $[O_2] = 1.0$ torr, the lifetime of SO is ~ 700 sec. From the method of Hudson and Heicklen *(24)* we estimate that wall removal of SO could account for the SO loss if one in 10^6 collisions were effective.

Nevertheless the discrepancy between the two results for k_5 from the two systems is alarming. There is another mechanism in the O + OCS system which can also explain the results. Reaction 16 can be replaced by

$$2SO \rightarrow S_2O_2 \tag{11}$$

which is followed either by

$$O + S_2O_2 \rightarrow SO + SO_2 \tag{19}$$

or by

$$S_2O_2 + SO_2 \rightarrow S_2O + SO_2 + O \tag{20}$$

$$O + S_2O \rightarrow 2SO \tag{21}$$

The sequence of reactions 11 and 19 or 20 and 21 is kinetically indistinguishable from reaction 16 if the rate constants for the reactions are sufficiently fast so that the steady-state approximation applies to each of the intermediates. For the oxygen atom reactions this would require rate constants in excess of about 5×10^9 ℓ mole^{-1} sec^{-1}.

The results in the O + OCS + O_2 system would then be interpreted as a competition between reactions 5 and 11. For the first three experiments in Table IV, the two reactions are approximately equal in rate, and k_5^2/k_{11} can be estimated to be ~0.5 ℓ mole^{-1} sec^{-1}. Unfortunately, this result is also about a factor 10^3 different from that found from the photooxidation of CS_2; the fate of SO is not clear.

Reaction of O_3 with CS_2

When CS_2 was added to the reaction cell containing O_3, the O_3 rapidly disappeared. The rate of disappearance was at least 100 times as fast as that due to the slow heterogeneous decay of pure O_3, which was too slow to measure. A typical plot of the reciprocal O_3 absorbance at 2537 Å versus reaction time is shown in Fig. 4. The monitoring light source was weak,

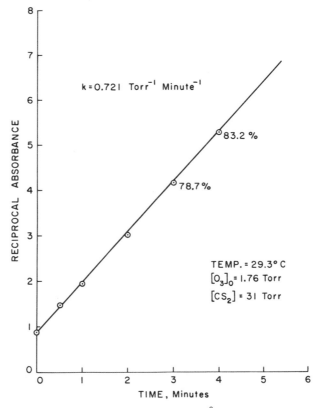

Fig. 4. Plot of reciprocal absorbance of O_3 at 2537 Å versus reaction time for an initial mixture of 1.76 torr O_3 and 31 torr CS_2 at 29.3°C. The numbers next to the data points indicate percent O_3 decomposed.

and separate experiments were done with the lamp off for the first few minutes of the reaction or with intermittent light. The results were the same in all cases, thus eliminating the possibility of a photoinduced decomposition.

The results in Fig. 4 clearly demonstrate that the decay is second-order in $[O_3]$, at least to 83% decomposition. Every experiment gave a second-order plot over the whole measurable range (at least 80% O_3 decomposition). The second-order rate constants, k, are listed in Table V for experiments with O_3 pressures between 0.147 and 4.0 torr and CS_2 pressures between 4.8 and 83 torr. The CS_2 was always in excess, the $[CS_2]/[O_3]_0$ ratio varying between 3.0 and 544, where $[O_3]_0$ is the initial O_3 pressure. Since the CS_2 is always in excess, its pressure may be considered constant throughout the experiment. The values obtained for k in the various experiments varied between 0.44 and 9.5 $torr^{-1}$ min^{-1}. They are plotted versus $[O_3]_0$ in Fig. 5. Except for three points, the data are well fitted

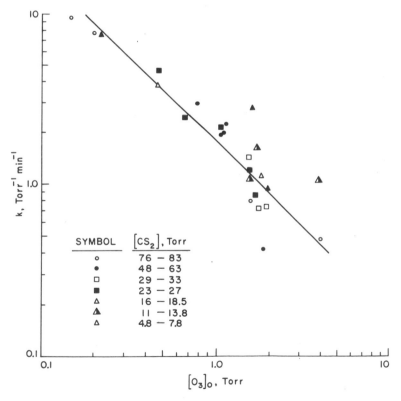

Fig. 5. Plot of the second-order rate constant, k, versus the initial O_3 pressure in the O_3-CS_2 reaction at room temperature.

Table V

Reaction of CS$_2$ with O$_3$

$[O_3]_0$ (torr)	$[CS_2]$ (torr)	Temperature (°C)	k^{-1} (torr min^{-1})	$\dfrac{[O_2]}{[O_3]_0}$	$\dfrac{[CO]}{[O_3]_0}$	$\dfrac{[CO_2]}{[O_3]_0}$	$\dfrac{[OCS]}{[O_3]_0}$	$\dfrac{[SO_2]}{[O_2]_0}$	$\dfrac{[P]/[O_3]_0}{\text{(absorbance/torr)}}$	$\dfrac{[OCS]+2[CO]+2[CO_2]}{[SO_2]}$	$\dfrac{\Sigma[O]}{3[O_3]_0}$
0.147	80	26	9.5	0.64	0.068	0.053	0.225	0.419	0.054	1.12	0.96
0.202	6.9	27.4	7.6	0.76	0.086	0.064	0.204	0.394	0.030	1.14	0.87
0.200	76	26	7.7	–	–	–	–	–	–	–	–
0.460	18.5	33.7	3.77	0.612	–	0.063	0.154	0.359	0.0065	–	–
0.480	26	32.8	4.65[a]	0.761	0.098	0.046	0.179	0.396	0.0083	1.19	0.89
0.666	23	28.8	2.45	0.806	0.114	–	0.189	0.410	0.015	–	–
0.772	51.7	34.1	2.95	–	–	–	0.165	0.456	0.0026	–	–
1.05	48	24.2	1.96	0.894	0.100	0.043	0.203	0.331	0.0057	1.46	0.87
1.06	23	30.6	2.16	0.895	0.118	0.038	0.178	0.440	0.021	1.10	0.985
1.08	60.4	36.6	1.97	0.794	0.106	0.034	0.160	0.343	0.013	1.28	0.865
1.12	56	24.7	2.24	0.728	0.080	0.045	0.223	–	0.0045	–	–
1.52	26.2	30.8	1.20	0.829	0.114	–	0.156	0.408	0.018	–	–
1.55	77.7	29.1	0.794	0.749	0.093	0.019	0.165	0.370	0.013	1.05	0.845
1.59	4.8	28.0	2.78	0.835	0.096	0.033	0.164	0.390	0.011	1.08	0.925
1.76	31	29.3	0.721	0.920	0.105	0.026	0.170	0.392	0.011	1.11	0.985
1.85	63	28.2	0.435	0.682	0.081	0.031	0.195	0.459	0.011	0.92	0.74
1.93	33	31.8	0.73	0.748	0.079	–	–	0.453	0.0093	–	–
1.97	7.8	26.5	0.93	0.910	0.085	0.043	0.169	0.434	0.0076	0.98	0.98
3.94	13.8	~26	1.04	–	–	0.024	0.167	0.371	0.0066	–	–
3.97	83	–	0.48	0.808	0.092	0.033	0.182	0.447	0.0073	0.965	0.945
				$\overline{0.787}\pm$ 0.072	$\overline{0.095}\pm$ 0.012	$\overline{0.040}\pm$ 0.011	$\overline{0.180}\pm$ 0.017	$\overline{0.404}\pm$ 0.031		$\overline{1.139}$	$\overline{0.912}$

[a]Monitoring light off until reaction ~70% complete.

by a line of negative unit slope. We have no explanation for the one low point. However, the two points that lie well above the line correspond to the experiments with the lowest $[CS_2]/[O_3]_0$ and are apparently real. The other points correspond to $[CS_2]/[O_3]_0$ in excess of 4.0 and lead to the surprising result that k is independent of $[CS_2]$ in this regime. The rate law which describes the results is

$$-d[O_3]/dt = k'[O_3]^2/[O_3]_0 \tag{XIV}$$

where k' is a constant independent of $[CS_2]$, $[O_3]_0$, or $[O_3]$. The intercept of the log-log plot gives $k' = 1.83$ min^{-1}.

After the O_3 was consumed, the products of the reaction were measured. The absorption never returned to zero, and a polymer was deposited on the cell wall. The polymer was measured from the residual absorption after the gases were removed. The gaseous products of the reaction were O_2, CO, CO_2, OCS, and SO_2. We looked for, but did not find, S_2O or significant amounts of SO_3. Several careful attempts were made to find SO_3, but to no avail. Certainly neither S_2O nor SO_3 is a major product, but minor amounts of either one might have been produced. The results of the analyses, normalized to $[O_3]_0$, are reported for the various experiments in Table V. The order of importance of the products is O_2, SO_2, OCS, CO, and CO_2. Within the experimental uncertainty, the relative amounts of the gaseous products remained the same for all the experiments; their average values and mean deviations are listed in the table. The experimental uncertainty in the polymer analysis is so large that it is difficult to make a judgment.

If the five gaseous products were the sole products, then mass balance requirements for carbon-sulfur and oxygen would lead to the respective expressions

$$[SO_2] = [OCS] + 2[CO] + 2[CO_2] \tag{XV}$$

$$3[O_3]_0 = \Sigma[O] \equiv 2[O_2] + [CO] + 2[CO_2]$$
$$+ [OCS] + 2[SO_2] \tag{XVI}$$

The ratios of the right-hand side to the left-hand side of the equations are tabulated in Table V for each experiment. The gaseous products are always deficient in oxygen and usually deficient in sulfur, though the deficiencies are not large and are within the experimental uncertainties. Consequently other products cannot be very significant. Of course, some of the deficiency could be accounted for by the polymer if it contained oxygen or had a sulfur-carbon ratio in excess of 2. The pressure of sulfur trioxide, if it is produced at all, must be $\lesssim 0.08[O_3]_0$.

In order to see if any of the products resulted from secondary reactions, some experiments were done in which the reaction mixture was removed from the reaction vessel before the O_3 was exhausted. The results are shown in Table VI. There is some indication that the polymer may be a secondary product. However, in view of the experimental uncertainties the evidence is not convincing. The ratios of the gaseous products are similar to those in Table V, and there is no evidence from these results to suggest that any of the gaseous products are secondary.

Table VI

Incomplete Reaction of CS_2 with O_3

$[O_2]_0$ (torr)	$[CS_2]$ (torr)	Temperature ($^\circ$C)	k (torr^{-1} min^{-1})	Time of Run (min)	O_3 Decomposed (%)
1.69	13	31.1	1.62	0.7	70
1.66	27	27.1	0.86	2.1	73
1.80	16	28.0	1.12	2.9	85
1.52	29	31.5	1.41	2.9	85
1.55	11	25.3	1.07	4.7	90

$\dfrac{[O_2]}{[O_3]_0}$	$\dfrac{[CO]}{[O_3]_0}$	$\dfrac{[CO_2]}{[O_3]_0}$	$\dfrac{[OCS]}{[O_3]_0}$	$\dfrac{[SO_2]}{[O_3]_0}$	$\dfrac{[P]}{[O_3]_0}$ (absorbance/torr)
–	–	–	–	–	0.0021
–	–	0.014	–	0.306	0.0036
0.784	0.089	0.031	0.165	0.382	0.0055
0.771	0.090	0.040	0.178	0.390	0.0046
0.814	0.084	0.023	0.153	0.373	0.0064

As a further check of the influence of the products on the reaction, O_3 was mixed with each gaseous product, one at a time. With O_2, CO_2, and SO_2, O_3 decay was no faster than in their absence. With $[CO]/[O_3]$ less than 5, there was also no enhancement of the decay, though at larger ratios O_3 removal can be very rapid indeed (C. Goldman, unpublished results, 1969). This reaction is currently being studied in our laboratory. With OCS added, O_3 removal appears to be somewhat enhanced, but it is still very much slower than in the presence of CS_2.

Finally, mixtures of CS_2, O_3, and each of the gaseous products were studied. The results are shown in Table VII. For none of the experiments was there any evidence that the ratio of product pressures was altered. This confirms that the products do not enter into the chemical reaction to any significant extent. Furthermore, at low initial pressure of each product gas, the constant $k' = k [O_3]_0$ was unaffected, even though more product gas was initially present than was produced in the reaction.

If larger pressures of O_2 were initially present, the rate constant, k', could be lowered, but the second-order relationship remained. An example of such a result is shown in Fig. 6. Even though 27 torr of O_2 was present, the plot is second-order in $[O_3]$ for at least 82% decomposition; yet k' is reduced from 1.83 to 0.66 min^{-1}.

At even higher pressures of added gas (60 torr of O_2, 180 torr of CO_2, or 4 to 8 torr of SO_2), the second-order plots deviate from linearity, indicating a further inhibition as the reaction progresses. An example of such a plot with 4.3 torr of SO_2 is shown in Fig. 7. Furthermore, with SO_2 present, k' seems to depend on $[CS_2]$, its value diminishing as $[SO_2]_0/[CS_2]$ increases.

The results can be summarized as follows: (1) For CS_2-O_3 mixtures with $[CS_2]/[O_3]_0 \geqslant 4$, the O_3 decays via equation XIV; (2) none of the gaseous products enters the reaction nor alters the rate law or rate constant, unless added in large excess initially. Presumably a chain mechanism is involved, but it is difficult to understand its nature. Experiments are currently being done at lower $[CS_2]/[O_3]_0$, where the rate law may be different. Also, the ratio of volume to surface area is being reduced to examine the possibility of wall effects. Nevertheless, it seems likely that both SO and CS are intermediates. If so, SO would be expected to produce SO_2 via

$$SO + O_3 \rightarrow SO_2 + O_2 \tag{22}$$

The CS species would be the precursor to the carbon compounds and could react with O_3 to initially produce a five-membered ring intermediate:

$$CS + O_3 \rightarrow \begin{array}{c} C - S \\ | \quad | \\ O \quad O \\ \diagdown \diagup \\ O \end{array} \tag{23}$$

which could then fragment in one of five ways:

Table VII

Reaction of CS_2 with O_3 in the Presence of Other Gases

$[O_3]_0$ (torr)	$[CS_2]$ (torr)	$[X]_0$ (torr)	Temperature (°C)	k, (torr^{-1} min^{-1})	$k[O_3]_0$ (min^{-1})	$\dfrac{[O_2]}{[O_3]_0}$	$\dfrac{[CO]}{[O_3]_0}$	$\dfrac{[CO_2]}{[O_3]_0}$	$\dfrac{[OCS]}{[O_3]_0}$	$\dfrac{[SO_2]}{[O_3]_0}$	$\dfrac{[P]/[O_3]_0}{\text{(absorbance/torr)}}$
						$X = O_2$					
1.11	70	10	37.8	2.9[a]	3.22	—	0.131	0.049	0.212	0.471	0.017
0.89	15	13	35.9	1.67	1.49	—	—	0.047	0.201	0.534	0.0135
1.01	56	27	31.3	0.655	0.66	—	—	0.065	0.272	0.465	0.002
0.524	41.8	52	31.0	1.29	0.68	—	0.229	0.029	—	0.668	~0.
1.26	30	~60	~30	0.55[a]	0.69[a]	—	—	0.054	0.276	0.465	0.0032
						$X = CO$					
1.46	35	1.2	26.4	1.10	1.61	0.904	—	0.027	0.171	0.416	0.015
						$X = CO_2$					
0.830	28.3	1.3	32.3	3.51	2.91	0.720	0.090	—	0.180	0.392	0.023
1.07	54.0	13	31.8	2.48	2.67	0.731	0.092	—	0.177	0.437	0.014
1.75	60.6	13	29.4	1.09	1.91	0.778	0.107	—	0.177	0.432	0.014
0.680	57.2	27	32.3	3.32	2.25	0.602	0.084	—	0.169	0.426	0.009
1.12	38	180	32.4	1.99[a]	2.41	0.965	0.113	—	—	0.425	0.0035
						$X = OCS$					
1.39	34.8	~0.40	27.1	1.19	1.66	0.827	0.109	—	—	0.424	0.0165
1.31	28	2.1	27.4	1.33	1.74	0.908	0.103	0.029	—	0.390	0.014
1.35	28.5	4.0	26.1	1.52	2.05	0.845	0.097	0.040	—	0.338	0.024
1.45	28	6.2	28.8	1.02	1.48	0.855	0.107	0.026	—	0.358	0.011
						$X = SO_2$					
0.785	23	1.2	33.0	3.02	2.38	0.856	0.099	0.051	0.213	—	0.0038
1.42	25	4.3	33.8	0.74[a]	1.05	0.676	0.060	0.056	0.170	—	0.0049
0.93	75	6.4	26.1	1.45[a]	1.35	0.821	0.092	0.033	0.202	—	—
0.90	6.9	8.1	27.8	~0.2[a]	0.2	0.864	0.058	0.064	0.132	—	—
0.680	23	8.4	27.2	0.37[a]	0.25	—	—	0.100	0.188	—	0.021

[a]From initial slope of reciprocal absorbance versus time.

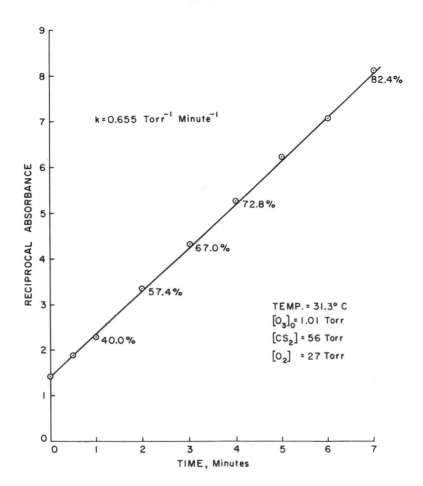

Fig. 6. Plot of reciprocal absorbance of O_3 at 2537 Å versus reaction time for an initial mixture of 1.01 torr of O_3, 56 torr of CS_2, and 27 torr of O_2 at 31.3°C. The numbers next to the data points indicate percent O_3 decomposed.

$$
\begin{array}{c}
C \!-\! S \\
| \quad | \\
O \quad O \\
\backslash \; / \\
O
\end{array}
\longrightarrow
\begin{cases}
CS + O_3 & \text{(24a)} \\
O_2 + OCS & \text{(24b)} \\
O_2 + CSO \to OCS & \text{(24c)} \\
CO + SOO \to SO_2 & \text{(24d)} \\
SO + COO \to CO_2 & \text{(24e)}
\end{cases}
$$

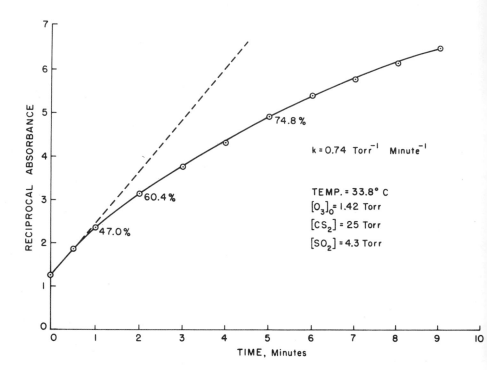

Fig. 7. Plot of reciprocal absorbance of O_3 at 2537 Å versus reaction time for an initial mixture of 1.42 torr of O_3, 25 torr of CS_2, and 4.3 torr of SO_2 at 33.8°C. The numbers next to the data points indicate percent O_3 decomposed.

Reaction 24a is the reverse of reaction 23. Both reactions 24b and 24c produce OCS, whereas reaction 24d produces CO and reaction 24e produces CO_2. Our results indicate that $(k_{24b} + k_{24c})/k_{24d}/k_{24e}$ is 0.180/0.095/0.040.

Acknowledgment

We wish to thank Dr. H. A. Wiebe for his many useful contributions.

References

1. V.N. Kondrat'ev, *Zh. Fiz. Khim.*, **13**, 1260 (1939); as reported in *Chem. Abstr.*, **35**, 354 (1941).

2. V.N. Kondrat'ev, *Zh. Fiz. Khim.*, **14**, 287 (1940); as reported in *Chem. Abstr.*, **36**, 4011⁶ (1942).
3. A.L. Myerson, F.R. Taylor, and P.L. Hanst, *J. Chem. Phys.*, **26**, 1309 (1957).
4. V.N. Kondrat'ev and A. Yakovleva, *J. Exptl. Theoret. Phys. (U.S.S.R.)*, **10**, 1038 (1940).
5. F.J. Wright, *J. Phys. Chem.*, **64**, 1648 (1960).
6. H.A. Wiebe and J. Heicklen, *Can. J. Chem.*, **47**, 2965 (1969).
7. J. Heicklen, *Advan. Photochem.*, **7**, 57 (1969).
8. R.J. Cvetanović, *Advan. Photochem.*, 1, 115 (1963).
9. R. Bent, W.R. Ladner, and W.J. Mullin, *Chem. Ind. (London)*, 461 (1967).
10. J. Heicklen, *J. Am. Chem. Soc.*, **85**, 3562 (1963).
11. M. de Sorgo, A.J. Yarwood, O.P. Strausz, and H.E. Gunning, *Can. J. Chem.*, **43**, 1886 (1965).
12. V.N. Kondrat'ev and E. Magaziner, *Zh. Fiz. Khim.*, **14**, 6 (1940); as reported in *Chem. Abstr.*, **35**, 979⁶ (1941).
13. N. Cohen and J. Heicklen, *Comprehensive Chem. Kinetics*, in press.
14. K.H. Homann, G. Krome, and H.G. Wagner, *Ber. Bunsenges. Physik. Chem.*, **72**, 998 (1968).
15. D.J. Williams, *Combus. Flame*, **12**, 165 (1968)
16. C.J. Halstead and B.A. Thrush, *Proc. Roy. Soc.*, **A295**, 363 (1966).
17. F. Kaufman and J.R. Kelso, *J. Chem. Phys.*, **40**, 1162 (1964).
18. A.B. Callear and I.W.M. Smith, *Nature*, **213**, 382 (1967).
19. I.W.M. Smith, *Trans. Faraday Soc.*, **64**, 378 (1968).
20. A.A. Westenberg and N. de Haas, *J. Chem. Phys.*, **50**, 707 (1969).
21. P.W. Schenk and R. Steudel, *Angew. Chem. Intern. Ed. Engl.*, **4**, 402 (1965).
22. H.W. Thompson and C.F. Kearton, *Z. Physik. Chem.*, **B14**, 359 (1931).
23. A.J. Yarwood, O.P. Strausz, and H.E. Gunning, *J. Chem. Phys.*, **41**, 1705 (1964).
24. J.L. Hudson and J. Heicklen, *J. Phys. Chem.*, **71**, 1518 (1967).

Discussion

J. HEICKLEN: I should like to reverse the procedure, and ask one short question. Can someone explain our ozone results?

J.G. CALVERT: How about an oxygen-atom-initiated reaction in the case of the ozone? If you add oxygen atoms to your reaction, do you get the same product distribution?

J. HEICKLEN: We have not done that and we are not sure how this could be done experimentally. When we mix ozone and CS_2, the main reaction is over in 2 or 3 minutes. There is not much time to study anything. We don't have any idea of how to get such a rate law. There may be some wall reaction, so we are going to change the surface-to-volume ratio by adding glass beads as a next step.

G. S. HAMMOND: There is an obvious class of mechanisms that handles this beautifully. Wouldn't the presence of an inhibitory impurity in the ozone explain the results?

B. WEINSTOCK: The other thing is the impurity in the CS_2 which you could test by purifying the CS_2.

J. HEICKLEN: We purified the CS_2.

J.G. CALVERT: How do you make your ozone?

J. HEICKLEN: We prepare our ozone by a Tesla coil discharge through oxygen and clean it up over liquid nitrogen.

J.G. CALVERT: What tank oxygen do you use? Is it oil-pumped or water-pumped?

J. HEICKLEN: I don't recall, but it is Matheson extra-dry-grade oxygen.

G.R.McMILLAN: The oxygen that you are using in your ozonizer, therefore, probably contains impurities.

J. HEICKLEN: Maybe that is the problem.

A. LEVY: When you say that N_2O is the third body in the O atom reaction, aren't you really competing with the N_2O-O atom reaction?

J. HEICKLEN: Yes, but the N_2O-O atom reaction is so slow that it is immeasurable under these conditions. The SO-O atom reaction is at least 10^7 times as fast.

J. G. CALVERT: What would you predict that SO does in an oxygen-rich environment?

J. HEICKLEN: What we wrote was the following:

$$SO + O_2 \rightarrow OSOO$$

$$OSOO + SO \rightarrow 2SO_2$$

which you will notice is exactly analogous to 2NO plus O_2. That is one possibility. But there are other possibilities. For example, again exactly analogous to NO:

$$2SO \rightarrow S_2O_2$$

$$S_2O_2 + O_2 \rightarrow 2SO_2$$

J. G. CALVERT: If you isolate SO in an oxygen environment, will your equilibrium eventually go to SO_3?

J. HEICKLEN: That is what we tried to do in the OCS experiments, but it did not work out too well. If we got the oxygen concentration high enough, we started getting the O atoms reacting with O_2 to give us ozone. There was a very small range within which we could work.

J.G. CALVERT: Is there any experimental measurement of that equilibrium constant?

J. HEICKLEN: No.

SESSION IV

The Photooxidation of Formaldehyde at Low Partial Pressures

J.J. Bufalini and K.L. Brubaker
National Air Pollution Control Administration
U.S. Department of Health, Education, and Welfare
Cincinnati, Ohio

Abstract

Photooxidation of formaldehyde at low partial pressures results in the production of hydrogen peroxide. The molecular imbalance between peroxide formed and formaldehyde consumed is explained by radical decomposition and surface effects. No other oxidants are produced. When formaldehyde is irradiated in the presence of nitrogen dioxide, the hydrogen peroxide yield is lowered and ozone is formed. The carbon fragments appear mostly as CO and CO_2. Little if any formic acid is produced.

Introduction

In a recent study by Purcell and Cohen *(1)*, hydrogen peroxide was found as a photooxidation product of formaldehyde. This observation contrasts with earlier work of Carruthers and Norrish *(2)*, who found formic acid, CO, CO_2, hydrogen, and a polymer. A similar study by Horner and Style *(3)* indicated that formic acid, CO, CO_2, and hydrogen were formed. Performic acid and hydrogen peroxide were not detected. The differences in results obtained by these investigators may arise from the concentrations used in the laboratory irradiations. Purcell and Cohen worked with very low concentrations, ranging from 1 to 30 ppm (v/v), whereas the earlier workers used millimeter partial pressures of formaldehyde. This difference suggests that the mechanism for the photooxidation of formaldehyde may be significantly altered at low concentrations. A similar observation was made by Altshuller and co-workers *(4)* with the photooxidation of propionaldehyde. Their results differed from those of McDowell and Sharples *(5)*, who observed peroxy acid but no hydroperoxide. Johnston and Heicklen *(6)* have shown that the mechanism of photooxidation of acetaldehyde is

References, pp. 237-238

altered at low concentrations. They observed methyl hydroperoxide at low partial pressure of acetaldehyde.

The purpose of this investigation was to extend the work of Purcell and Cohen by observing all the carbon fragments resulting from the photooxidation of formaldehyde by irradiation at two different wavelengths (3130 Å and 3660 Å) in the presence and absence of oxides of nitrogen.

Experimental Procedure

Formaldehyde in air was irradiated either in a 72-liter borosilicate flask or in 160-liter plastic bags made from fluorinated ethylene-propylene copolymer (Dupont FEP Teflon). The irradiations were carried out in a thermostatted irradiation chamber described elsewhere *(7)* at a temperature of $23° \mp 1°C$ and at ambient atmospheric pressure. The irradiation chamber was fitted with either 24 General Electric F40BLB blacklights with maximum intensity at 3600 Å or with 28 Westinghouse FS40 sunlamps with maximum intensity at about 3100 Å. The irradiation container was filled by injecting either or both nitrogen dioxide and formaldehyde solution through a rubber septum onto the inner wall of a glass tube through which a gas, usually air, was passing. The glass was then heated gently to ensure complete evaporation of the reactants.

Analysis for formaldehyde was performed by the chromotropic acid method *(8)*; nitrogen dioxide concentration was measured by the method of Saltzman *(9)*; hydrogen peroxide concentration was measured by a titanium-8-quinolinol method *(10)*; and nitrate was determined as nitrite by reduction with hydrazine in a hot alkaline solution. The nitrite was then diazotized with sulfanilamide and N(1-naphthyl)ethylenediamine dihydrochloride. Carbon monoxide and carbon dioxide were measured by gas chromatography, with a catalytic converter of the type originally developed by Schwenk *et al. (11)* to convert the carbon monoxide to methane for easy detection with a flame ionization detector.

The formaldehyde solution was Matheson, Coleman, and Bell reagent-grade 36.0 to 38.0% in water with 10 to 15% methanol added as a preservative. This solution was used without further purification. Baker dry air and prepurified nitrogen and nitrogen dioxide (Matheson, 99.5% pure) were used.

Light intensity of the irradiation chamber was determined by measuring the initial rate of disappearance of nitrogen dioxide in an inert atmosphere, as described by Tuesday *(12)*. Bufalini and Stephens *(13)* derived an expression for this rate, which involves the bimolecular rate constant, k_3, of the reaction between oxygen atoms and nitrogen dioxide, the termolecular rate constant, k_2, of the reaction of oxygen atoms with nitrogen dioxide in the presence of a third body, M, and the rate of photochemical dissociation, $k_a\phi$, of nitrogen dioxide into nitric oxide and oxygen atoms. Here $k_a\phi$ is the rate at which nitrogen dioxide is absorbing incident photons, and ϕ is the quantum yield for dissociation. The expression is

$$\frac{d(NO_2)}{dt} = \frac{-2k_3k_a\phi(NO_2)}{k_2(M) + k_3}$$

Bufalini and Stephens *(13)* used values for k_2 and k_3 quoted in Leighton's book *(14)*. Schuck *et al. (15)* recently remeasured these rate constants and found them to be $k_2 = 4.24 \times 10^{10}$ liters^2 mole^{-2} sec^{-1} and $k_3 = 5.26 \times 10^9$ liters mole^{-1} sec^{-1}. These values differ substantially from those appearing in Leighton's treatise; we used the more recent values in our calculations.

If one observes the rate of disappearance of NO_2, the value of $k_a\phi$ can be obtained. This value was all that was needed in our studies, but the absolute light intensity (photons cm^{-2} sec^{-1}) can be obtained by using the relationship between k_a, the absorption coefficient of NO_2, and the incident light intensity. The quantum yield, ϕ, is taken as unity for the wavelengths employed in this work. The values obtained for the first-order dissociation constants, $k_a\phi$, were 0.32 min^{-1} and 0.14 min^{-1} for 24 blacklights and 28 sunlamps, respectively.

Results

During the early stages of this work, we were uncertain about the suitability of formalin solution because of the presence of methanol. We compared the formaldehyde consumption and H_2O_2 production of formalin and paraformaldehyde, shown in Fig. 1. This figure shows that the presence of methanol has very little, if any, effect on photooxidation rate of formaldehyde. In further tests, methanol was irradiated with nitrogen dioxide; these data are shown in Table I. Apparently some methanol does react, since carbon monoxide and formaldehyde are observed as products. The yield is small, however. Also, since the concentration of methanol present during the formaldehyde irradiations is one-third that shown in Table I, we concluded that methanol interference is minimal.

Data from the photooxidation of formaldehyde in the presence and absence of nitrogen dioxide with sunlight fluorescent lights (wavelength

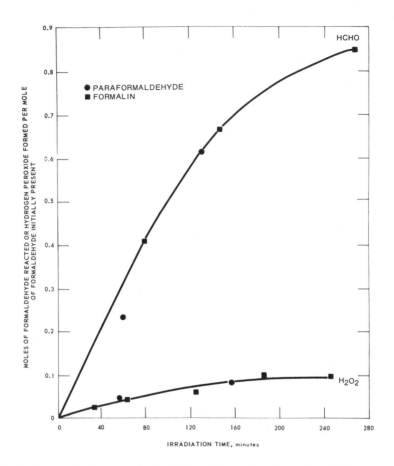

Fig. 1. Comparison between the irradiation of formalin and paraformaldehyde.

Table I

Photooxidation of Methanol with Nitrogen Dioxide and Blacklights

MeOH (ppm)	NO$_2$ (ppm)	Irradiation Time (min)	Products Formed (ppm)	
			CO	CH$_2$O
12.0	1.3	60	0.253	0
12.3	0.27	120	0.153	0.280
12.8	0.20	120	0.109	0.242

maximum at 3100 Å) are shown in Fig. 2. Results from the photooxidation of formaldehyde, again in the presence and absence of nitrogen dioxide but with blacklight fluorescent lights (wavelength maximum at 3600 Å),
are shown in Figs. 3 and 4. The reduced data are shown in Tables II, III, IV, and
V for the various conditions, where $(HCHO)_i$ and $(HCHO)_r$ refer to the initial
HCHO concentration and the concentration reacted at time, t, respectively.

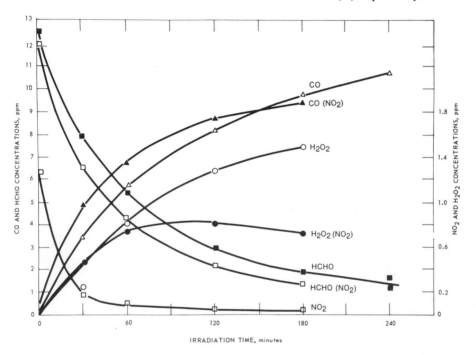

Fig. 2. Formaldehyde irradiated with and without NO_2 in the presence of sunlights.

Table II

Formaldehyde (12.5 PPM) in Air Irradiated with Sunlamps

Irradiation Time (min)	$\dfrac{(HCHO)}{(HCHO)_i}$	$\dfrac{(CO)}{(HCHO)_r}$	$\dfrac{(H_2O_2)}{(HCHO)_r}$
30	0.633	0.732	0.052
60	0.400	0.724	0.115
120	0.224	0.796	0.127
180	0.156	0.836	0.140
240	0.106	0.833	0.090

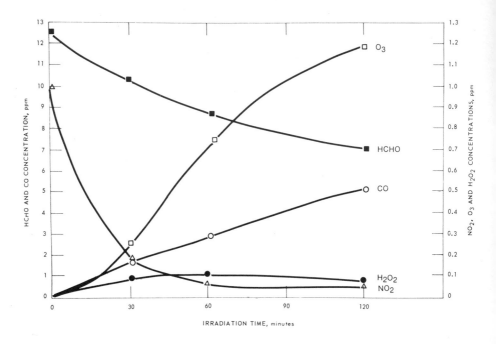

Fig. 3. Formaldehyde irradiated with blacklights and nitrogen dioxide.

Table III

Formaldehyde (12 PPM) Irradiated with 1.2 PPM Nitrogen Dioxide in Air and Sunlamps

Irradiation Time (min)	$\dfrac{(HCHO)}{(HCHO)_i}$	$\dfrac{(CO)}{(HCHO)_r}$	$\dfrac{(H_2O_2)}{(HCHO)_r}$	$\dfrac{(NO_2)}{(NO_2)_i}$	O_3(ppm)
30	0.503	0.771	0.073	0.133	–
60	0.336	0.824	0.0867	0.080	0.68
120	0.190	0.896	0.0871	0.039	0.93
180	0.118	0.881	0.0713	0.030	0.81

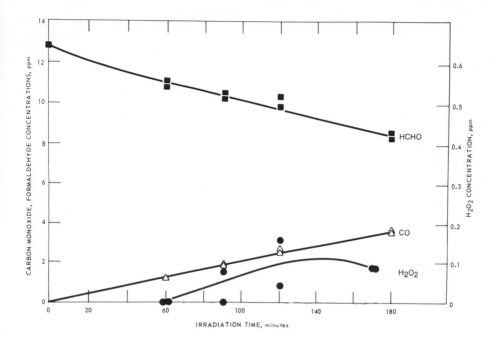

Fig. 4. Formaldehyde irradiated with blacklamps.

Table IV

Formaldehyde (12.9 PPM) in Air Irradiated with Blacklights

Irradiation Time (min)	$\dfrac{\text{(HCHO)}}{\text{(HCHO)}_i}$	$\dfrac{\text{(CO)}}{\text{(HCHO)}_r}$	$\dfrac{\text{(H}_2\text{O}_2)}{\text{(HCHO)}_r}$
60	0.861	0.717	0
90	0.813	0.814	0.018
120	0.759	0.861	0.035
180	0.669	0.883	0.021

Table V

Formaldehyde (12.7 PPM) Irradiated with 1.01 PPM of Nitrogen Dioxide in Air and Blacklights

Irradiation Time (min)	$\dfrac{\text{(HCHO)}}{\text{(HCHO)}_i}$	$\dfrac{\text{(CO)}}{\text{(HCHO)}_r}$	$\dfrac{\text{(H}_2\text{O}_2)}{\text{(HCHO)}_r}$	$\dfrac{\text{(NO}_2)}{\text{(NO}_2)_i}$	O_3(ppm)
30	0.814	0.819	0.050	0.152	0.27
60	0.714	0.864	0.020	0.064	0.75
120	0.527	0.825	0.028	0.089	1.19

Gas chromatographic analyses indicated carbon monoxide as the major product. As shown in the tables, this product can account for as much as 90% of the total carbon. Limited data from two experiments with a closed glass system indicated that between 12 and 20% of the carbon appears as CO_2. The remaining carbon appeared as carbon monoxide.

Various techniques were employed to test whether any oxidant other than H_2O_2 was formed in the photooxidation of formaldehyde. These tests were performed by the titanium-8-quinolinol method for H_2O_2, and with the neutral potassium iodide reagent, the molybdate-catalyzed potassium iodide reagent, the Mast instrument equipped with an olefin injection system, and a Mark IV ultraviolet photometer for ozone. After obtaining some contradictory results, we found that formaldehyde interfered with the molybdate-catalyzed potassium iodide reagent, giving more oxidant than is actually present. No other oxidants, such as performic acid or peroxyformyl nitrate, were observed as products. Ozone was observed only when oxides of nitrogen were present prior to irradiation. The H_2O_2 yield was lower when formaldehyde was irradiated with sunlamps in the presence of nitrogen oxide. Production of H_2O_2 was low and reproducibility poor when formaldehyde was irradiated with blacklights. The stability of H_2O_2 to thermal and surface decomposition was linear and was 10^{-3} ppm/min at the 2-ppm level. At 6 ppm, the decomposition was again linear but three times as great. However, as the air volume in the Teflon bag decreased (that is, the ratio of volume to area decreased), the rate of decomposition increased. All experiments were performed at near maximum volume. The data shown in the figures and tables are not corrected for decomposition.

Analyses for formic acid were performed in several experiments under the various conditions of these studies. The formic acid data were inconclusive, probably because of the difficulty of the analytical method. In one experiment, no formic acid was observed when formaldehyde was reacted with NO_2 and sunlights for 30 and 60 minutes. At 120 minutes, when 9.69 ppm formaldehyde had reacted, 0.73 ppm formic acid was observed. At 180 minutes, when 10.16 ppm formaldehyde had reacted, 0.64 ppm formic acid was observed.

Since most if not all of the carbon from formaldehyde can be accounted for by the formation of carbon monoxide and carbon dioxide, it was necessary to determine the fate of nitrogen dioxide. We showed recently *(16)* that, when hydrocarbons are photooxidized in the presence of oxides of nitrogen, much of the nitrogen oxide is oxidized to nitric acid on the walls of the reaction vessel. Since Teflon bags could not be used for this study, we repeated some of the work with a large borosilicate flask. Two experiments were performed with the large flask for this purpose. Formaldehyde (6 ppm) was irradiated for 6 hours with 2.3 ppm nitrogen dioxide. After the irradiation, 2.25 ppm of the nitrogen was recovered; 1.79 ppm appeared as nitrate on the walls, and 0.46 ppm appeared as nitrite in the gas phase. This experiment was repeated again with 6 ppm formaldehyde and 1.9 ppm nitrogen dioxide. After 17 hours of irradiation, no nitrate or nitrite was observed in the gas phase but 0.18 ppm nitrite and 1.8 ppm nitrate were observed on the walls of the reaction vessel.

The results from the reaction of atomic oxygen and formaldehyde are shown in Table VI. All the data were obtained by irradiating formaldehyde and nitrogen dioxide in nitrogen for 7.5 min. The approximate atomic oxygen concentration was determined by use of a steady-state approximation similar to that of Ford and Endow *(17)*. This approximate atomic oxygen concentration was then employed in the second-order rate expression for the disappearance of formaldehyde, to obtain the approximate rate constant for the reaction. This rate constant was then placed back into the steady-state expression for the atomic oxygen concentration, and a more correct value of oxygen atom concentration was obtained. The values in the column of Table VI were obtained by this iteration procedure.

Discussion

The photolysis of formaldehyde has been reported *(18)* in terms of two primary processes:

$$HCHO + h\nu \rightarrow H + HCO \tag{I}$$

$$\rightarrow H_2 + CO \tag{II}$$

The importance of both processes at different wavelengths has been discussed by McQuigg and Calvert *(19)* and by DeGraff and Calvert *(20)*. In the presence of nitrogen dioxide and high partial pressures of oxygen, the following sequence of reactions can also occur:

$$NO_2 + h\nu \rightarrow NO + O \tag{1}$$

$$O + O_2 \xrightarrow{M} O_3 \tag{2}$$

$$O + HCHO \rightarrow OH + HCO \tag{3}$$

Table VI

Rate Constant for Formaldehyde-Atomic Oxygen Reaction

Experiment	$(HCHO)_i$	$(HCHO)_f$	$(NO_2)_i$	$(NO_2)_f$	Time (min)	$k \times 10^{-8}$ (liters mole^{-1} sec^{-1})
3-17	12.69	11.40	1.26	.865	7.5	5.85
3-19	12.71	12.10	1.29	1.03	7.5	1.70
4-15	12.70	11.48	2.20	1.23	7.5	3.85
5-23	12.79	11.72	1.88	1.27	7.5	3.24
5-28	13.22	11.67	1.60	1.37	7.5	5.92
8-20	12.79	11.52	1.41	1.27	7.5	4.55
						4.2 ± 1.6

$$H + O_2 \rightarrow HO_2 \tag{4}$$

$$HCO + O_2 \rightarrow HCO_3 \tag{5}$$

$$HO_2 + HCHO \rightarrow H_2O_2 + HCO \tag{6}$$

$$HCO_3 + HCHO \rightarrow HCO_3H + HCO \tag{7}$$

$$HCO_3 \rightarrow CO + HO_2 \tag{8}$$

$$\rightarrow CO_2 + OH \tag{9}$$

$$HO_2 \overset{wall}{\rightarrow} destruction \tag{10}$$

$$HCO_3H \rightarrow CO + H_2O + \tfrac{1}{2}O_2 \tag{11}$$

$$\rightarrow CO_2 + H_2 + \tfrac{1}{2}O_2 \tag{12}$$

$$H_2O_2 \rightarrow H_2O + \tfrac{1}{2}O_2 \tag{13}$$

$$OH + HCHO \rightarrow HCO + H_2O \tag{14}$$

$$NO + HO_2 \rightarrow NO_2 + OH \tag{15}$$

$$O_3 + NO \rightarrow NO_2 + O_2 \tag{16}$$

$$NO_2 + O_3 \rightarrow NO_3 + O_2 \tag{17}$$

$$NO_3 + NO_2 \rightarrow N_2O_5 \tag{18}$$

$$N_2O_5 + H_2O \rightarrow 2HNO_3 \tag{19}$$

$$OH + NO_2 \rightarrow HNO_3 \tag{20}$$

$$OH + CO \rightarrow CO_2 + H \tag{21}$$

From the sequence of reactions written, it isn't obvious how formic acid can be formed in the absence of oxides of nitrogen. In their presence, reactions 22 and 23 can occur.

$$HCO_3 + NO \rightarrow HCO_2 + NO_2 \tag{22}$$

$$HCO_2 + HCHO \rightarrow HCO_2H + HCO \qquad (23)$$

In the present work, as in the work of Purcell and Cohen *(1)*, the molecular balance between hydrogen peroxide formed and aldehyde consumed is clearly lacking. This is especially true of prolonged irradiations, as shown in Figs. 2 and 3. This discrepancy can be explained by reactions 10 and 13 in the absence of nitrogen oxides. In the presence of nitrogen oxides the amount of H_2O_2 produced is significantly lower. This indicates that reaction 15 is important. It is doubtful that reaction 7 occurs, since no oxidants other than hydrogen peroxide and ozone have been observed. It is also probable that the peroxyformyl radical (reaction 5) is not formed at all and that the HCO radical decomposes directly after combining with oxygen to form the products of reactions 8 and 9. Evidence for this is found in the work of Horner and co-workers *(21)* and in the more recent work of Dimitriades (private communication), who was unable to produce peroxyformyl nitrate.

In one respect, the data shown in the tables do not fit the reaction scheme shown. In Tables II and III, the third columns show the CO/HCHO ratios for the various irradiation times in the absence and presence of oxides of nitrogen. The ratios are higher in the presence of nitrogen oxides and with increasing irradiation time. Reaction 21 shows OH radicals reacting with CO. If this reaction were important, there should be a relative decrease in CO concentration after prolonged irradiation. The ratio should also be lower when oxides of nitrogen are present. Unless the rate constant for OH and HCHO is much greater than 2×10^{-13} cc/molecule sec *(22)*, which is the OH-CO rate constant, it must be concluded that OH radicals do not play an important role in the reaction of formaldehyde. However, comparison of Figs. 3 and 4 shows that the rate of disappearance of formaldehyde is 50 to 200 times as great as the rate that can be explained by just the atomic oxygen reaction. Since the H_2O_2 yield is low in the presence of NO_2, and since little if any formic acid was formed and no peracid was observed, the types of free radicals operative in this system are clearly limited. Therefore, it must be concluded that OH radicals are the most important free radicals operative in this system and that the rate constant for formaldehyde and OH is much greater than that for CO and OH. This conclusion is not in agreement with the work of Avramenko and Lorentzo *(23)* but seems compatible with the observations of Herron and Penzhorn *(24)*. The former found a rate constant of 10^{-13} cc/molecule sec for the OH-formaldehyde reaction, while the latter found a lower limit of 6×10^{-12} cc/molecule sec. Since the rate constant is so large, the rate constant for O atom and formaldehyde shown in Table VI is too large by a factor of 2. This arises from the fact that, for every O atom reacting, a hydroxyl radical is formed that will also react with formaldehyde. The rate constant for reaction 3 is then 3.5×10^{-13} cc/molecule sec. Other published values are 1.5×10^{-13} cc/molecule sec *(24)* and 3.5×10^{-14} cc/molecule sec *(25)*.

Reactions 19 and 20 are included in the reaction scheme as a possible source of nitrate formation. However, since no nitrate was observed in the gas phase, either the reactions occur on the walls of the reaction vessel or are of little importance.

The data shown in Tables II and III indicate that more hydrogen peroxide is formed when formaldehyde is irradiated with sunlamps (λ = 3100 Å) than when it is irradiated with blacklamps (λ = 3600 Å). This suggests that process I is less important at the longer wavelength, an observation that is compatible with the work of McQuigg and Calvert *(19)* and earlier investigators and incompatible with the observations of DeGraff and Calvert *(20)*.

This work is obviously incomplete. The CO/HCHO ratios increased with irradiation time, which suggests that the carbon exists in some intermediate that dissociates further to CO. However, no such compound was found. More complete and better analyses are needed at earlier irradiation times for definitive answers.

References

1. T.C. Purcell and I.R. Cohen, *Environ. Sci. Technol.,* 1, 845 (1967).

2. J.E. Carruthers and R.G.W. Norrish, *J. Chem. Soc.,* 1036 (1936).

3. E.C.A. Horner and D.W.G. Style, *Trans. Faraday Soc.,* 50, 1197 (1954).

4. A.P. Altshuller, I.R. Cohen, and T.C. Purcell, *Can. J. Chem.,* 44, 2973 (1966).

5. C.A. McDowell and L.K. Sharples, *Can. J. Chem.,* 36, 258 (1958).

6. H.S. Johnston and J. Heicklen, *J. Am. Chem. Soc.,* 86, 4259 (1964).

7. A.P. Altshuller and I.R. Cohen, *Intern. J. Air Water Pollution,* 8, 611 (1964).

8. A.P. Altshuller, D.L. Miller, and S.F. Sleva, *Anal. Chem.,* 33, 621 (1961).

9. B.E. Saltzman, *Anal. Chem.,* 26, 1949 (1954).

10. I.R. Cohen and T.C. Purcell, *Anal. Chem.,* 39, 131 (1967).

11. U. Schwenk, H. Hachenberg, and M. Forderreuther, *Brennstoff-Chem.,* 42, 295 (1961).

12. C.S. Tuesday in "Chemical Reactions in the Lower and Upper Atmosphere," (R.D. Cadle, ed.), Interscience, New York, 1961, pp. 1-49.

13. J.J. Bufalini and E.R. Stephens, *Intern. J. Air Water Pollution,* 9, 123 (1965).

14. P.A. Leighton, "Photochemistry of Air Pollution," Academic Press, New York, 1961.

15. E.A. Schuck, E.R. Stephens, and R.R. Schrock, Rate Constant Ratios during Nitrogen Dioxide Photolysis, presented at the 59th Annual Meeting of the Air Pollution Control Association, San Francisco, California, June 20-24, 1966.

16. B.W. Gay and J.J. Bufalini, Nitric Acid: Formation by Photooxidation of Hydrocarbons in the Presence of Oxides of Nitrogen, presented at the 158th National American Chemical Society Meeting, New York, New York, September 7-12, 1969.

17. H.W. Ford and N. Endow, *J. Chem. Phys.*, 27, 1277 (1957).

18. J.G. Calvert and J.N. Pitts, Jr., "Photochemistry," Wiley, New York, 1966, p. 371.

19. R.D. McQuigg and J.G. Calvert, *J. Am. Chem. Soc.*, 91, 1590 (1969).

20. B.A. DeGraff and J.G. Calvert, *J. Am. Chem. Soc.*, 89, 2247 (1967).

21. E.C.A. Horner, D.W.G. Style, and D. Summers, *Trans. Faraday Soc.*, 50, 1201 (1954).

22. G. Dixon-Lewis, W.E. Wilson, and A.A. Westenberg, *J. Chem. Phys.*, 44, 2877 (1966).

23. L.I. Avramenko and R.V. Lorentzo, *Dokl. Akad. Nauk. SSSR*, 69, 205 (1949).

24. J.T. Herron and R.D. Penzhorn, *J. Phys. Chem.*, 73, 191 (1969).

25. H. Niki, *J. Chem. Phys.*, 45, 2330 (1966).

Discussion

J.T. HERRON: Rate constants have been reported by Dr. Penzhorn and myself* for both the O + CH_2O reaction and the OH + CH_2O reaction. At 300°K, the rate constants are $k(O + CH_2O)$ = 9 × 10^{10} cm^3 mole^{-1} sec^{-1}, and $k(OH + CH_2O)$ = 4 × 10^{12} cm^3 mole^{-1} sec^{-1}. The latter, although only a limiting value, is based on a direct measurement.

J.G. CALVERT: Dr. Bufalini, you referred to the work of McQuigg and Calvert and DeGraff and Calvert (references *19* and *20* of preceding paper), concerning the relative importance of process I and process II at different wavelengths. Process I is formaldehyde photodissociating to a hydrogen atom and HCO, and process II is formaldehyde photodissociating to a hydrogen molecule and CO. DeGraff's work suggested that process I was favored at longer wavelengths over process II, while McQuigg found just the opposite.

I should like to comment on that particular problem. There was one wavelength where both of them agreed (3130 Å). At this wavelength, about equal amounts of processes I and II occur. In the McQuigg experiments, we were looking for isotopic exchange. In the DeGraff experiments, we measured quantum yields of the suppressed type I process. I think McQuigg's results are our best estimate of the relative importance of the two processes. Dr. Bufalini's results agree with McQuigg's work.

---

*J.T. Herron and R.D. Penzhorn, *J. Phys. Chem.*, 73, 191 (1969).

It is interesting that, if we integrate over the formaldehyde band for the wavelengths of sunlight, we would predict about five times as much process II as process I. It would be interesting if we could demonstrate that there is a peak in the molecular hydrogen concentration in the atmosphere that follows the formaldehyde peak. Some measurements of molecular hydrogen in the atmosphere have recently been made. Although there was a background hydrogen concentration from cracking and other refinery processes, there was an indication of a peak in the hydrogen concentration around noontime, which would suggest a photochemical origin for molecular hydrogen. Conceivably, this might come from the photolysis of formaldehyde.

W.E. WILSON: It was not clear to me, Dr. Bufalini, what form of formaldehyde you were looking at, monomeric or polymeric.

J.J. BUFALINI: I used formalin in this work. As you know, it is extremely difficult to work with formaldehyde. This is one of the reasons, I think, why Dr. Altshuller's initial work was on propionaldehyde. It is so easy to handle.

W.E. WILSON: Unless you went through a process to prepare monomer, you were looking at some polymeric form. I am not sure what relationship this might have to the reactions of monomeric formaldehyde, which presumably is what is found in the atmosphere.

J.J. BUFALINI: As shown in Fig. 1 of our paper, the formaldehyde consumption and H_2O_2 production were the same whether we prepared the formaldehyde from formalin or from paraformaldehyde. This suggests that, if the formaldehyde from formalin is in polymeric form, the formaldehyde from paraformaldehyde is in the same form. Of course, another possibility is that different forms of formaldehyde react similarly.

R.J. CVETANOVIC: In the presentation of his paper, Dr. Bufalini raised the question of the relevance of the stoichiometric number to the determination of rate constants from rate measurements. This is a point of considerable importance. In the reaction of $O(^3P)$ atoms with formaldehyde the OH radicals formed in the primary step rapidly react with another molecule of formaldehyde. Allowance must be made for this secondary reaction when the rate constant of the primary step is determined from the rate of consumption of formaldehyde. In view of the conventional definition of the rate constant of an elementary reaction, failure to allow for complex stoichiometry will lead to confusion and inaccuracies. Difficulties arise, of course, when the stoichiometric number is not known accurately. This difficulty is not uncommon, for example, in some ESR measurements of rate constants in the gas phase. These must, of necessity, be conducted at low pressures where secondary reactions tend to be very important. Another example is the value of the rate constant of the elementary reaction of $O(^3P)$ atoms with ethylene obtained by Elias and Schiff,* which has been quoted earlier in this Symposium. Brown and Thrush† have pointed out that this value is somewhat high because the reaction rate was determined from the loss of ethylene, assuming simple stoichiometry and thus neglecting the secondary reaction of ethylene with hydrogen atoms.

J.T. HERRON: R.E. Huie and I have from time to time measured the rate constant for the ethylene reaction. Our results seem to agree with the higher values for the rate constant reported by Elias.‡ Our measurements are made under conditions where the concentration of atomic oxygen greatly exceeds that of ethylene. Total conversions are small, so that secondary reactions are negligible. I would emphasize, however, that these measurements were not part of a systematic study of the ethylene reaction.

E.E. DABY: I have to disagree with you, Dr. Herron. We have also measured the ethylene-oxygen atom reaction¶ and get a factor of 2, approximately, lower than Elias‡. We also followed formaldehyde formation in this system. By using a large excess of O atoms, we had pseudo first-order consecutive reactions going from ethylene to formaldehyde to other products. From the maximum concentration of formaldehyde formed, you can calculate relative rate constants for the reactions of ethylene and formaldehyde with O atoms. If you take this ratio and insert Dr. Herron's value for the formaldehyde rate constant, then the value which we derive for the ethylene rate constant is the same as the value which we measured directly.

J.T. HERRON: In view of the controversy surrounding this rate constant, it would appear that further detailed studies are in order.

---

*L. Elias and H. I. Schiff, *Can. J. Chem.,* **38**, 1657 (1960).

†J.M. Brown and B.A. Thrush, *Trans. Faraday Soc.,* **63**, 630 (1967).

‡L. Elias, *J. Chem. Phys.,* **38**, 989 (1963).

¶H. Niki, E.E. Daby, and B. Weinstock, in "Twelfth Symposium (International) on Combustion," p. 277, The Combustion Institute, 1969.

The Photochemical Formation of Aerosols in Urban Atmospheres

P.J. Groblicki and G.J. Nebel
Fuels and Lubricants Department
General Motors Research Laboratories
Warren, Michigan

Abstract

The photochemical reactions involving some of the gaseous contaminants of urban atmospheres that result in the formation of aerosols have been investigated in a large irradiation chamber. Aerosol formation was measured with a light-scattering photometer and a condensation nuclei counter. The reactions at atmospheric concentrations of various mixtures of several different hydrocarbons, sulfur dioxide, nitric oxide, and ozone were studied.

The propylene-nitric oxide-sulfur dioxide system was studied systematically to determine the effects of several reaction variables. The amount of aerosol formed after irradiation was significantly increased with increased concentrations of propylene or sulfur dioxide. On the other hand, increasing the nitric oxide concentration at first increased and then gradually decreased aerosol formation. Increasing the temperature from 80° to 95°F or decreasing the water vapor pressure from 17 to 3 torr also increased aerosol formation. Reducing the light intensity to one-half the usual level delayed the formation of aerosol but did not affect the amount ultimately formed.

The amount of aerosol formed on irradiation in the hydrocarbon-nitric oxide-sulfur dioxide system depended on the nature of the hydrocarbon as well as the concentration. Of the reactive hydrocarbons investigated, α-pinene and cyclohexene formed the most aerosol, and ethylene the least. The amount of aerosol formed with the unreactive hydrocarbons was similar to the amount formed in "blank" runs.

The aerosol formed from all the hydrocarbons investigated except cyclohexene and α-pinene was found to be predominantly ammonium sulfate. Cyclohexene and α-pinene formed aerosols which contained carbonaceous material as well as ammonium sulfate.

Cyclohexene and α-pinene, unlike the other hydrocarbons investigated, produced as much aerosol when irradiated with nitric oxide alone as when irradiated with nitric oxide and sulfur dioxide. These two hydrocarbons also produced appreciable aerosol when reacted with ozone in the dark. Other reactive hydrocarbons such as 1-heptene and styrene also reacted rapidly with ozone in the dark but did not form significant amounts of aerosol.

Although only minor amounts of aerosol were formed by the dark reaction of sulfur dioxide and ozone, significant aerosol was formed when propylene was also present.

These results indicate that two distinct types of aerosol (sulfate and carbonaceous) can be formed by some of the gaseous contaminants of urban atmospheres. Ozone

---

References, p. 263

appears to be a key reactant in the formation of both types, and irradiation and nitric oxide may be involved only to the degree that they form ozone.

Introduction

Poor visibility is one of the most obvious manifestations of photochemical smog. Visibility is reduced because of small particles (0.1 to 1 micron in diameter) suspended in the atmosphere which scatter light very effectively. This particulate or aerosol material may come directly from various sources, or it may be formed by chemical reactions between trace gaseous constituents such as hydrocarbons, nitrogen oxides, and sulfur dioxide. The complete conversion of all the reactive gases in a typical urban atmosphere will yield a suspended particulate concentration of several thousand micrograms per cubic meter. The actual concentrations are only 1 to 10% of this amount, with the latter condition producing a severe haze. Charlson has presented a useful correlation between suspended particulates and visibility *(1)*. It states that the product of the concentration in micrograms per cubic meter and visibility or visual range in kilometers is about 1800. Hence, on a hazy day with only 5 kilometers visibility, one would expect a mass loading of about 360 micrograms per cubic meter.

It is difficult to distinguish between aerosol produced by atmospheric reactions and other aerosol. One approach is to follow diurnal changes. However, the low concentrations make it difficult to collect enough sample in a short time period. Lundgren's recent study is probably the best available on this subject *(2)*. He collected successive 4-hour aerosol samples (at Riverside, California) and analyzed them for a number of chemical species. His results suggest that inorganic material (sulfates and nitrates) is largely responsible for the increased aerosol loading and reduced visibility during photochemical smog episodes. Previously, it had been believed that organic material was responsible.

The difficulty of field investigations has led to the study of photochemical aerosol formation in laboratory irradiation chambers. Several studies have been made, and in general they have shown (1) that few hydrocarbons will form aerosol when irradiated with NO_2 unless SO_2 is also present, and (2) that the aerosol will contain sulfate if SO_2 is present. Harkins and Nicksic *(3)* concluded that sulfuric acid was formed, since they found no carbon in the aerosol when ^{14}C-tagged ethylene or propylene was irradiated with NO and SO_2. Earlier, Endow *et al.* *(4)* found less than 1% carbon and no organic functional groups in the aerosol formed by the irradiation of propylene-NO_2-SO_2 mixtures. There is little information available on the composition of the aerosols formed by the irradiation of higher-molecular-weight hydrocarbons, with or without sulfur dioxide.

This study was undertaken to learn more about the composition of photochemical aerosols, and how they are formed. The effects of different hydrocarbons, sulfur dioxide, nitric oxide, nitrogen dioxide, ozone, humidity, temperature, and illumination intensity were studied in a large irradiation chamber. The aerosol formed was measured and characterized.

Experimental Procedure

In this study, dilute mixtures of hydrocarbons, nitric oxide, and sulfur dioxide in clean air were irradiated in a laboratory chamber, and the aerosol material formed by the photochemical reactions was measured. The apparatus and procedures used are described briefly below. The smog chamber facility was completely described previously *(5)*.

Irradiation Chamber and Associated Equipment. The irradiation chamber is a 300-cubic-foot cylindrical vessel of stainless steel. Inside the chamber, Pyrex tubes contain fluorescent lamps, the number and type of which were selected to duplicate sunlight. The radiation intensity as measured by the NO_2 photolysis method is 0.25 min^{-1}. A large tube-axial fan thoroughly mixes the chamber contents.

Clean air for the experiments is obtained through an inlet on the roof of the building. The air is passed through a coarse filter, a bed of $KMnO_4$-impregnated alumina pellets, a spray-type humidifier, and an absolute filter. This treatment removes the natural aerosols (small particle count is less than 100 per cubic centimeter) but not all the gaseous impurities. To avoid excessive background reactivity, no experiments are made if the total hydrocarbon concentration of the chamber air exceeds 0.6 ppm as hexane.

Gaseous reactants are added to the chamber from a gas-handling system consisting of calibrated glass volumes and a precision pressure gauge. Liquid reagents are added with a microsyringe.

The chamber is equipped with gas analyzers for the reactants and some of the products. Table I lists the constituents determined and the analyzers used.

The chamber is maintained at a small positive pressure (0.1 inch H_2O) by automatically adding cylinder air to make up for the gas samples withdrawn by the analyzers. The makeup air is passed through a water bubbler to keep the humidity in the chamber constant.

Materials. Pure hydrocarbons were obtained from several sources. The majority were Phillips hydrocarbons of the following grades:

Table I

Gas Analysis Methods

Constituent	Instrument	Remarks
Total hydrocarbon	Beckman 107 flame ionization analyzer	
Individual hydrocarbon	Hewlett Packard 402 gas chromatograph	Flame detector. Porapak or Durapak column. Column length and temperature optimized for test hydrocarbon. 5-cc sample.
NO_x, NO_2	Beckman Acralyzers	Saltzman reagent. Dichromate oxidant in NO_x sample train; NO determined by difference.
SO_2	Beckman 906 coulometric KI analyzer	Proprietary scrubber to minimize interferences.
O_3	Mast coulometric KI analyzer	Chromium trioxide scrubber to eliminate SO_2 interference. Results corrected for NO_x interference.
CO	Beckman 21 NDIR analyzer	CO added as tracer.
H_2O	Aminco Hygrometer	

Research grade. Methane, ethylene, propylene, 1,3-butadiene, isoprene, cyclopentene, 2,2,4-trimethylpentane, 2,4,4-trimethyl-1-pentene, ethylbenzene.
Pure grade. Benzene, cyclohexene.
Technical grade. 1-Octene, 3-heptene.

a-Pinene was obtained from the Chemical Procurement Laboratories. Gas chromatographic analysis showed that it contained about 25% of an unknown impurity, most likely the β-isomer. Mesitylene was a 99.95% pure API sample. Styrene was redistilled from material of unknown origin. 1-Heptene was obtained from Humphrey-Wilkinson, Inc. Its purity is not known.

Sulfur dioxide and nitric oxide were cp grade, obtained from the Matheson Company. Nitrogen dioxide was prepared from nitric oxide and oxygen in the gas-handling system as needed.

Typical Experimental Procedure. The chamber was thoroughly flushed with filtered air of controlled humidity and preheated to the test temperature, 95°F unless otherwise noted. The reactants were added as much as 30 minutes before the beginning of a run, so that the slower responding analyzers could reach equilibrium. About 50 ppm of (inert) carbon monoxide was added as a tracer to determine dilution. Once the analyzer readings had stabilized, the lights were turned on and the chamber contents were irradiated for 6 hours. The gaseous reactants and products were monitored continuously. Aerosol samples were collected on filters during the last 2 hours of the run.

Aerosol Measurements. The principal instrument used for the aerosol measurements was a Sinclair-Phoenix smoke photometer or smokemeter *(6)*. This instrument measures the amount of light scattered in the near-forward direction by a stream of aerosol particles flowing through a dark-field optical system. The response of this instrument depends on both the concentration of the aerosol particles and their physical properties such as size, shape, and refractive index. (These same factors also affect visibility in the atmosphere.) In this study, the smokemeter was adjusted so that the second calibration filter (3% transmission) gave a full-scale reading of 5. For comparison, outside air registered ½ to 1 on clear bright days, and about 2.7 on one day of poor visibility (about 1 mile).

During these experiments, many comparisons between smokemeter reading and aerosol sulfate concentration were obtained. These can be used to estimate the relative changes in total aerosol concentration, since sulfate was the major aerosol constituent in several of the systems studied.* The relationship between smokemeter reading and sulfate for all the propylene-NO-SO$_2$ runs is shown in Fig. 1. These data suggest that a change of one smokemeter unit in this study represents a two- to threefold change in total aerosol concentration. This is considerably less than the tenfold change often quoted for one smokemeter unit, but this is because our instrument was operated at a higher-than-normal sensitivity.

---

*Total aerosol concentrations were measured in a few runs, by collecting the sample on a Nuclepore filter and weighing it with a sensitive electrobalance. The very limited results confirm that the propylene-NO-SO$_2$ aerosol is mostly ammonium sulfate.

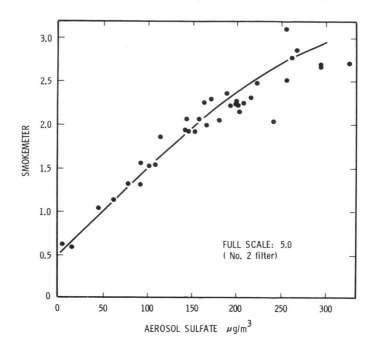

Fig. 1. Comparison of sulfate and smokemeter values for all propylene runs.

The smokemeter sample was pumped back into the irradiation chamber. A separate, filtered airstream was used to cool the lamp.

The smokemeter was supplemented by a condensation nuclei counter during the later runs. The instrument was a Gardner Associates small particle detector *(7)*. Condensation nuclei (CN) include all particles from molecular cluster size up to about 5 microns. Condensation nuclei counts per cubic centimeter can vary widely, from a few hundred for very clean air to tens of millions for dirty air. By varying the initial supersaturation, the CN counter can also provide an estimate of particle size.

Samples of the aerosol were collected on Millipore type TH membrane filters 13 mm in diameter. The volume sampled was 10 to 15 cubic feet, depending on how much the filter plugged during the 2-hour sampling period. The filters are supplied as pairs of matched thickness. By placing the filter with the aerosol sample in one beam of a Perkin-Elmer Model 337 grating infrared spectometer, and the unused filter in the reference beam, a spectrum of the aerosol material only was obtained. The wavelengths between 2 and 25 microns were scanned. The infrared spectra were used to identify chemical groups in the aerosol.

The sulfur content of the aerosol was determined by an x-ray fluorescence method. The same filter sample was used for both the infrared and the sulfur analyses. In the x-ray method, the sample is exposed to a beam of hard x-rays. The sulfur (or other element) absorbs some of the hard radiation and reradiates or fluoresces its own soft x-rays of a characteristic frequency. The fluorescent radiation, which is proportional to the number of sulfur atoms on the filter, is measured. The method is extremely sensitive (less than 1 microgram of sulfur can be determined) and rapid (less than 5 minutes per sample, after 30 minutes for calibration and setup) and has a linear response. The absolute calibration was derived by comparing the x-ray and turbidimetric analyses of several sulfate aerosol samples. The absolute accuracy of the sulfate values is estimated to be ±25%, although the relative precision is considerably better.

Irradiation of Propylene-NO-SO$_2$ Mixtures

This system was chosen to study the effects of several "atmospheric" variables on aerosol formation. Propylene was selected because it is a common atmospheric hydrocarbon and is moderately reactive photochemically. The variables were reactant concentration, humidity, temperature, and light intensity.

Typical Experimental Results. The data from a typical experiment with 4 ppm propylene, 2 ppm NO, and 1 ppm SO$_2$ are plotted in Fig. 2. The interesting feature of this smog profile is the sharp increase in aerosol concentration (smokemeter reading) after about 75 minutes of irradiation. This coincides with the complete oxidation of NO to NO$_2$, and the appearance of ozone. The aerosol concentration reached a maximum after about 270 minutes and then gradually declined. Subsequent smokemeter readings used in this report are the maximum values. Unless otherwise noted, they are not corrected for the initial readings, which ranged from 0.1 to 0.4 smokemeter units.

In Fig. 2 and in other experiments, approximately 10% of the NO was unavoidably oxidized to NO$_2$ before irradiation began. The NO was oxidized when it was flushed into the chamber (about 15 minutes before the lights were turned on), even though it was diluted with nitrogen in the gas-handling system. The initial NO concentrations given in this report include this small amount of NO$_2$.

When pure NO$_2$ was substituted for NO, the results were similar to those shown in Fig. 2, except that the starting time was moved up to coincide approximately with the NO$_2$ peak and the appearance of ozone.

Slightly more aerosol was formed from NO_2 than from the same concentration of NO. This may have been caused by the slight loss of reactants (from dilution or reaction) during the NO oxidation period. Prager *et al.* *(8)* found the same results for mixtures of 2-pentene, SO_2, and NO or NO_2.

Reactant Concentration. The effect of varying the SO_2 concentration on the amount of aerosol produced is shown in Fig. 3 for mixtures containing 4 ppm propylene, 2 ppm NO, and up to 1 ppm SO_2. Increasing the SO_2 concentration from 0 to 1 ppm increased the smokemeter reading significantly, from 0.6 to 2.2. This was accompanied by a similar increase in the sulfate concentration. With no SO_2 added, practically no sulfate was found. With 1 ppm added, about 200 $\mu g/m^3$ of sulfate was recovered as aerosol. We have concluded from these results that SO_2 concentration is an important factor in the formation of photochemical aerosol. We have also concluded (from results not shown here) that SO_2 concentration does not affect the amount of ozone formed nor the rate of oxidation of nitric oxide, two other photochemical smog parameters.

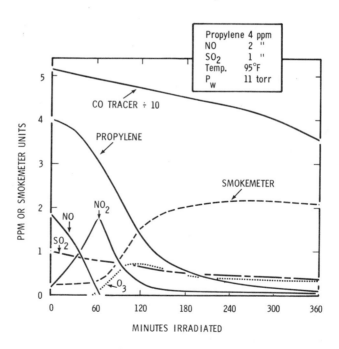

Fig. 2. Typical smog profile.

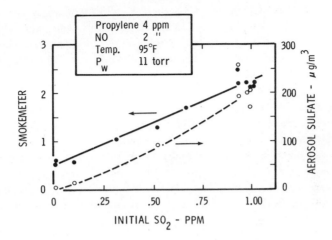

Fig. 3. Effect of sulfur dioxide on aerosol formation.

The effect of propylene concentration on the amount of aerosol formed is shown in Fig. 4. Increasing the propylene concentration from 0 to 4 ppm increased the smokemeter reading from 1.0 to 2.2, and the sulfate from about 40 to 200 $\mu g/m^3$. These are significant changes, and we have concluded that the concentration of propylene (or other reactive hydro-carbon) is an important factor in the formation of this kind of aerosol.

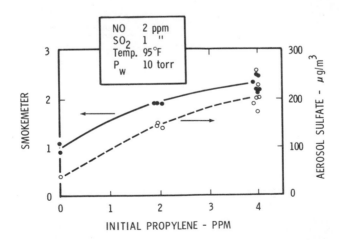

Fig. 4. Effect of propylene on aerosol formation.

The effects of NO concentration on the amount of aerosol formed are shown in Fig. 5. The top graph is for 4 ppm propylene and 1 ppm SO_2; the bottom, 2 ppm propylene and 1 ppm SO_2. At each propylene concentration, NO had relatively little effect on either the smokemeter reading or the sulfate concentration, once the concentration reached some minimum value. No special effort was made to determine this minimum concentration, but it appeared to be about 0.2 ppm. We have concluded that nitric oxide is not an important factor in aerosol formation, provided that at least a small amount is present.

The concentration effects generally agree with other investigations *(8-12)*.

Humidity and Temperature. The effect of humidity on the amount of aerosol formed is shown in Fig. 6. The irradiated mixtures contained 4

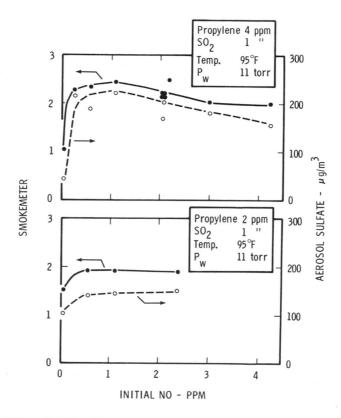

Fig. 5. Effect of nitric oxide on aerosol formation.

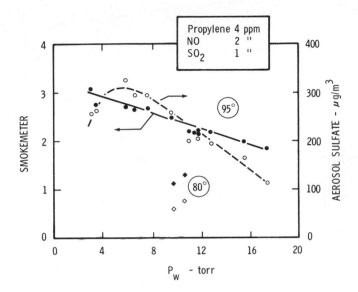

Fig. 6. Effect of humidity and temperature on aerosol formation.

ppm propylene, 2 ppm NO, 1 ppm SO_2, and varying amounts of water vapor. Increasing the water vapor pressure from 3 to 17 torr decreased the smokemeter reading from about 2.9 to 1.8. This change is significant. Increasing the humidity generally decreased the sulfate values also, although there was a maximum at around 6 torr.

The literature data on the humidity effects are conflicting. Wilson and Levy *(13)* using 1-butene, NO, and SO_2, and Nicksic and Harkins *(3)* using auto exhaust from a high-sulfur fuel, agree with our results that increasing humidity decreases light-scattering aerosol. Prager *et al. (8)* reported no effect of humidity on the aerosol formed by irradiating 2-pentene, NO_2, and SO_2 mixtures. In contrast, Schuck *et al. (14)* reported that increasing humidity increased the aerosol formed in irradiated mixtures of 2-methyl-2-butene, NO, and SO_2. We cannot explain these discrepancies.

Also shown in Fig. 6 are the results of two tests made at 80°F rather than the usual 95°F. Both the smokemeter and the sulfate data show that considerably less aerosol was formed at 80°F, perhaps only 30 to 40% as much. These results do not agree with those of Harkins and Nicksic *(3)*, who found about a threefold decrease in aerosol when the temperature was increased from 50° to 100°F. Again, we cannot explain this disagreement. However, what little information is available on temperature effects in photochemical systems indicates that increasing temperature increases reaction rates and product yields *(15)*.

We have concluded that higher temperatures and lower humidities favor aerosol formation.

Light Intensity. Reducing the light intensity to one-half the normal level did not affect the maximum amount of aerosol formed from the standard 4 : 2 : 1 mixture. However, it did delay the time of the maximum by about 30 minutes. Reducing the light intensity also delayed the oxidation of NO and the appearance of ozone, which probably explains the aerosol delay. The maximum ozone concentration was also reduced from 0.7 to 0.5 ppm.

Reckner *et al (12)* reported that reducing light intensity reduced aerosol formation. This conclusion does not conflict with our findings, because they used a continuous-flow or dynamic system where a slower reaction rate will yield a lower equilibrium concentration. On the other hand, Harkins and Nicksic *(3)* also reported that reducing light intensity reduced aerosol formation. Since their experiments, like ours, were batch-type, the two sets of results disagree.

Aerosol Composition. The propylene-NO-SO_2 aerosol material was predominantly composed of ammonium sulfate. This conclusion is based on the infrared spectra of the filter samples, a typical one of which is shown in Fig. 7. The spectrum of pure ammonium sulfate is also shown. The two spectra match very well. There are no absorption bands in the aerosol spectrum which are not found in the ammonium sulfate. This means that there could not have been much, if any, organic material or nitrate in the aerosol.

The only time the aerosol spectra did not match the ones shown in Fig. 7 was at relatively dry conditions, when the water vapor pressure was less than 6 torr. Then, the spectrum more nearly resembled that of NH_4HSO_4.

The sulfate analyses also suggest that the aerosol was mostly ammonium sulfate. Up to 300 $\mu g/m^3$ of sulfate was found, which is a relatively high value even for total aerosol.

A few aerosol samples were also analyzed for ammonium ion by the colorimetric method of Tetlow and Wilson *(16)*. The results confirmed that the aerosol was $(NH_4)_2SO_4$.

The ammonia in the ammonium sulfate probably came from the air, since it is not likely that ammonia was formed in the chamber. Later, we analyzed the air in the vicinity of our laboratory and found about 90 $\mu g/m^3$ of NH_3. This is just about enough to combine with the highest sulfate concentrations in this study. It is also within the 60 to 150 $\mu g/m^3$ range recently reported by Morgan *et al. (17)* in a survey of several U.S. cities.

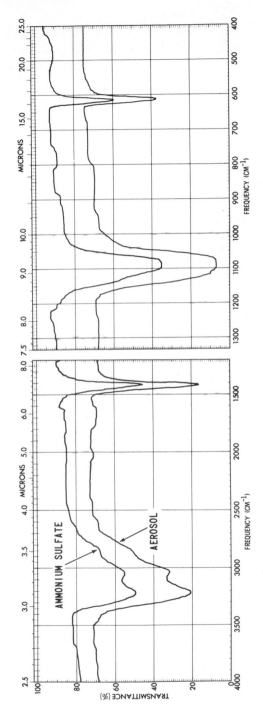

Fig. 7. Infrared spectra of propylene-NO-SO$_2$ aerosol and ammonium sulfate.

Sulfur Balance. Only a small fraction of the sulfur dioxide "reacted" was recovered as sulfate aerosol. In a typical experiment, the SO_2 concentration decreased from 1 to 0.5 ppm (2850 to 1425 $\mu g/m^3$), and about 150 $\mu g/m^3$ of sulfate was recovered. We believe that most of the SO_2 unaccounted for was oxidized to SO_3 and adsorbed on the walls of the chamber. This helps to explain why relatively high SO_2 concentrations were needed in this study to produce significant amounts of aerosol. Presumably, much lower SO_2 concentrations are needed in the atmosphere where absorption on surfaces is less important.

Irradiation of Other Hydrocarbon-NO-SO_2 Mixtures

Several hydrocarbons besides propylene were irradiated with NO and SO_2. Most were selected because of their photochemical reactivity, and it was expected that they would form aerosols readily. The results are shown in Table II.

On the basis of the smokemeter readings, the terpene a-pinene was by far the strongest aerosol former. The olefins were next. The two aromatics, ethyl benzene and mesitylene, formed much less aerosol than the higher-molecular-weight olefins, and were comparable to ethylene and propylene. The paraffins, methane and isooctane, formed very little aerosol. Although cyclohexene and isooctene were irradiated with NO_2 rather than NO, this difference does not appear to be important enough to alter the above rankings.

Most of the sulfate results fell into one of two categories, 40 to 80 or 180 to 240 $\mu g/m^3$, depending to a considerable degree on whether the hydrocarbon was a weak or strong aerosol former. This suggests that there may be two different oxidation mechanisms for SO_2, depending on the hydrocarbon in the system.

A few tests were also made without SO_2; results are shown in parentheses in Table II. The results for a-pinene and cyclohexene are particularly interesting, because as much or more aerosol was formed when no SO_2 was present. Prager *et al. (8)*, Schuck and Doyle *(11)*, and Stevenson *et al. (10)* all previously reported that cyclohexene formed large amounts of aerosol when irradiated with NO_2 but without SO_2. Most hydrocarbon-NO_x systems require SO_2 to form aerosol *(15)*. The reasons for the unique aerosol-forming characteristics of cyclohexene and a-pinene are not known.

Prager *et al. (8)* also reported that 2,4,4-trimethyl-1-pentene formed equally large amounts of aerosol when irradiated with NO_2 alone as when

Table II

Aerosol Formed from Various Hydrocarbons, NO, and SO_2 [a]

Hydrocarbon	Aerosol Formed	
	Smokemeter [b,c]	Sulfate ($\mu g/m^3$) [c]
Isooctane	0.4 (0.2)	48 (5)
Methane	0.8	45
Ethylene	1.4	84
Mesitylene	1.6	40
Ethylbenzene	2.2	84
Propylene	2.2 (0.4)	200 (5)
Propylene (NO_2)	2.6	176
Isoprene	2.4	222
Isooctene [d]	(0.6)	(4)
Isooctene (NO_2)	2.6 (0.9)	208 (5)
1,3-Butadiene	2.7	189
1-Octene	2.8	350
Cyclohexene (NO_2)	2.9 (3.2)	242 (9)
α-Pinene	4.4 (4.5)	246 (2)

[a] HC 4 ppm, NO 2 ppm, SO_2 1 ppm.
[b] Corrected for initial readings.
[c] Values in parentheses: no SO_2 added.
[d] 2,4,4-Trimethyl-1-pentene.

irradiated with NO_2 and SO_2. In this study, 2,4,4-trimethyl-1-pentene and NO_2 formed much more aerosol when SO_2 was present. We cannot explain this discrepancy.

As expected, the sulfate concentrations were very low when no SO_2 was added to the system. The background SO_2 concentration in the chamber air was estimated at one to two parts per hundred million, which is enough to account for the small amounts of sulfate actually found.

The infrared spectra of the aerosol samples from all the hydrocarbons showed ammonium sulfate bands when SO_2 was present. With the paraffins and the light olefins, only ammonium sulfate bands were found. With the heavier hydrocarbons, and particularly with cyclohexene and α-pinene, bands other than those of ammonium sulfate were present. These other bands were the same as those found when no SO_2 was added to the system. Fig. 8 shows spectra of the a-pinene aerosols with and without SO_2. The outstanding features of these spectra are the strong scattering-type absorption between 2.5 and 5.0 microns, and the strong absorption band at 5.9 microns. The scattering absorption may be due to an organic polymer; the 5.9-micron band is probably carbonyl absorption.

No evidence of the benzene ring structure was found in the mesitylene or ethylbenzene (or any other) spectra.

Dark Reactions of Hydrocarbons and Ozone

All hydrocarbons tested in the preceding section had one feature in common: they did not form aerosol in significant amounts until ozone was present. (Ozone was formed within a few minutes in mixtures containing NO_2. In mixtures containing NO, it took anywhere from a half hour to a few hours to form, depending on the hydrocarbon present and the hydrocarbon and NO concentrations.) This suggested that ozone might be a key ingredient in the formation of aerosols, both with and without SO_2.

There is some evidence in the literature that aerosols can be formed by the reaction of hydrocarbons and ozone alone. Wei and Cvetanovic *(18)* and Rasmussen *(19)* reported the formation of aerosols from high concentrations of hydrocarbons and ozone. Prager *et al. (8)* found that aerosols could be formed at much lower concentrations (but still above atmospheric) from cyclopentene, cyclohexene, or 1,3-hexadiene and ozone. In this study, we investigated at still lower concentrations the reactions between ozone and several hydrocarbons including a-pinene and cyclohexene, both of which had formed large amounts of aerosol when irradiated with NO or NO_2. The results are shown in Table III.

a-Pinene and cyclohexene formed relatively large amounts of aerosol, and cyclopentene a moderate amount. These results agree with those of Prager *et al. (8)*. The other hydrocarbons formed little or no aerosol, even though they all (except isooctane) reacted readily with ozone.

The effect of ozone concentration on the aerosol formed by the dark reaction of cyclohexene and ozone was also studied (Table IV). Increasing the ozone concentration greatly increased the amount of aerosol formed. Apparently, the availability of ozone was the limiting factor. The cyclohexene-ozone reaction was very fast, about 90% of the ozone reacting in 6 or 7 minutes.

Only the cycloolefins formed enough aerosol to provide a usable infrared sample. The aerosol spectra from the a-pinene-ozone and cyclohexene-

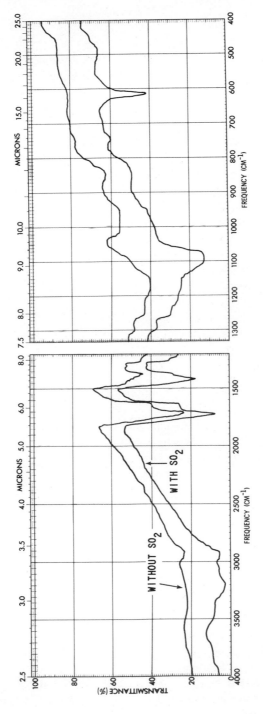

Fig. 8. Infrared spectra of α-pinene-NO₂ aerosol with and without SO₂.

Table III

**Aerosol Formed by the Dark Reaction
of Various Hydrocarbons and Ozone[a]**

Hydrocarbon	Smokemeter Reading[b]
a-Pinene	3.0, 3.2
Cyclohexene	2.2, 2.6
Cyclopentene	1.4
Propylene	0.25
1-Heptene	0.25
Benzene	0.25
Isooctene	0.20
Isooctane	0.15
3-Heptene	0
Styrene	0

[a]HC 4 ppm, ozone 0.6 ppm.
[b]Corrected for initial values.

Table IV

**Aerosol Formed by Dark Reaction
of Cyclohexene and Ozone[a]**

Ozone (ppm)	Smokemeter
0.2	0.2
0.75	2.2
1.35	3.5[b]

[a]Cyclohexene 4 ppm.
[b]Aerosol mass concentration 245 $\mu g/m^3$.

ozone dark reactions were identical to the corresponding spectra from the hydrocarbon-NO_x photoreactions. The a-pinene-NO_2 spectrum was previously shown in Fig. 8.

The small particle detector was used to measure the condensation nuclei formed in the ozone-hydrocarbon reactions. a-Pinene, 1-heptene, 3-heptene, and styrene immediately produced a large number of nuclei (10,000,000 per cubic centimeter) when added to the chamber containing ozone. Cyclohexene, cyclopentene, propylene, and 2,4,4-trimethyl-1-pentene also immediately formed particles, but only about 37,000 per cubic centimeter for cyclohexene and about 400,000 per cubic centimeter for the others. Benzene and isooctane did not form any significant number of condensation nuclei when mixed with ozone. In the case of cyclohexene, the relatively large amount of light scattering from so few particles implies that the particles must have grown to the optimum size range for light scattering. (This is usually given as 0.1 to 1.0 micron.) This seems to be the case, since the small particle counter, when operated as a crude sizing instrument, indicated that the condensation diameter *(7)* of the cyclohexene aerosol particles was larger than 0.3 micron.

Propylene-Sulfur Dioxide-Ozone Reactions

The close relationship between ozone and aerosol formation in the variables study suggested that the sulfate aerosol might be formed by the direct oxidation of SO_2 by ozone. Accordingly, the reaction between SO_2 and ozone was studied. The results are plotted in Fig. 9. Surprisingly, ozone

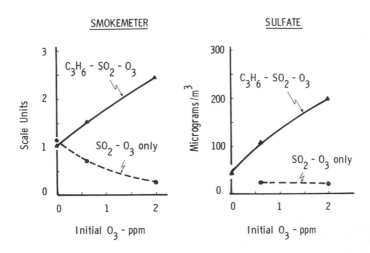

Fig. 9. Aerosol formed by irradiation of propylene-SO_2-ozone.

appeared to inhibit the (slow) photooxidation of SO_2 in air. These tests clearly prove that SO_2 was not oxidized directly by ozone in the irradiated hydrocarbon-NO-SO_2 reactions.

As a next step, the reaction between a typical hydrocarbon, propylene, SO_2, and ozone was studied. These results are also plotted in Fig. 9. With propylene present, both the smokemeter reading and the sulfate concentration increased with the amount of ozone added to the system. This clearly shows that SO_2 was being oxidized, and that propylene was in some way taking part in the reaction. The amount of SO_2 oxidized appeared to be limited by the availability of ozone, since the smokemeter leveled off at about the time all the ozone had reacted. The ozone reacted fairly quickly, decreasing from 2.0 ppm to 1.0 ppm in about 13 minutes and to 0.1 ppm in 55 minutes. During this time, about half the propylene (initially 4 ppm) was consumed.

The effect of irradiation on the propylene-SO_2-ozone reaction was not clear from these tests, so they were repeated without irradiation. The dark reaction results are shown in Fig. 10. They show essentially the same trends and effects as when irradiated. That is, no aerosol is formed unless propylene, SO_2, and ozone are all present, and then the aerosol increases with the amount of ozone added to the system. The only significant difference was the slightly lower smokemeter and sulfate values in the dark reactions. This may have been due as much to the lower temperature ($80°F$) at which the dark reactions were carried out as to the absence of

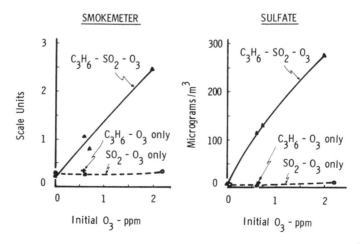

Fig. 10. Aerosol formed by dark reaction of propylene-SO_2-ozone.

irradiation. It was not possible to run the dark reactions at the usual 95°F.

Also shown in Fig. 10 is a single test between propylene and ozone. No aerosol was formed, even though the olefin and ozone reacted rapidly to form unknown products.

Thus, it appears that all three constituents – propylene, SO_2, and ozone – are necessary to form aerosol in this system. Any two of them are not enough. Moreover, the composition of the propylene-SO_2-ozone aerosol also was ammonium sulfate.

This strongly suggests that the role of nitrogen oxides and of irradiation in all prior experiments was simply to generate ozone. This partly explains why NO concentration and light intensity had relatively little effect on the amount of aerosol formed.

The mechanism by which SO_2 is oxidized to SO_3 is not clear, but the oxidizing agent is probably some intermediate in the propylene-ozone reaction. It may be an ozonide, an epoxide, or a free radical. These species have all been identified in olefin-ozone reactions.

The only other investigators to study aerosol formation from the dark, gas phase reaction of olefins, SO_2, and ozone were Reckner *et al.* (12). Their results (for 2-pentene) were similar to ours, and they also concluded that some intermediate from the olefin-ozone reaction oxidized SO_2. For some reason, however, they never continued this work.

We consider this finding to be an important clue to the formation of particulate matter in the atmosphere, particularly during photochemical smog episodes. The oxidation of sulfur dioxide in the atmosphere is far from understood *(20)*. The reactive olefin-SO_2-ozone reaction may be an important atmospheric reaction. We have not looked at other hydrocarbons besides propylene to see whether they also "catalyze" the oxidation of SO_2 by ozone, but it seems reasonable to expect that some of them will. If so, it would implicate all reactive hydrocarbons in the atmospheric visibility problem, not just those few that form carbonaceous aerosol.

Discussion

The influence of the walls makes any irradiation chamber a less-than-perfect tool for the quantitative study of atmospheric processes. An indication of wall effects in our chamber is that, typically, less than one quarter of the sulfur dioxide reacted appears in the aerosol. In spite of this limitation, aerosol concentrations of hundreds of micrograms per cubic meter were attained in these studies. This is the same order of magnitude as the total mass loading in urban areas, although our reactant concentrations were somewhat higher than in urban areas. One special experiment was performed at more typical atmospheric levels: 2 ppm propylene, 0.4 ppm NO, and 0.1 ppm SO_2. After irradiation, the smokemeter reading was 0.5 and the sulfate concentration was 16 micrograms per cubic meter. Both were considerably lower than in the other experiments, but only 6% of the SO_2 which reacted was recovered as sulfate. The chamber walls can act as a sink for the aerosol and reactive intermediates. It also seems unlikely that a species formed on the surface would be desorbed from the walls as a particle. These problems suggest that the aerosol concentrations observed in the chamber indicate the minimum effect that would occur in the atmosphere.

The composition of the aerosols produced in chamber studies should be typical of the aerosol produced in the atmosphere. In accord with past studies, we found the aerosol produced from the irradiation of light olefins with nitrogen oxides and sulfur dioxide to be predominately sulfate, neutralized by ammonia from the ambient air. Some sulfate was produced whenever a reactive hydrocarbon was irradiated with nitrogen oxides and sulfur dioxide. In some cases, the infrared spectrum indicated that, in addition to the ammonium sulfate, a carbonaceous material was also present which gave strong scattering in the infrared and had a carbonyl absorption band. Such spectra were obtained from several different reactions involving cycloolefins: (1) irradiation with nitrogen oxides; (2) irradiation with nitrogen oxides and sulfur dioxide; and (3) reaction in the dark with ozone. The spectra of the aerosols produced from (1) and (3) appeared to be identical. The key to the outstanding ability of the cycloolefins (including the terpenes) to form carbonaceous aerosols may be the production of a species with oxygenated functional groups at both ends due to ozonolysis and ring rupture. The low vapor pressure of this species may allow condensation to particles, or the active ends may undergo subsequent polymerization.

In addition to the carbonaceous aerosol formed by the reaction of cycloolefins and ozone in the dark, sulfate aerosol was produced from the dark reaction of ozone and sulfur dioxide in the presence of propylene. The formation of both sulfate and carbonaceous aerosols by a dark reaction with ozone and the similarity of the carbonaceous aerosol formed in the irradiated and dark reactions involving cycloolefins suggest that it may be the reaction with ozone that is important in the photochemical systems. This further suggests that reactions with ozone may be responsible for the formation of aerosol in the atmosphere, and that the effects of reactant concentrations and light intensity may be important only insofar as they affect the production of ozone.

Ozone is a natural constituent of the atmosphere, as well as a product of photochemical smog. In the present tests, ozone reacted rapidly with cycloolefins and with propylene and sulfur dioxide to form aerosol. These relatively fast reactions suggest that olefins should be able to compete with other atmospheric constituents for ozone, and that ozone-olefin reactions may play an important role in the formation of aerosol material in the atmosphere.

References

1. R.J. Charlson, *Environ. Sci. Technol.*, **3**, 913 (1969).
2. D.A. Lundgren, *J. Air Pollution Control Assoc.*, **20**, 603 (1970).
3. J. Harkins and S.W. Nicksic, *J. Air Pollution Control Assoc.*, **15**, 218 (1965).
4. N. Endow, G.J. Doyle, and J.L. Jones, *J. Air Pollution Control Assoc.*, **13**, 141 (1963).
5. C.S. Tuesday, B.A. D'Alleva, J.M. Heuss, and G.J. Nebel, Paper 65-19, presented at the 58th Annual Meeting of the Air Pollution Control Association, Toronto, Canada, June 1965.
6. D. Sinclair, *Air Repair*, **3**, 51 (1953).
7. T.A. Rich, *Geofis. Pura Appl.*, **31**, 60 (1955).
8. M.J. Prager, E.R. Stephens, and W.E. Scott, *Ind. Eng. Chem.*, **6**, 521 (1960).
9. A.P. Altshuller, S.L. Kopczynski, W.A. Lonneman, T.L. Becker, and D.L. Wilson, *Environ. Sci. Technol.*, **2**, 696 (1968).
10. H.J.R. Stevenson, D.E. Sanderson, and A.P. Altshuller, *Intern. J. Air Water Pollution*, **9**, 367 (1965).
11. E.A. Schuck and G.J. Doyle, Air Pollution Foundation Report No. 29, 1959.
12. L.R. Reckner, W.E. Scott, and R.H. Linnell, paper presented at the 145th National Meeting, American Chemical Society, New York, September 1963.
13. W.E. Wilson and A. Levy, *J. Air Pollution Control Assoc.*, **20**, 385 (1970).
14. E.A. Schuck, G.J. Doyle, and N. Endow, Air Pollution Foundation Report No. 31, 1960.
15. A.P. Altshuller and J.J. Bufalini, *Photochem. Photobiol.*, **4**, 97 (1965).
16. J.A. Tetlow and A.L. Wilson, *Analyst*, **89**, 453 (1964).
17. G.B. Morgan, C. Golden, and E.C. Tabor, *J. Air Pollution Control Assoc.*, **17**, 300 (1967).
18. Y.K. Wei and R.J. Cvetanovic, *Can. J. Chem.*, **41**, 913 (1963).
19. R.A. Rasmussen, Ph.D. Thesis, Washington University, Saint Louis, Missouri, 1964.
20. P. Urone and W.H. Schroeder, *Environ. Sci. Technol.*, **3**, 436 (1969).

Discussion

W.E. WILSON: I have been doing some work sponsored by the American Petroleum Institute, looking at the relationships between fuel composition and visibility reduction due to photochemical smog aerosols. Some of our results are shown in Fig. 11. A lot of aerosol is formed at 0% relative humidity, but as the humidity increases the amount of aerosol formed decreases. At 65% relative humidity no aerosol was formed. This agrees well with the work just presented, but unfortunately it is wrong. What we are observing is not a change in aerosol formation per se, but a change in the type of aerosol that is formed. In dry systems, the aerosol bounces off the wall and off the fan blades, but as you add water vapor, it sticks somewhere. If I turn the fan off, I no longer get a downward trend with relative humidity. Of course, from what we know about aerosols in the atmosphere we would expect that as relative humidity goes up, so does light scattering. I mentioned this to Dr. Altshuller, and he indicated that if you want to measure aerosol you should slow down your fan speed. I feel somewhat better to see that others have made the same mistake. So I would suggest that you try some of these reactions with your fan slowed down or with your fan turned off. And I encourage all of you who are interested in aerosol formation to see what happens when you turn the fan off.

P.J. GROBLICKI: I have not checked the lifetime of aerosols in our chamber, but they do not decay very rapidly once they have been formed.

W.E. WILSON: Once an aerosol is formed in our system, the fan takes it out very slowly. If the reaction is run with the fan off, and the fan is then turned on, the aerosol half-life is several hours. So the fan is doing something in the aerosol formation step. It is not just the common aerosol loss due to a fan that everyone who has worked with chambers knows about. It is something different which I don't understand at all.

A.P. ALTSHULLER: I am concerned that when we use chambers for particulate research which were developed initially for homogeneous gas reaction research, we may be in trouble in several ways. One way is the stirring problem that has been mentioned. The second is that most of the sulfur isn't in the vapor state as sulfate aerosol; it is on the walls. Thirdly, not only is most of the sulfur on the walls, but most of the nitrogen is on the walls as nitrate. The point I am making is that one must be very careful in the use of chambers in the aerosol field. You can make quite erroneous conclusions if you are not careful.

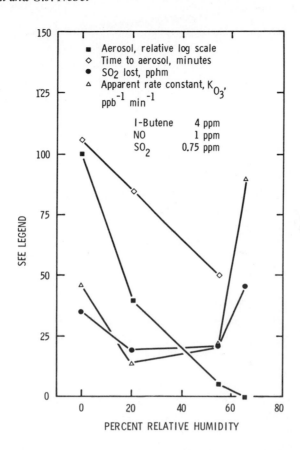

Fig. 11. Effect of humidity on the 1-butene-NO-SO$_2$ system.

P.J. GROBLICKI and G.J. NEBEL (Note added)

Dr. Wilson has recently presented* comparisons of the amount of light scattering from the aerosol formed in photochemical reactions in the presence and absence of stirring. We have also made a few similar comparisons in our chamber. In some cases, stirring greatly reduced aerosol formation. Mixtures

---

*W.E. Wilson, E.L. Merryman, A. Levy, and H.R. Taliaferro, "Aerosol Formation in Photochemical Smog. I. Effect of Stirring," presented at 63rd Annual Meeting, Air Pollution Control Association, St. Louis, Missouri, June 14, 1970.

that formed large amounts of aerosol, however, were affected less than those that formed little aerosol. Based on all the results now available, the qualitative trends shown in our paper are still valid. The relative ranking of some of the less effective aerosol formers, however, might change somewhat.

Smog chambers have a much greater surface-to-volume ratio than the atmosphere. Vigorous stirring might accentuate the effectiveness of the surface in removing particles and reactive gas phase species. Although smog chamber experiments cannot exactly duplicate the atmosphere, they certainly give insights into atmospheric reactions which are, nevertheless, quite valuable.

J.L. MONKMAN: I was very impressed with Dr. Groblicki's infrared spectra of ammonium sulfate. But I should like to point out that the sulfate which we have found in ambient air is mostly calcium sulfate. You can isolate this from any high-volume sample in milligram amounts. You can extract it, filter it, recrystallize it in conventional ways, and have amounts which you can weigh. That is not to say that ammonium sulfate is not present, but ammonium sulfate is not the only sulfate in the air. We have analyzed two thousand high-volume samples over two or three years. We have measured calcium and we have measured water-soluble sulfate, and the ratio of the two is about 1 : 1. We have measured sulfuric acid, and it is roughly 10% of the total soluble sulfate. We have not measured ammonium, not because we disregard it or don't think it should be measured, but because we don't think a high-volume sampler retains it properly. Finally, I have a question. You mentioned that Lundgren found 80 $\mu g/m^3$ of nitrate and 20 $\mu g/m^3$ of sulfate at Riverside. Are those figures correct?

P.J. GROBLICKI: Yes. This is from a paper that Lundgren presented at an APCA meeting (reference 2 of preceding paper).

J. HEICKLEN: Can anyone tell us what the concentration of ammonia in the atmosphere is and how it varies from place to place?

B. WEINSTOCK: Elmer Robinson recently gave a paper in which he analyzed, in detail, the circulation of nitrogen compounds through the atmosphere.*

A.P. ALTSHULLER: The measurements which are available, using the colorimetric method for ammonia, indicate values of 0.2, 0.3, even 0.4 ppm in a number of U.S. cities.

S. BENSON: Was that ammonia or ammonium ions?

A.P. ALTSHULLER: Those values are for free ammonia.

T.R. WELCH: McKay, at Harwell, recently published some relevant

---

*E. Robinson and R.C. Robbins, *J. Air Pollution Control Assoc.*, **20**, 303 (1970).

information on the presence of ammonium sulfate in the atmosphere.* Its concentration is very great in the atmosphere at Tees-side, England. He came to the conclusion that this was largely formed by the interaction between SO_2 and ammonia from the land.

J.P. FRIEND: I happened to hear McKay's speech in Heidelberg last month, and he suggested that the global source for atmospheric ammonia is probably the decay of animal urine. McKay and his co-workers collected aerosol particles in the Tees-side valley where there happens to be a large ammonia plant. These particles turned out to be virtually pure ammonium sulfate. They also collected aerosol particles in Harwell, in the open country with no industrial facilities nearby and no conspicuous sources of ammonia, and also found almost pure ammonium sulfate. Also, stratospheric aerosol particles consist largely of ammonium sulfate. I would suggest that much, if not most, of the sulfate in the atmosphere is ammonium sulfate or perhaps ammonium bisulfate, as opposed to calcium sulfate or other materials.

P.J. GROBLICKI: Jim Lodge has also identified ammonium sulfate in atmospheric aerosols.†

J. WAGMAN: I can offer another piece of supporting evidence. At NAPCA, we have measured the size distribution of particles containing ammonium ion and sulfate. We have done this in several cities and find that the particle size distributions of the two are quite similar.‡ This would seem to indicate that ammonium sulfate is present in the atmosphere.

P.A. LEIGHTON: Is there any evidence for the presence of calcium in photochemically formed particulates?

A.P. ALTSHULLER: In response to Dr. Leighton's inquiry, I think that the ammonium species is far more likely to be associated with photochemical air pollution than calcium. As I recall, Dale Lundgren mentioned at the Gordon Conference this summer that he found ammonium nitrate at Riverside, California.

J.J. BUFALINI: Did you look for nitrate either in the gas phase or on the walls?

P.J. GROBLICKI: We did not check for nitrate on the walls. We attempted to measure nitrate in the aerosol collected on the filter, but at that time we did not have a very good nitrate method. We're still working on this. We did not see any absorption bands in the infrared spectrum which we could attribute to nitrate, so there could not have been much there.

---

*H.A.C. McKay, *Chem. Ind. (London)* 1162 (1969).
†E.R. Frank and J.P. Lodge, Jr., *J. Microscopie,* 6, 449 (1967).
‡J. Wagman, R.E. Lee, Jr., and C.J. Axt, *Atmos. Environ.,* 1, 479 (1967); R.E. Lee, Jr., and R.K. Patterson, *ibid.,* 3, 249 (1969).

Participant List

P. D. Agarwal
GM Research Laboratories
Warren, Michigan

W. G. Agnew
GM Research Laboratories
Warren, Michigan

W. A. Albers, Jr.
GM Research Laboratories
Warren, Michigan

E. R. Allen
National Center for Atmospheric
Research
Boulder, Colorado

F. C. Alley
Clemson University
Clemson, South Carolina

*A. P. Altshuller
National Air Pollution Control
Admin.
U.S. Dept. of Health, Education,
and Welfare
Cincinnati, Ohio

P. R. Ballinger
Chevron Research Company
Richmond, California

S. E. Beacom
GM Research Laboratories
Warren, Michigan

C. R. Begeman
GM Research Laboratories
Warren, Michigan

H. S. Bender
GM Research Laboratories
Warren, Michigan

J. E. Bennethum
GM Research Laboratories
Warren, Michigan

*S. W. Benson
Stanford Research Institute
Menlo Park, California

C. E. Billings
GCA Corporation
Bedford, Massachusetts

F. Bonamassa
California Air Resources Board
Los Angeles, California

F. W. Bowditch
GM Engineering Staff
Warren, Michigan

K. L. Brubaker
National Air Pollution Control Admin.
U.S. Dept. of Health, Education,
and Welfare
Cincinnati, Ohio

**J. J. Bufalini
National Air Pollution Control Admin.
U.S. Dept. of Health, Education,
Welfare
Cincinnati, Ohio

---

*Denotes Session Chairman
**Denotes Speaker

M. Bufalini
National Air Pollution Control
Admin.
U.S. Dept. of Health, Education,
and Welfare
Cincinnati, Ohio

I. G. Burstain
Shell Development Company
Emeryville, California

A. V. Butterworth
GM Research Laboratories
Warren, Michigan

L. R. Buzan
GM Research Laboratories
Warren, Michigan

**R. D. Cadle
National Center for Atmospheric
Research
Boulder, Colorado

**J. G. Calvert
The Ohio State University
Columbus, Ohio

R. J. Campion
Esso Research and Engineering
Company
Linden, New Jersey

J. D. Caplan
GM Research Laboratories
Warren, Michigan

V. J. Castrop
GM Industrial Hygiene
Warren, Michigan

E. Cehelnik
The Pennsylvania State University
University Park, Pennsylvania

P. F. Chenea
GM Research Laboratories
Warren, Michigan

J. E. Christian
Purdue University
Lafayette, Indiana

J. M. Colucci
GM Research Laboratories
Warren, Michigan

W. H. Corcoran
California Institute of Technology
Pasadena, California

W. Cornelius
GM Research Laboratories
Warren, Michigan

K. E. Cowser
Oak Ridge National Laboratory
Oak Ridge, Tennessee

L. S. Cressler
General Motors Institute
Flint, Michigan

*R. J. Cvetanovic
National Research Council of Canada
Ottawa, Canada

E. E. Daby
Ford Motor Company
Dearborn, Michigan

B. A. D'Alleva
GM Research Laboratories
Warren, Michigan

B. N. Dewitt
General Motors Institute
Flint, Michigan

**B. Dimitriades
Bureau of Mines
U.S. Dept. of the Interior
Bartlesville, Oklahoma

J. Durham
Oak Ridge National Laboratory
Oak Ridge, Tennessee

D. S. Eddy
GM Research Laboratories
Warren, Michigan

A. Eschenroeder
General Research Corporation
Santa Barbara, California

F. L. Estes
Gulf South Research Institute
Baton Rouge, Louisiana

W. L. Faith
San Marino, California

J. P. Friend
New York University
Bronx, New York

D. L. Fry
GM Research Laboratories
Warren, Michigan

J. W. Gall
Ohio State University
Columbus, Ohio

K. D. Gardels
GM Research Laboratories
Warren, Michigan

Z. G. Gardlund
GM Research Laboratories
Warren, Michigan

W. A. Glasson
GM Research Laboratories
Warren, Michigan

F. T. Greene
Midwest Research Institute
Kansas City, Missouri

M. E. Griffing
Ethyl Corporation
Ferndale, Michigan

**P. J. Groblicki
GM Research Laboratories
Warren, Michigan

J. P. Guarino
Mobil Research and Development
Corporation
Princeton, New Jersey

W. A. Guillory
Drexel Institute of Technology
Philadelphia, Pennsylvania

L. R. Hafstad
National Research Council
Washington, D. C.

J. W. Hall
Clemson University
Clemson, South Carolina

G. S. Hammond
California Institute of Technology
Pasadena, California

J. L. Hartman
GM Research Laboratories
Warren, Michigan

**J. Heicklen
The Pennsylvania State University
University Park, Pennsylvania

D. J. Henry
GM Research Laboratories
Warren, Michigan

R. Herman
GM Research Laboratories
Warren, Michigan

J. T. Herron
National Bureau of Standards
U.S. Dept. of Commerce
Washington, D. C.

J. M. Heuss
GM Research Laboratories
Warren, Michigan

R. F. Hill
GM Research Laboratories
Warren, Michigan

I. C. Hisatsune
The Pennsylvania State University
University Park, Pennsylvania

C. J. Hochanadel
Oak Ridge National Laboratory
Oak Ridge, Tennessee

G. A. Hollinden
The Catholic University of America
Washington, D. C.

J. C. Holzwarth
GM Research Laboratories
Warren, Michigan

M. W. Jackson
GM Research Laboratories
Warren, Michigan

**S. Jaffe
California State College
at Los Angeles
Los Angeles, California

F. E. Jamerson
GM Research Laboratories
Warren, Michigan

R. S. Kapner
The Cooper Union
New York, New York

M. Katz
York University
Toronto, Canada

J. C. Kent
GM Research Laboratories
Warren, Michigan

C. E. Kircher
Detrex Chemical Industries, Inc.
Detroit, Michigan

R. Klein
National Bureau of Standards
U.S. Dept. of Commerce
Washington, D. C.

R. L. Klimisch
GM Research Laboratories
Warren, Michigan

S. L. Kopczynski
National Air Pollution Control
Admin.
U.S. Dept. of Health, Education,
and Welfare
Fairfax, Ohio

J. Kumari
Case Western Reserve University
Cleveland, Ohio

R. H. Kummler
General Electric Company
Philadelphia, Pennsylvania

A. Kuppermann
California Institute of Technology
Pasadena, California

F. Lamb
Ethyl Corporation
Ferndale, Michigan

H. F. LeFevre
The Catholic University of America
Washington, D. C.

*P. A. Leighton
Stanford University (Emeritus)
Palo Alto, California

A. Levy
Battelle Memorial Institute
Columbus, Ohio

L. L. Lewis
GM Research Laboratories
Warren, Michigan

B. Linsky
West Virginia University
Morgantown, West Virginia

C. Marks
GM Engineering Staff
Warren, Michigan

J. N. Mattavi
GM Research Laboratories
Warren, Michigan

W. J. Mayer
GM Research Laboratories
Warren, Michigan

J. C. McElhany
GM Research Laboratories
Warren, Michigan

**G. R. McMillan
Case Western Reserve University
Cleveland, Ohio

S. R. Miller
University of Colorado
Boulder, Colorado

J. L. Monkman
Occupational Health Division
Dept. of National Health and Welfare
Ottawa, Canada

C. E. Moser
Texaco, Inc.
Beacon, New York

J. C. Mulac
Gulf Research and Development
Company
Pittsburgh, Pennsylvania

B. E. Nagel
GM Research Laboratories
Warren, Michigan

G. J. Nebel
GM Research Laboratories
Warren, Michigan

E. E. Nelson
GM Engineering Staff
Warren, Michigan

G. W. Niepoth
GM Engineering Staff
Warren, Michigan

J. P. Nolta
GM Research Laboratories
Warren, Michigan

P. E. Oberdorfer, Jr.
Sun Oil Company
Marcus Hook, Pennsylvania

K. J. Olszyna
The Pennsylvania State University
University Park, Pennsylvania

H. W. Otto
Esso Research and Engineering
Company
Linden, New Jersey

G. H. Patterson
E. I. du Pont de Nemours and
Company
Wilmington, Delaware

J. N. Pattison
University of Cincinnati
Cincinnati, Ohio

W. H. Percival
GM Research Laboratories
Warren, Michigan

S. M. Pier
The Pace Company
Houston, Texas

J. M. Pierrard
E. I. du Pont de Nemours and
Company
Wilmington, Delaware

**J. N. Pitts, Jr.
University of California, Riverside
Riverside, California

R. A. Reck
GM Research Laboratories
Warren, Michigan

H. F. Richards
Shell Development Company
Emeryville, California

L. A. Ripperton
University of North Carolina
Chapel Hill, North Carolina

J. C. Romanovsky
National Air Pollution Control
Admin.
U.S. Dept. of Health, Education,
and Welfare
Durham, North Carolina

N. R. Roobol
General Motors Institute
Flint, Michigan

D. J. Rose
Oak Ridge National Laboratory
Oak Ridge, Tennessee

G. F. Ryckman
GM Research Laboratories
Warren, Michigan

P. R. Ryason
Chevron Research Company
Richmond, California

I. E. Schaumberg
General Motors Institute
Flint, Michigan

N. A. Schilke
GM Research Laboratories
Warren, Michigan

L. J. Schoen
National Bureau of Standards
U. S. Dept. of Commerce
Washington, D. C.

R. C. Schwing
GM Research Laboratories
Warren, Michigan

F. Scofield
National Paint, Varnish and Lacquer
Assoc.
Washington, D. C.

R. L. Scott
GM Research Laboratories
Warren, Michigan

D. A. Skinner
Union Oil Company
Brea, California

D. H. Slater
Ohio State University
Columbus, Ohio

R. G. Smith
Wayne State University
Detroit, Michigan

D. L. Snyder
Case Western Reserve University
Cleveland, Ohio

R. S. Spindt
Gulf Research and Development
Company
Pittsburgh, Pennsylvania

**E. R. Stephens
University of California, Riverside
Riverside, California

R. Sugimoto
Houston Chemical Company
Houston, Texas

D. M. Teague
Chrysler Corporation
Detroit, Michigan

R. J. Templin
GM Research Laboratories
Warren, Michigan

J. D. Thomas
GM Research Laboratories
Warren, Michigan

R. F. Thomson
GM Research Laboratories
Warren, Michigan

**R. B. Timmons
The Catholic University of America
Washington, D. C.

M. Tsou
GM Research Laboratories
Warren, Michigan

C. S. Tuesday
GM Research Laboratories
Warren, Michigan

A. F. Underwood
GM Research Laboratories
Warren, Michigan

J. Wagman
National Air Pollution Control
Admin.
U.S. Dept. of Health, Education,
and Welfare
Cincinnati, Ohio

L. G. Wayne
University of Southern California
Los Angeles, California

E. E. Weaver
Ford Motor Company
Dearborn, Michigan

B. Weinstock
Ford Motor Company
Dearborn, Michigan

T. R. Welch
British Petroleum (North America),
Ltd.
New York, New York

E. F. Weller
GM Research Laboratories
Warren, Michigan

K. Westberg
Aerospace Corporation
Los Angeles, California

M. L. Whisman
U.S. Dept. of the Interior
Bartlesville, Oklahoma

K. W. Wilson
Stanford Research Institute
South Pasadena, California

W. E. Wilson
Battelle Memorial Institute
Columbus, Ohio

D. B. Wimmer
Phillips Petroleum Company
Bartlesville, Oklahoma

W. P. Wood
The Pennsylvania State University
University Park, Pennsylvania

W. S. Zimmt
E. I. du Pont de Nemours and
Company
Philadelphia, Pennsylvania

Author Index

Numbers in parentheses indicate the numbers of the references when these are cited in the text without the names of the authors.

Numbers set in **boldface** refer to the first page of a contributor's paper.

Ackerman, R.A., 12(45), 14(45), 15(45), 16, 31(45, 46)
Akhtar, M., 36(4)
Allen, E.R., **63**, 66, 70 (17, 18), 79, 84 (18), 86, 184
Altshuller, A.P., 3 (2, 8), 4 (8), 48 (2, 4), 54, 55, 59, 63, 68(16), 79, 81, 87, 96 (6), 100, 114 (16, 18), 159, 225, 226 (7, 8), 239, 250 (9, 10), 252, 254 (10, 15), 264, 266, 267
Ando, W., 11 (41), 20 (41), 176 (32)
Arden, E. A., 38, 40 (12)
Arnold, S. J., 7, 9 (25), 14, 16 (25), 17, 26 (25), 31
Avery, H. E., **64** (7), 84, 123
Avramenko, L.I., 64 (8, 9, 10, 11), 77, 86, 87, 236
Axt, C.J., 267

Badger, R.M., 8 (30), 22
Bagley, K.W., 70 (18), 84 (18)
Baurer, T., 6 (17), 21 (17), 26 (17)
Bayes, K.D., 6, 13, 15, 21
Becker, T.L., 55, 160 (1), 250 (9)
Benson, S., 156-158, 266
Bent, R., 195 (9)
Bielski, B.H.J., 105, 130
Black, G., 17 (53)
Bonnamassa, F., 51 (6)
Bonner, W.A., 176 (30)
Borkman, R.F., 148 (9)
Bortner, M.H., 6 (17, 18), 12, 17, 21 (17), 22, 25 (18), 26 (17)
Bowen, E.J., 9, 10
Broadbent, A.D., 9 (32), 13, 16 (32), 18 (32, 50), 22 (32, 50), 25 (32, 50)
Brown, F.B., 176 (31)
Brown, J.F., Jr., 104 (7)
Brown, J.M., 240
Browne, R.J., 9
Browning, L., 125
Brubaker, K.L., **225**

Bufalini, J.J., 3 (2), 48 (4), 56, 59, 96 (6), 99, 114 (16, 18), **225**, 226, 227, 232 (16), 239, 252, 254 (15), 267
Burleson, F.R., 51 (5), 51 (8), 52 (5)
Busfield, W.K., 148 (8), 152 (8), 161 (13)

Cadle, R.D., **63**, 66 (15), 72, 77, 79, 86, 87, 103, 105, 108, 184
Callear, A.B., 205 (18)
Calvert, J.G., 8 (29), 36 (3, 4), 40 (15), 59, 130, **133**, 134 (3, 4), 153 (17), 155-158, 160 (11, 12), 162 (20), 172 (11, 12), 174 (11, 12), 176 (12), 189, 221, 222, 233, 237, 238
Carruthers, J.E., 225
Caton, R.B., 155
Cehelnik, E., 189, **191**, 193
Charlson, R.J., 242
Christie, M.I., 64 (12), 77, 79, 87
Clark, I.D., 15
Cohen, I.R., 48 (2), 63, 79, 81, 225, 226, 236
Cohen, N., 37 (8), 40 (8), 55, 56, 58, 201 (13), 203, 206 (13), 209 (13), 210 (13)
Collier, S.S., 156, 160 (11, 12), 172 (11, 12), 174 (11, 12), 176 (12), 189
Collin, J., 113
Collins, B.M., 64 (12), 77, 79, 87
Coomber, J.W., 22 (59), 23 (59, 60), 24 (60), 25 (60)
Corey, E.J., 19
Cottrell, T.L., 103, 105, 108
Cram, D.J., 165 (23)
Crist, R.H., 176 (31)
Crosby, H.J., 18 (57)
Cundall, R.B., 149
Cventanovic, R.J., 3 (3), 32, 54, 55, 64 (6, 7), 77, 79, 80, 84, 86, 87, 100, 113, 114 (12, 17), 123, 126, 195 (8), 239, 256

Daby, E.E., 32, 54, 85, 114 (14), 240

Subject Index